RHS

THE
GARDENER'S
BOTANICAL

RHS The Gardener's Botanical

Author: Dr Ross Bayton

First published in Great Britain in 2019
by Mitchell Beazley, an imprint of Octopus Publishing Group Ltd,
Carmelite House, 50 Victoria Embankment, London EC4Y 0DZ

www.octopusbooks.co.uk

An Hachette UK Company
www.hachette.co.uk

Published in association with the Royal Horticultural Society

ISBN: 978-1-78472-620-1
A CIP record of this book is available from the British Library
Printed and bound in China

MITCHELL
BEAZLEY

Mitchell Beazley Publisher: Alison Starling
RHS Head of Editorial: Chris Young
RHS Publisher: Rae Spencer-Jones
RHS Consultant Editors: Simon Maughan, Rosalyn Marshall

Conceived, designed and produced by
The Bright Press, an imprint of The Quarto Group
The Old Brewery, 6 Blundell Street
London N7 9BH
United Kingdom
(0)20 7700 6700
www.QuartoKnows.com

Design: Greg Stalley
Layout: Ginny Zeal

The Royal Horticultural Society is the UK's leading gardening charity
dedicated to advancing horticulture and promoting good gardening. Its charitable
work includes providing expert advice and information, training the next generation
of gardeners, creating hands-on opportunities for children to grow plants and
conducting research into plants, pests and environmental issues
affecting gardeners.

For more information visit www.rhs.org.uk or call 0845 130 4646.

THE
GARDENER'S
BOTANICAL

An Encyclopedia of Latin Plant Names

ROSS BAYTON

MITCHELL BEAZLEY

Contents

Introduction

For any gardener, knowing the names of the plants in your care is crucial. Not only does it allow you to share what you're growing with friends and family, it unlocks a world of useful information, both in books and online, helping you to make the best of the plants you grow. But why do the names have to be in Latin? Many garden plants have English names that are much easier to remember. The trouble is, those names vary depending on who you talk to. In Scotland, a bluebell is *Campanula rotundifolia*, while in England it's *Hyacinthoides non-scripta*. Not surprisingly, there are other bluebells too, including desert bluebell (*Phacelia campanularia*) in America (California) and royal bluebell (*Wahlenbergia gloriosa*) in Australia. There are even bluebell creepers, *Billardiera heterophylla* in Australia and *Clitoria ternatea* in Asia and America. With 'bluebells' occurring seemingly worldwide, it is essential for each to have its own unique name, as the cultivation requirements for an English bluebell differ widely from those of its Antipodean namesakes.

The decision to use Latin for this naming system stems largely from its historical use by scholars. A university education in the 18th century required familiarity with both Latin and Greek, allowing students to access the works of classical writers from ancient Greece and Rome. Much of the 'Latin' in use in horticulture is actually derived from Greek. How botanical Latin has changed over time, and botanical art alongside, is discussed on pages 12 and 17.

The enduring benefits of using this botanical tongue are that scientists, growers and gardeners can communicate about plants with accuracy, no matter what language they speak. So whether it's bluebell (Scotland), harebell (England), bluebell-bellflower (United States), *campanilla* (Spanish), *campanule à feuilles rondes* (French) or *rundblättrige glockenblume* (German), it is universally *Campanula rotundifolia*. Latin names are not static though and new information is always being discovered – on page 20 we look at how DNA is revealing old and new relationships between plants.

Understanding Latin names brings other benefits. Most obviously, they can reveal useful information that's helpful to the gardener. *Armeria maritima* thrives by the sea, while *Geum rivale* doesn't mind getting its feet wet. *Toxicodendron* is best avoided, while silky soft *Alchemilla mollis* is a pleasure to touch. Botanical Latin has other practical uses too, which are discussed on page 22.

Latin names also reveal fascinating stories, such as the tale of French diplomat Jean Nicot, who popularised tobacco, which now bears his name (*Nicotiana*), or the moving account of a promising Scottish botanist who fell during the First World War and is commemorated for evermore (*Briggsia*). Delve into our dictionary of botanical Latin and you'll find interest, inspiration and intrigue in equal measure.

LEFT: French diplomat Jean Nicot is immortalised in the Latin name for tobacco, *Nicotiana tabacum*.

How to use this book

The following section of the book contains about 5,000 Latin botanical terms arranged alphabetically. These are terms that you might come across either for the genus or the species name of a plant. The term appears first, then a guide to pronunciation. The following line provides the feminine and neuter versions of the name, if applicable, followed by the etymology of the word. This will explain the meaning (or meanings) behind the Latin term. For the genus entries, the family name is also included in brackets at the end. An example of a plant name that features the term is also supplied.

Where variations in spelling occur, they are grouped together, as in:

> ## cashmerianus
> kash-meer-ee-AH-nus
> cashmeriana, cashmerianum
> –
> ## cashmirianus
> kash-meer-ee-AH-nus
> cashmiriana, cashmirianum
> –
> ## cashmiriensis
> kash-meer-ee-EN-sis
> cashmiriensis, cashmiriense
> From or of Kashmir, as in *Cupressus cashmeriana*

Where a genus term can also be used for a species, it is included in brackets afterwards.

At the end of the book is an index of 2,000 of some of the most frequently used common names. Here you can look up a plant that you know by its common name and find out the Latin name. You can then look up what the Latin term means in the alphabetical listings section.

Pronunciation of botanical Latin can vary so the examples provided here are a guide rather than a definitive directive. Capital letters indicate where the stress should fall. Where gender variations occur, pronunciation is given only for the masculine version.

Most gardeners will have encountered plants that seem to have not only numerous common names but also variations in their Latin appellations. Some epithets, which were once in wide usage, have now become obsolete, perhaps due to reclassification of the plants to which they were once applied. However, as these names may still sometimes be found in old horticultural works, as synonyms in modern texts or when browsing the varied sources of the internet, they have been included for completeness. The *RHS Plant Finder* provides a general guide to current nomenclatural opinion, if required.

Helped by an informed understanding of botanical nomenclature, it is hoped that gardeners will be able to make better gardens filled with better plants; plants that sit well in their site, thrive in the conditions provided for them, and have the form, habit and colour that make for the most aesthetically pleasing association with their neighbours.

Genus name in Latin (if the name can also be used as a species name, this appears in brackets afterwards).

A guide to pronunciation is provided and capital letters indicate where the emphasis should fall.

Alyogyne
al-ee-oh-GY-nee
From Greek *alytos* meaning 'undivided' and *gyne* meaning 'female', as the styles are undivided (*Malvaceae*)

Origin of the term is explained and Latin meaning.

Family name

Genus spotlight focusses on interesting details about key genera.

Species name in Latin. The masculine version appears first with other versions listed below.

amphibius
am-FIB-ee-us
amphibia, amphibium
Growing both on land and in water, as in *Persicaria amphibia*

When appropriate, an example is given of a plant name that features the Latin term.

Lines link entries that are different spelling variations with the same meaning.

Fact spotlight provides fascinating insights into botanical Latin.

Extensive index of common names allows readers to find the Latin name for common plants, which can then be cross-referenced to the alphabetical listings.

A guide to the use of Latin

When writing Latin names, it is important to order the various elements in the correct sequence and observe typographical conventions. This is a simplified outline of the binomial system, so there are exceptions to these rules, along with further complexities of structure. As this is a book aimed at gardeners, not botanists, only the broad principles are dealt with here.

Family
(for example, *Sapindaceae*)
This appears as uppercase and lowercase, and the International Code of Botanical Nomenclature also recommends italics. Family names are easily recognised, as they end in *-aceae*.

Genus
(for example, *Acer*)
This appears in italics with an uppercase initial letter. It is a noun and has a gender: masculine, feminine or neuter. The plural term is genera. When listing several species of the same genus together, the genus name is often abbreviated, for example: *Acer amoenum*, *A. barbinerve* and *A. calcaratum*.

Species
(for example, *Acer palmatum*)
The species is a specific unit within the genus and the term is often referred to as the specific epithet. This appears in lowercase italics. It is mostly an adjective, but can sometimes be a noun (for example, *Agave potatorum*, where the epithet means 'of drinkers'). Adjectives always agree in gender with the genus name they follow, but nouns used as specific epithets are invariable. It is the combination of the generic and specific epithet that gives us the species name in the binomial, or two-word, system.

Subspecies
(for example, *Acer negundo* subsp. *mexicanum*)
This appears as lowercase italics and is preceded by the abbreviated form subsp. (or occasionally ssp.), which appears as lowercase roman type. It is a distinct variant of the main species.

Varietas
(for example, *Acer palmatum* var. *coreanum*)
This appears as lowercase italics and is preceded by the abbreviated form var., which appears as lowercase roman type. Also known as the variety, it is used to recognise slight variations in botanical structure.

Forma
(for example, *Acer pseudoplatanus* f. *purpureum*)
This appears as lowercase italics and is preceded by the abbreviated form f., which appears in roman type. Also known as the form, it distinguishes minor variations such as the colour of the flower.

Cultivar
(for example, *Acer forrestii* 'Alice')
This appears as uppercase and lowercase roman type with single quotation marks. Also known as a named variety, it is applied to artificially maintained plants. Modern cultivar names (i.e., those after 1959) should not include Latin or Latinised words.

Acer palmatum,
Japanese maple

Hybrid

(for example, *Hamamelis × intermedia*)

This appears as uppercase and lowercase italics and is denoted by a × that is not italicised (note that this is a multiplication sign, not the letter x). This may be applied to plants that are the product of a cross between species of the same genus. If a hybrid results from the crossing of species from different genera then the hybrid generic name is preceded by a multiplication sign. However, if a hybrid results from the grafting of species from different genera, this is indicated by an addition sign rather than a multiplication sign.

Synonyms

(for example, *Plumbago indica*, syn. *P. rosea*)

Within a classification a plant has only one correct name, but it may have several incorrect ones. These are known as synonyms (abbreviated as syn.) and may have arisen due to two or more botanists giving the same plant different names or from a plant being classified in different ways.

Common names

Where common names are used, they appear as lowercase roman type except where they derive from a proper name, such as that of a person or a place. (For example, common soapwort, but London pride.) Note that Latinised versions of proper names do not have capital letters, for example, *forrestii* or *freemanii*.

Many Latin genus names are in ordinary use as common names, for example fuchsia; in this context, they appear in lowercase roman type, and can also be used in the plural (fuchsias, rhododendrons).

Gender

In Latin, adjectives must agree with the gender of the noun that they qualify; therefore in botanical names, the species must agree with the genus. An exception to this rule is made if the species name is a noun (for example, *forrestii*, 'of Forrest'); in this instance, there is no genus and species agreement. To help familiarise the reader with the different gender forms, where a specific epithet appears, the masculine, feminine and neuter versions are usually listed – for example, *grandiflorus* (*grandiflora*, *grandiflorum*).

Plumbago indica,
Indian leadwort

Why botanical Latin is used for plant names

John David, Head of Horticultural Taxonomy, RHS

The system of plant names we use today dates back to the scheme first devised by the Swedish botanist Carolus Linnaeus (Carl von Linné) in his *Species Plantarum* of 1753, but the names he used in many cases were far older. Linnaeus drew heavily on earlier works, particularly the many herbals published in the previous two centuries that in turn are ultimately derived from the *De Materia Medica* of Dioscorides (around AD 77). Although he mined these early sources for names, Linnaeus did not always choose to use the name for the same plant as was originally intended.

The innovation Linnaeus employed, known as the binomial system, was to refer to each plant by a unique combination of two words and was developed as a kind of *aide-memoire*. By the Renaissance, plants had become known by long phrase names that could include over 20 words, but usually between five and ten. These could be difficult to remember, so a shorthand of just two words was a godsend. Linnaeus's system was quickly taken up by other botanists; one of the earliest works in Britain to fully adopt the system being the eighth edition of Miller's *Gardener's Dictionary* (1768). Linnaeus developed this system for animals as well.

The two elements of a Latin name are a combination of the name of a genus (plural genera) and the name of a species, such that closely related species share the same genus (generic) name. The genera were included by Linnaeus in classes, and this is where his so-called sexual system comes in. His classes were defined by the number and combination of male and female parts in the flower. An example being Hexandria Monogyna, for flowers with six stamens (male parts) and only one style (female part). This was more controversial than it might seem today as Linnaeus described these combinations in terms of marriages. For a conservative and deeply religious society, the thought of six husbands in

bed with one wife – or in the case of Polyandria, twenty or more husbands in one marriage – was shocking. It was felt at the time that Linnaeus's system was not something for polite conversation.

ABOVE: Swedish botanist Carolus Linnaeus, in the traditional dress of Lapland, is shown here carrying his favourite flower, *Linnaea borealis*.

RIGHT: The system of classification created by Linnaeus emphasised the sexual anatomy of flowers.

Another reason why Linnaeus's system of naming plants was so important is that until the era of exploration, of the Americas, Africa and Asia, Europeans had needed names only for European plants, which numbered in the low thousands. By the early 18th century, plants were flowing in from all over the world and needed to be described and named quickly. With so many plants being discovered and described, and the establishment of a more sophisticated understanding of how they were related, came the need for more ranks in the classification which were inserted between genus and class. These were the family (ending with *-aceae*) and order (ending with *-ales*) in the 19th century, with the class (*-opsida*) being redefined and the rank of phylum (*-phyta*) added above the class in the 20th century. Like the genus and species names, these are all in Latin form, but are plural adjectives. In addition, there is provision for ranks in between: variety, tribe, section, series and any number of sub- or super- ranks, as well as hybrids. Though this complex arrangement of ranks is important for botanists looking at the plant kingdom as a whole, it does not detract from the simplicity of Linnaeus's binomial system for other users of plant names.

The adoption of Latin for naming and, indeed, describing plants comes from the status of that language as the common language of learned discourse for centuries, allowing students to access the works of classical writers from ancient Greece and Rome. Botanical Latin would hardly be recognised by a Roman for it is an end point of the development, through medieval Church Latin, of a language, which from the 7th century onwards was no one's native tongue. The formal publication of a new plant required a description in Latin up until 2012 and even now it is still one of only two alternatives, the other being English. However, despite its advantage in removing almost all ambiguity, the technicalities of case, number, gender, tense, mood and declension, grammatical features almost non-existent in many of the world's languages, meant that the use of Latin presented an almost insurmountable challenge for botanists around the globe. While it is no longer required for describing plants, it is retained for plant names and an understanding of Latin is helpful for the creation of new names of plants, an appreciation of their meaning and their pronunciation.

LEFT: The binomial system of Linnaeus was timely as it provided a system for naming the many plants found during the age of discovery.

BELOW: Plant hunter Frederick Burbidge (1847–1905) discovered several new species while collecting for the Veitch Nurseries in Asia.

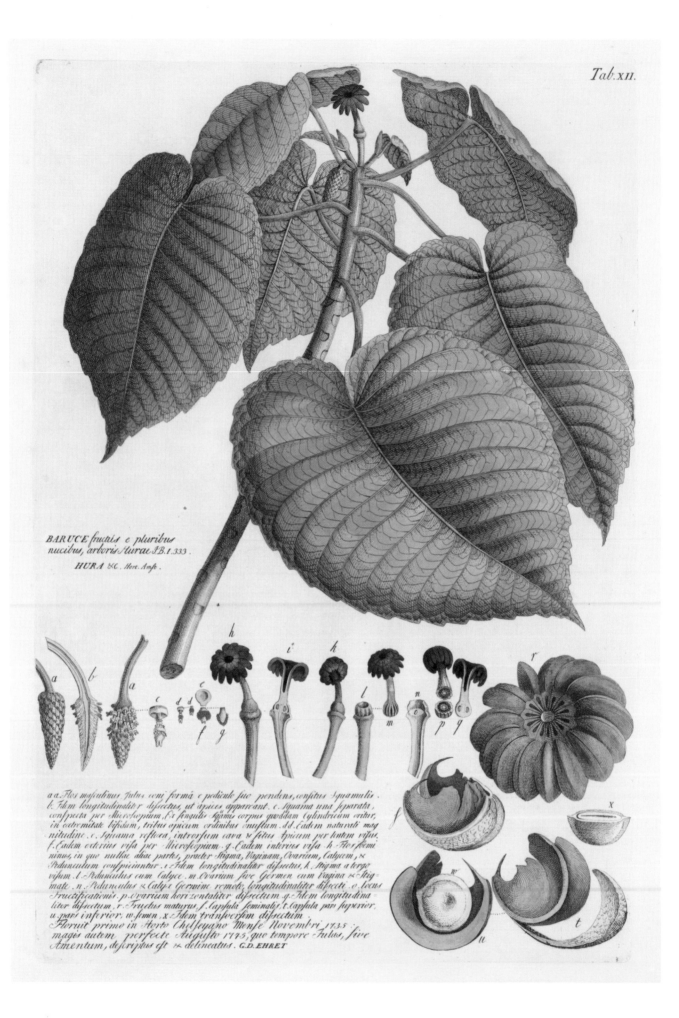

Tab. XII.

BARUCE fructus e pluribus
nucibus, arboris Hurae I.B.1.333.
HURA &c. Hort. Amst.

a a. Flos masculinus Iulus coni formâ e pediculo suo pendens, consitus Squamulis.
b. Idem longitudinaliter dissectus, ut apices appareant. c. Squama una separata,
conspecta per Microscopium, Ex singulis Squamis corpus quoddam Cylindricum oritur,
in extremitate bifidam, tribus apicum ordinibus onustum. d d. Eadem naturali mag
nitudine. e. Squama reflexa, introrsum cava & situs apicum per lentem visus.
f. Eadem exterius visa per Microscopium. g. Eadem interius visa. h. Flos foemi
ninus, in quo nullae aliae partes, praeter Stigma, Vaginam, Ovarium, Calycem, &
Pedunculum conspiciuntur. i. Idem longitudinaliter dissectus, k. Stigma a tergo
visum. l. Pedunculus cum Calyce. m. Ovarium sive Germen cum Vagina & Stig
mate. n. Pedunculus & Calyx Germine remoto, longitudinaliter dissecti. o. locus
Fructificationis. p. Ovarium horizontaliter dissectum. q. Idem longitudi
naliter dissectum. r. Fructus maturus. s. Capsula seminalis. t. Capsula pars superior.
u. pars inferior. w. semen. x. Idem transversim dissectum.
Floruit primo in Horto Chelseyano Mense Novembri 1755,
magis autem, perfecte Augusto 1745, quo tempore Iulus, sive
Amentum, descriptus est & delineatus. G.D. EHRET.

A brief history of botanical art

Brent Elliott, RHS Librarian (retired)

Botanical art is art that serves the purposes of botanists, and throughout history this has usually facilitated the accurate identification of plants. To be worthwhile, illustrations need to be available in multiple copies: a picture that exists in a single copy may be an excellent portrait of a plant, but it can be of little use other than to local botanists. We know from Pliny the Elder, writing in the 1st century AD, that scholars had tried to produce illustrated books about plants; but the only way of distributing books then was by hand-copying, and illustrations copied by hand over and over again gradually ceased to resemble the originals sufficiently to be reliable identification guides. So the attempt to illustrate books on plants was abandoned, and scholars had to rely on written descriptions alone.

The printing press changed all that. The first printed botanical books simply copied the poor schematic illustrations found in medieval manuscripts, but in 1530 Otto Brunfels published his *Herbarum vivae eicones*, with the first printed images of plants drawn from actual plant specimens, made by an artist named Hans Weiditz. This was followed in 1542 by the *De historia stirpium commentarii insignes* of Leonhart Fuchs, the first textbook on plants where both text and pictures were based on studying living specimens. Albrecht Meyer's illustrations for Fuchs established the conventions of botanical art for the next century: plants were depicted at life size where possible; the complete plant was shown, including the root system; the plants were shown in outline, with little attempt at illustrating surface texture.

Fuchs's reasoning for the use of outlines was that readers might want to colour the pictures. Amateur colouring remained a problem for generations. How could you ensure that people using the book in different places actually saw the same pictures, if in some cases they had been coloured,

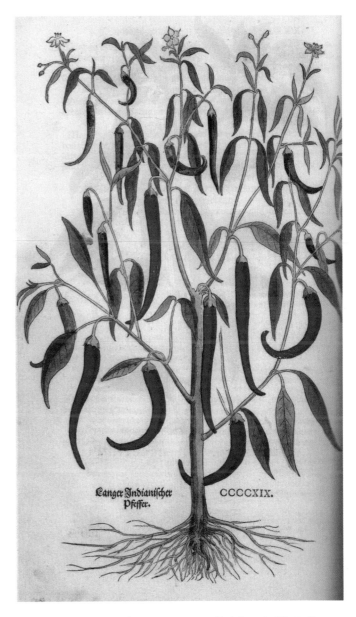

LEFT: Botanical illustrations from the mid-1700s (here, *Hura crepitans* in *Euphorbiaceae*) show detailed dissections of the flowering parts.

ABOVE: Early botanical illustrations, such as this chilli (*Capsicum annuum*) from Fuchs's 1543 German edition, rely on outlines instead of texture.

Pl. CCXIX.

RICINUS, *foliis peltatis inæqualiter serratis, capsulis hispidis.*

G. D. Ehret delin.   I. Miller Sculp.

Published according to Act of Parliament by P. Miller March 21. 1758.

18

Hibiscus mutabilis 31
Flina-Paretti

LEFT: The illustrations to Philip Miller's *Gardeners Dictionary* included this one by G.D. Ehret, showing the castor oil plant (*Ricinus communis*).

ABOVE: This picture of *Hibiscus mutabilis* from Rheede's *Hortus Malabaricus* (1678-1703) shows how such illustrations spread knowledge of the world's flora.

perhaps by someone not familiar with the plants? In the late 17th century, artists for prestigious publications began to depict the surface texture of leaves and stems in as much detail as possible, simply to deter people from colouring the illustrations. The first experiments in colour printing took place in the 18th century, but it would not be until the mid-19th century that satisfactory results were obtained.

Most botanical illustration in the 16th and 17th centuries was made for herbals – books on the plants used in medicine. During the 18th century the emphasis shifted to floras of particular parts of the world, and monographs on particular plant genera or families. In the 1730s, the botanist Carl Linnaeus popularised a system of classification based on the number and arrangement of the parts of the flower, and artists began to add detailed dissections of the flower to their works. These dissections came to be presented in rows, usually below the main figure. Leaf structure was considered subordinate, and frequently an outline of the leaf was shown as a background to the main image.

Linnaeus's sexual system of classification was superseded in the 19th century by systems that no longer focused exclusively on the flower, and artists returned to depicting all parts of the

plant. By this time they had a new tool to help them: the microscope. The first plant drawings to be created with the assistance of a microscope had been made as long ago as the 1620s, but these were not published at the time, and the power of the microscope as an aid to botany was widely recognised only in the 1830s, with the publication of Franz Bauer's drawings of orchid anatomy. A new type of botanical illustration appeared, one that used anatomical details to compare different species in the same genus or family.

In the 20th century, despite the increasing use of photography to portray plants, botanical works continued to use artists' drawings. It would take several photographs to provide all the information that can be conveyed in a single good drawing. This situation may be changing in the 21st century, with the advent of digital photography and the use of computer software to assemble multiple photographs into a single image. The coming decades promise to be an exceedingly interesting period in the history of botanical art.

How the study of DNA is changing plant names

Alastair Culham, Curator of the University of Reading Herbarium

As both a botanist and a gardener I often have to justify my use of two languages that are not natively spoken today: Latin, the international language of scientific communication for many centuries, which forms the basis for plant names, and the language of DNA sequences, the code that tells most living organisms what they are, how they should interact with the environment and even when to die. Latin causes people to ask me why plant names are so difficult and DNA data evokes questions about why plant names change so often.

DNA structure has been understood since the 1950s, but only since the 1990s has it been possible to read long stretches of DNA in a fairly cheap and efficient way. DNA provides a complex and highly detailed story of how things are related to each other, written by DNA from parents combining in offspring and the accumulation and stabilisation of chance mutations in the DNA bases. Plants have a particularly complex pattern of inheritance of DNA. Most DNA is in the cell nucleus, arranged in chromosomes and inherited 50/50 from each parent. However, there are two much smaller sets of DNA: one is in the mitochondrion, which provides energy for cell functions, the other, unique to plants, is in the plastid (including chloroplasts) with genes linked to photosynthesis and other functions. Both mitochondrial and plastid DNA are usually inherited only from the female (seed) parent. The result is that a plant cell has DNA with a mix of different histories, therefore different bits of DNA can tell very different stories about how plants are related.

To get from DNA to a theory of how species are related to each other, to form genera, families and orders, involves the comparison of DNA sequences through alignment and analysis of the changes in the DNA between samples. This is called phylogenetic analysis, which is about building a theory

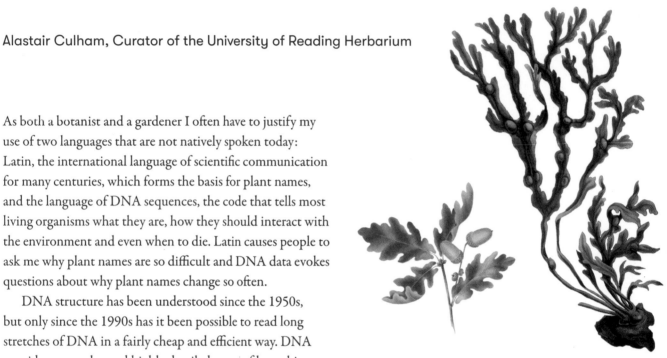

ABOVE: The acorn-like structures on bladderwrack (*Fucus vesiculosus*, right), a type of seaweed, once led to its inclusion in the oak genus *Quercus*, together with English oak, *Quercus robur* (left).

of what is related to what through reconstruction of changes in DNA sequence over time. The resulting tree of relationships, the phylogeny, is hierarchical and the tips are generally species. These in turn form larger groups, genera, and these yet larger families and so on.

There are many hidden levels of complexity. It is not easy to align one strand of DNA against another because they can change in the DNA sequence and can both extend and contract in length. Over millions of years, DNA strands can become so different it is almost impossible to tell which bit from one species is derived from which bit of another. As plants become more closely related, the differences become smaller and alignment is easier. This goes on until the DNA sequences are effectively the same, at which point species can't be told apart. Until about 2015 it was very expensive to read large portions of DNA in a single plant (it took ten years to read 90% of the smallest plant genome) but new

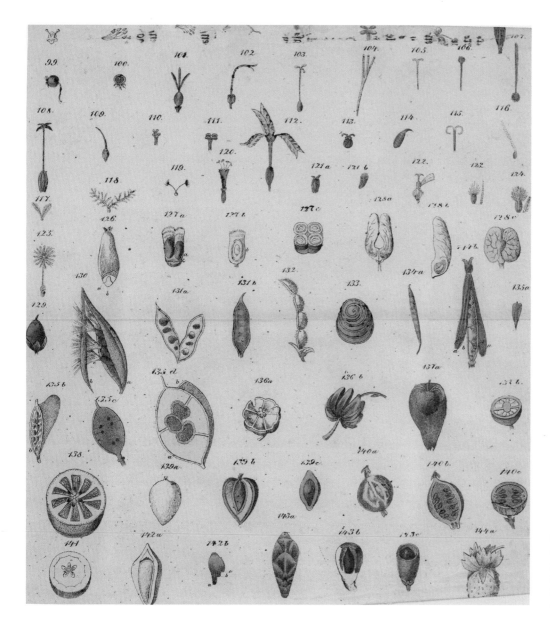

technology has made reading a whole genome more cost-effective. Now it is possible to uniquely identify most individuals based on DNA sequence.

The phylogenies constructed for plants were originally based on one gene and gradually more genes have been added. However, the easy sources of data have been only the chloroplast DNA and the DNA that codes for ribosomes (protein manufactures). When these limited data sets were analysed and used to build phylogenetic trees, some startling new relationships among plants were found, resulting in many changes of plant names. As more DNA data have been read, some of those early ideas of relationship have been replaced with newer, more robust ideas, leading to further name changes.

Most botanists try to ensure that plant names are informative of the relationships among those plants. That has big practical advantages, for instance most gardeners would

know that plants in the mint family, *Lamiaceae*, are likely to be aromatic, or that *Capsicum* species will have hot fruit. My favourite way to illustrate how name changes have helped us understand what we see is to look in a botany book by Clusius, published in 1601. He included bladderwrack (the seaweed) in his genus *Quercus* (the oak) due to the common presence of acorn-like structures. Imagine the disappointment if you bought a *Quercus* from a catalogue and got brown seaweed! DNA data helps improve the way classification reflects relationships among plants. Think of every name change as an improved model, rather than a nuisance.

Practical uses of botanical Latin

James Armitage, Editor of *The Plantsman*

Many gardeners will have thought at some point that Latin names just get in the way. Even the keenest plant enthusiast will be familiar with the experience of trying to recall some impossibly antediluvian epithet, clutching their forehead and muttering feebly, 'I know it begins with a D...'. Common names are so charming and memorable – foxglove, Jack-in-the-pulpit, handkerchief tree – why not just use these?

There are several excellent reasons why we need a fixed scientific set of names constructed from a dead language. One great advantage of Latin is its universality. No nation can claim it as its mother tongue, so it is at once everyone's and no one's, neither advantaging nor disadvantaging any one user. In the vast, shifting diversity of language and script found across the globe, Latin stands as a constant, unchanging point, so a plant name is the same in New Zealand as it is in Korea, Sweden, Morocco, Brazil or Canada.

Latin names are also predictive in a way common names tend not to be. There is nothing in the colloquialisms skunkbush and stag's-horn sumach to suggest any particular relationship or similarity. However, once you know that they both refer to species of the genus *Rhus* you are able to predict that each plant is likely to have pinnate leaves and good autumn colour.

Aside from other considerations, an important justification for the use of Latin names is that they have so much to tell us that is of practical value. Colour, form, size, ethnobotany, habitat, geography, history – all these things and many more are referred to in the names of plants, and all impart practical information that helps to make us better gardeners.

It is always helpful to gain some idea of a plant's appearance from a mere glance at its name. Those developing a colour scheme in blue and white, for instance, might wish to keep an eye out for plants bearing the epithets *cyanus* and *caeruleus* (blue) or *albus* and *lacteus* (white). More fiery colours are represented by *aurantiacum* (orange), *coccineus* (scarlet) and *ruber* (red), among many others.

It is not just characteristics as obvious as colour that are indicated in plant names. Epithets with the suffix *-folius* refer to details of the leaves. So we have *angustifolius* (narrow leaves), *brevifolius* (short leaves) and *grandifolius* (big leaves).

Stature might be indicated in names like *grandis* (big), *minima* (smallest) and *nana* (dwarf), and growth habit in names like *fastigiata* (erect, upright branches), *pendula* (hanging) and *scandens* (climbing). For plants that satisfy with their aroma, the epithet *odorata* (with a fragrant scent) might be sought out, while the name *foetida* (with a bad smell) forewarns of a less agreeable experience.

Once acquaintance is made with the richness and diverse derivation of botanical Latin, scientific names can become every bit as romantic, evocative and charming as common names. And nearly as easy to remember!

RIGHT: Though exhibiting many different colours, foxglove (*Digitalis*) flowers are usually tubular, like the thimble from which their Latin name derives.

Genre Digitale

1. D. Purpurea
4. D. Cunariensis
2. D. Lanata
5. D. Tomentosa
6. D. Ambigua
7. D. Minor
8. D. Orientalis

115

a-
Used in compound words to denote without or contrary to

abbreviatus
ab-bree-vee-AH-tus
abbreviata, abbreviatum
Shortened; abbreviated, as in *Buddleja abbreviata*

Abelia
uh-BEE-lee-uh
Named after Clarke Abel (1780–1826), British surgeon and naturalist (*Caprifoliaceae*)

Abeliophyllum
uh-BEE-lee-oh-fil-um
Leaves resembling *Abelia*, from Greek *phyllon* meaning 'leaf' (*Oleaceae*)

Abies (also abies)
A-bees
From Latin name for fir tree, published by Pliny the Elder in 77 AD (*Pinaceae*)

—

abietinus
ay-bee-TEE-nus
abietina, abietinum
Like fir tree (*Abies*), as in *Campanula patula* subsp. *abietina*

abortivus
a-bor-TEE-vus
abortiva, abortivum
Incomplete; with parts missing, as in *Oncidium abortivum*

abrotanifolius
ab-ro-tan-ih-FOH-lee-us
abrotanifolia, abrotanifolium
With leaves like southernwood (*Artemisia abrotanum*), as in *Euryops abrotanifolius*

Abutilon
uh-BEW-ti-lon
From Latin, derived from Arabic (*abu-tilun*) for Indian mallow (*Malvaceae*)

abyssinicus
a-biss-IN-ih-kus
abyssinica, abyssinicum
Connected with Abyssinia (Ethiopia), as in *Aponogeton abyssinicus*

Acacia [1]
uh-KAY-sha
From Greek *akantha*, meaning 'thorn'. Many species bear prominent spines (*Fabaceae*)

Acaena
uh-SEE-nuh
From Greek *akantha*, meaning 'thorn' as the fruits are spiny (*Rosaceae*)

Acalypha
uh-KA-lee-fuh
From Greek *akaluphe* meaning 'nettle', to which some species resemble (*Euphorbiaceae*)

acanth-
Used in compound words to denote spiny, spiky or thorny properties

acanthifolius
uh-kan-thi-FOH-lee-us
acanthifolia, acanthifolium
With leaves like *Acanthus*, as in *Carlina acanthifolia*

Acantholimon
uh-KAN-tho-lim-on
From Greek *akantha* meaning 'thorn', and *Limonium*, a related genus (*Plumbaginaceae*)

Acanthostachys
uh-KAN-tho-stak-is
From Greek *akantha* meaning 'thorn' and *stachys*, an 'ear of grain', as the inflorescences are spiny and similar in shape to a cereal seed head (*Bromeliaceae*)

Acacia acinacea, **gold-dust wattle**

1

A
B
C
D
E
F
G
H
I
J
K
L
M
N
O
P
Q
R
S
T
U
V
W
X
Y
Z

i

25

Acanthus

uh-KAN-thus

From Greek *akantha* meaning 'thorn', as floral bracts and leaves may be spiny (*Acanthaceae*)

acaulis

a-KAW-lis

acaulis, acaule

Short-stemmed: without a stem, as in *Gentiana acaulis*

Acca

AK-uh

From Peruvian indigenous name *aca* (for *A. macrostemma*) (*Myrtaceae*)

-aceae

Denoting the rank of family

Acer

AY-sa

From Latin name for maple tree, derived from Latin for 'sharp' or 'pointed', as maple wood was used in manufacturing spears (*Sapindaceae*)

acerifolius

a-ser-ih-FOH-lee-us

acerifolia, acerifolium

With leaves like maple (*Acer*), as in *Quercus acerifolia*

acerosus

a-seh-ROH-sus

acerosa, acerosum

Like a needle, as in *Melaleuca acerosa*

acetosella

a-kee-TOE-sell-uh

With slightly sour leaves, as in *Oxalis acetosella*

Achillea

uh-KEY-lee-ah

Named after Greek warrior Achilles, who used the plant to heal wounds (*Asteraceae*)

achilleifolius

ah-key-lee-FOH-lee-us

achilleifolia, achilleifolium

With leaves like common yarrow (*Achillea millefolium*), as in *Tanacetum achilleifolium*

Achimenes

uh-KIM-en-eez

From Greek *cheimanos* meaning 'tender', as plants are not frost-hardy or from Greek Achaemenes, the mythical ancestor of a Persian royal house (*Gesneriaceae*)

Achlys

AK-liss

Named after Greek goddess of mist and darkness, as plants grow in shade (*Berberidaceae*)

acicularis

ass-ik-yew-LAH-ris

acicularis, aciculare

Shaped like a needle, as in *Rosa acicularis*

acinaceus

a-sin-AY-see-us

acinacea, acinaceum

In the shape of a curved sword or scimitar, as in *Acacia acinacea*

GENUS SPOTLIGHT

Acanthus

The Greek word *akantha* meaning 'thorn' or 'thorny' is a common component of plant Latin names, as in *Acanthostachys* or *Pyracantha*, warning that the plant may be spiny to touch. *Acanthus* itself can have spiny leaves, as in *A. spinosus* and *A. sennii*, but some species have softer foliage (e.g. *A. mollis*) and the spines are restricted to the flower spikes, where spine-tipped bracts enclose the buds. Consider carefully before planting herbaceous *Acanthus*, as their deep roots are difficult to extract and resprout if cut, turning unwanted plants into pernicious weeds.

Acanthus mollis,
bear's breech

Acinos
uh-SEE-nos
From Greek *akinos* used by Dioscorides for a small fragrant plant (*Lamiaceae*)

Aciphylla
a-si-FILL-uh
From Greek *akis* meaning 'point' and *phyllon* meaning 'leaf', as plants have sharply pointed foliage (*Apiaceae*)

Acis
A-kis
Named after Greek mythological character Acis, killed by a cyclops and transformed into a Sicilian river of the same name (*Amaryllidaceae*)

Acmena
AK-mee-na
From Greek *acmene*, a beautiful wood nymph (*Myrtaceae*)

acmopetala
ak-mo-PET-uh-la
With pointed petals, as in *Fritillaria acmopetala*

Acoelorrhaphe
a-see-lo-RAY-fee
From Greek *a* ('without'), *koilos* ('hollow') and *rhaphis* ('seam'), as the seeds lack the characteristic ridge or depression commonly found in related palms (*Arecaceae*)

Acokanthera
ah-ko-KAN-ther-ah
From Greek *akoke* meaning 'point' and *anthera*, referring to the pointed anthers (*Apocynaceae*)

aconitifolius
a-kon-eye-tee-FOH-lee-us
aconitifolia, aconitifolium
With leaves like aconite (*Aconitum*), as in *Ranunculus aconitifolius*

Aconitum
ah-kon-EYE-tum
From Greek *akoniton*, used by Theophrastus to refer to a very poisonous plant, possibly derived from *akon*, a poison-tipped dart or javelin (*Ranunculaceae*)

Acorus
a-CORE-us
From Greek *coreon* meaning 'pupil', as used to treat ailments of the eye (*Acoraceae*)

Acradenia
ak-ra-DEEN-ee-uh
From Greek *akros* meaning 'tip', and *aden* meaning 'gland', referring to the glands on top of the ovary (*Rutaceae*)

acraeus
ak-ra-EE-us
acraea, acraeum
Dwelling on high ground, as in *Euryops acraeus*

GENUS SPOTLIGHT

Achillea

Named after the hero of Greek mythology, Achilles, who is said to have used an extract of yarrow (*A. millefolium*) to staunch the flow of blood from wounds. The inflorescences in many ways resemble those of the carrot family (*Apiaceae*), in that many flowers cluster together to form an umbrella-like platform that is readily accessed by butterflies, hoverflies and other pollinating insects. But yarrow is in the daisy family (*Asteraceae*), and each of the small 'flowers' is itself an inflorescence, composed of several much smaller florets. By gathering together so many blooms, yarrows produce a long-lasting and nectar-rich display, much loved by gardeners and insects alike.

Achillea millefolium,
common yarrow

Actaea

ak-TAY-uh

From the Greek word for elder (*Sambucus*), as the foliage is similar (*Ranunculaceae*)

Actinidia

ak-tin-ID-ee-uh

From Greek *aktin* meaning 'ray', as the floral styles radiate outwards from the centre of the flower (*Actinidiaceae*)

actinophyllus

ak-ten-oh-FIL-us

actinophylla, actinophyllum

With radiating leaves, as in *Schefflera actinophylla*

acu-

Used in compound words to denote sharply pointed

aculeatus

a-kew-lee-AH-tus

aculeata, aculeatum

Prickly, as in *Polystichum aculeatum*

aculeolatus

a-kew-lee-oh-LAH-tus

aculeolata, aculeolatum

With small prickles, as in *Arabis aculeolata*

acuminatifolius

a-kew-min-at-ih-FOH-lee-us

acuminatifolia, acuminatifolium

With leaves that taper sharply to long narrow points, as in *Polygonatum acuminatifolium*

acuminatus

ah-kew-min-AH-tus

acuminata, acuminatum

Tapering to a long, narrow point, as in *Magnolia acuminata*

acutifolius

a-kew-ti-FOH-lee-us

acutifolia, acutifolium

With leaves that taper quickly to sharp points, as in *Begonia acutifolia*

acutilobus

a-KEW-ti-low-bus

acutiloba, acutilobum

With sharply pointed lobes, as in *Hepatica acutiloba*

acutissimus

ak-yoo-TISS-ee-mus

acutissima, acutissimum

With a very acute point, as in *Ligustrum acutissimum*

acutus

a-KEW-tus

acuta, acutum

With a sharp but not tapering point, as in *Cynanchum acutum*

Adansonia digitata, baobab

ad-

Used in compound words to denote to

Ada

A-duh

Named after Ada, Queen of Caria and adopted mother of Alexander the Great. Could also refer to the Hebrew *adah* meaning 'beauty' (*Orchidaceae*)

Adansonia [1]

ad-an-SOWN-ee-ah

Named after Michel Adanson (1727–1806), French explorer and biologist (*Malvaceae*)

aden-

Used in compound words to denote that a part of the plant has glands

Adenia

ah-DEE-nee-uh

From Arabic *aden*, the vernacular name for the outwardly similar *Adenia venenata* and *Adenium obesum* in Arabia (*Passifloraceae*)

Adenium

ah-DEE-nee-um

From Arabic *aden*, the vernacular name for the outwardly similar *Adenia venenata* and *Adenium obesum* in Arabia (*Apocynaceae*)

Adiantum capillus-veneris,
maidenhair fern

Adenocarpus
ad-en-oh-CARP-us
From Greek *aden* meaning 'gland' and *karpos*, meaning 'fruit', as the seed pods are glandular (*Fabaceae*)

Adenophora
ah-den-OFF-or-uh
From Greek *aden* meaning 'gland' and *phoros* meaning 'to bear', as the nectaries are glandular (*Campanulaceae*)

adenophorus
ad-eh-NO-for-us
adenophora, adenophorum
With glands, usually in reference to nectar, as in *Salvia adenophora*

adenophyllus
ad-en-oh-FIL-us
adenophylla, adenophyllum
With sticky (gland-bearing) leaves, as in *Oxalis adenophylla*

adenopodus
a-den-OH-poh-dus
adenopoda, adenopodum
With sticky pedicels (small stalks), as in *Begonia adenopoda*

adiantifolius
ad-ee-an-tee-FOH-lee-us
adiantifolia, adiantifolium
With leaves like maidenhair fern (*Adiantum*), as in *Anemia adiantifolia*

Adiantum [2]
ad-ee-AN-tum
From Greek *adiantos* meaning 'unwettable', as the fronds shed water (*Pteridaceae*)

adlamii
ad-LAM-ee-eye
Named after Richard Wills Adlam (1853–1903), a British collector who supplied plants to London's Royal Botanic Gardens, Kew, in the 1890s

Adlumia
ad-LOOM-ee-uh
Named after John Adlum (1759–1836), American surveyor, judge and viticulturist (*Papaveraceae*)

admirabilis
ad-mir-AH-bil-is
admirabilis, admirabile
Of note, as in *Drosera admirabilis*

adnatus
ad-NAH-tus
adnata, adnatum
Joined together, as in *Sambucus adnata*

Adonis
ad-OWN-iss
Named after Greek mythological character Adonis, a lover of the goddess Aphrodite (*Ranunculaceae*)

adpressus
ad-PRESS-us
adpressa, adpressum
Pressed close to; refers to the way hairs (for example) press against a stem, as in *Cotoneaster adpressus*

Adromischus
ad-roh-MISS-kus
From Greek *hadros* meaning 'stout' and *mischos* meaning 'stalk', referring to the thick flower stems (*Crassulaceae*)

adscendens
ad-SEN-denz
Ascending; rising, as in *Aster adscendens*

adsurgens
ad-SER-jenz
Rising upwards, as in *Phlox adsurgens*

aduncus
ad-UN-kus
adunca, aduncum
Hooked, as in *Viola adunca*

Aechmea
EK-mee-uh
From Greek *aichme* meaning 'point', as the floral bracts are sharp-tipped (*Bromeliaceae*)

Aegopodium

ie-go-POH-dee-um

From Greek *aigos* meaning 'goat' and *podion* meaning 'foot', as the leaves are said to resemble goat hooves (*Apiaceae*)

aegyptiacus

eh-jip-tee-AH-kus

aegyptiaca, aegyptiacum

—

aegypticus

eh-JIP-tih-kus

aegyptica, aegypticum

—

aegyptius

eh-JIP-tee-us

aegyptica, aegypticum

Connected with Egypt, as in *Achillea aegyptiaca*

aemulans

EM-yoo-lanz

—

aemulus

EM-yoo-lus

aemula, aemulum

Imitating; rivalling, as in *Scaevola aemula*

Aeonium

ie-OH-nee-um

From Greek *aionios* meaning 'everlasting', as these succulents are evergreen (*Crassulaceae*)

aequalis

ee-KWA-lis

aequalis, aequale

Equal, as in *Phygelius aequalis*

aequinoctialis

eek-wee-nok-tee-AH-lis

aequinoctialis, aequinoctiale

Connected with the equatorial regions, as in *Cydista aequinoctialis*

aequitrilobus

eek-wee-try-LOH-bus

aequitriloba, aequitrilobum

With three equal lobes, as in *Cymbalaria aequitriloba*

Aerangis

air-AN-gis

From Greek *aer* meaning 'air' and *angos* meaning 'vessel', as the flower has a pendulous spur that holds nectar (*Orchidaceae*)

Aerides

air-id-EEZ

From Greek *aer* meaning 'air', referring to the epiphytic habit (*Orchidaceae*)

aerius

ER-re-us

aeria, aerium

From high altitudes, as in *Crocus aerius*

aeruginosus

air-oo-jin-OH-sus

aeruginosa, aeruginosum

The colour of rust, as in *Curcuma aeruginosa*

Aeschynanthus

ay-shi-NAN-thus

From Greek *aischyne* meaning 'shame' and *anthos* meaning 'flower', possibly alluding to the shocking red colour of the flowers of many species (*Gesneriaceae*)

aesculifolius

es-kew-li-FOH-lee-us

aesculifolia, aesculifolium

With leaves like horse chestnut (*Aesculus*), as in *Rodgersia aesculifolia*

Aesculus [1]

ES-kew-lus

From Latin name for edible acorn (*Sapindaceae*)

aestivalis

ee-stiv-AH-lis

aestivalis, aestivale

Relating to summer, as in *Vitis aestivalis*

aestivus

EE-stiv-us

aestiva, aestivum

Developing or ripening in the summer months, as in *Leucojum aestivum*

Aethionema

ee-thee-oh-NEEM-uh

From Greek *aethes* meaning 'irregular' or *aitho* meaning 'burnt', plus *nema* meaning 'filament', referring to some characteristic of the stamens (*Brassicaceae*)

aethiopicus

ee-thee-OH-pih-kus

aethiopica, aethiopicum

Connected with Africa, as in *Zantedeschia aethiopica*

aethusifolius

e-thu-si-FOH-lee-us

aethusifolia, aethusifolium

With pungent leaves like *Aethusa*, as in *Aruncus aethusifolius*

aetnensis

eet-NEN-sis

aetnensis, aetnense

From Mount Etna, Italy, as in *Genista aetnensis*

aetolicus

eet-OH-lih-kus

aetolica, aetolicum

Connected with Aetolia, Greece, as in *Viola aetolica*

afer

A-fer

afra, afrum

Specifically connected with North African coastal countries such as Algeria and Tunisia, as in *Lycium afrum*

affinis

uh-FEE-nis

affinis, affine

Related or similar to, as in *Dryopteris affinis*

afghanicus

af-GAN-ih-kus

afghanica, afghanicum

—

afghanistanica

af-gan-is-STAN-ee-ka

Connected with Afghanistan, as in *Corydalis afghanica*

aflatunensis

a-flat-u-NEN-sis

aflatunensis, aflatunense

From Aflatun, Kyrgyzstan, as in *Allium aflatunense*

africanus

af-ri-KAHN-us

africana, africanum

Connected with Africa, as in *Sparrmannia africana*

Agapanthus

a-guh-PAN-thus

From Greek *agape* meaning 'love' and *anthos* meaning 'flower', though the reason for this name is unknown (*Amaryllidaceae*)

Agapetes
ag-ah-PEET-ees
From Greek *agapetos* meaning 'beloved' or 'desirable', due to their great beauty (*Ericaceae*)

Agastache
ag-AH-sta-kee
From Greek *agan* meaning 'very much' and *stachys*, an 'ear of grain', an allusion to the plentiful flower heads (*Lamiaceae*)

agastus
ag-AS-tus
agasta, agastum
With great charm, as in *Rhododendron ×
agastum*

Agathis
AG-ah-thiss
From Greek *agathis* meaning 'ball of thread', as the seed cones are spherical (*Araucariaceae*)

Agathosma
ag-uth-OZ-ma
From Greek *agathos* meaning 'good' and *osme* meaning 'fragrance' (*Rutaceae*)

Agave
uh-GAH-vee
From Greek *agavos* meaning 'great', in reference to the impressive inflorescence of many species (*Asparagaceae*)

agavoides
ah-gav-OY-deez
Resembling *Agave*, as in *Echeveria agavoides*

ageratifolius
ad-jur-rat-ih-FOH-lee-us
ageratifolia, ageratifolium
With leaves like *Ageratum*, as in *Achillea ageratifolia*

Ageratina
aj-err-ah-TEE-na
Resembling the related genus *Ageratum* (*Asteraceae*)

ageratoides
ad-jur-rat-OY-deez
Resembling *Ageratum*, as in *Aster ageratoides*

Ageratum
aj-err-AH-toom
From Greek *ageraton* meaning 'not growing old', in reference to the long-lasting flowers (*Asteraceae*)

aggregatus
ag-gre-GAH-tus
aggregata, aggregatum
Denotes aggregate flowers or fruits, such as raspberry or strawberry, as in *Eucalyptus aggregata*

Aglaomorpha
uh-glay-oh-MOR-fa
From Greek *aglaos* meaning 'beautiful' and *morpha* meaning 'shape' or 'form' (*Polypodiaceae*)

Aglaonema
uh-glay-oh NEE-ma
From Greek *aglaos* meaning 'beautiful' and *nema* meaning 'filament', possibly referring to the stamens, though these are typically small in this genus (*Araceae*)

agnus-castus
AG-nus KAS-tus
From *agnos*, Greek name for *Vitex agnus-castus*, and *castus*, chaste, as in *Vitex agnus-castus*

Agonis
ah-GO-niss
From Greek *agon* meaning a 'gathering', in reference to the clustered flowers or copious seeds (*Myrtaceae*)

Agoseris
ag-OSS-er-iss
From Greek *aigos* meaning 'goat' and *seris* meaning 'lettuce' (*Asteraceae*)

agrarius
ag-RAH-ree-us
agraria, agrarium
From fields and cultivated land, as in *Fumaria agraria*

**Aesculus glabra,
Ohio buckeye**

1

agrestis

ag-RES-tis

agrestis, agreste

Found growing in fields, as in *Fritillaria agrestis*

agrifolius

ag-rih-FOH-lee-us

agrifolia, agrifolium

With leaves with a rough or scabby texture, as in *Quercus agrifolia*

Agrimonia

ah-gree-MOH-nee-ah

From Greek *argemone* meaning poppy, though several alternative meanings also possible as this plant does not closely resemble a poppy (*Rosaceae*)

agrippinum

ag-rip-EE-num

Named after Agrippina, mother of the Emperor Nero, as in *Colchicum agrippinum*

Agrostemma [1]

ah-gro-STEM-uh

From Greek *agros* meaning 'field' and *stemma* meaning 'wreath' (*Caryophyllaceae*)

Agrostis

ah-GROS-tis

The Latin and Greek name for 'grass', 'weed' or 'couch grass' (*Poaceae*)

Aichryson

ie-CRY-son

From Greek *aei* meaning 'always' and *khrysos* meaning 'gold', as the flowers are yellow (*Crassulaceae*)

Ailanthus [2]

ay-LAN-thoos

From Ambonese (Indonesia) *ailanto* meaning 'reach for the sky' or 'tree of heaven' (*Simaroubaceae*)

aitchisonii

EYE-chi-soh-nee-eye

Named after Dr J.E.T. Aitchison (1836–98), a British doctor and botanist who collected plant material in Asia, as in *Corydalis aitchisonii*

aizoides

ay-ZOY-deez

Like the genus *Aizoon*, as in *Saxifraga aizoides*

ajacis

a-JAY-sis

A species name that honours the Greek hero Ajax, as in *Consolida ajacis*

ajanensis

ah-yah-NEN-sis

ajanensis, ajanense

From Ajan on the Siberian coast, as in *Dryas ajanensis*

1

Agrostemma githago,
corncockle

2

Ailanthus altissima,
tree of heaven

Ajania
ah-JAH-nee-uh
Named for the city of Ajan (now Ayan) on the Pacific coast of Russia (*Asteraceae*)

Ajuga [3, 4]
ah-JOO-ga
Origins uncertain, though could derive from Greek *a* meaning 'without' and *iugum*, a 'yoke', as the calyx is undivided (*Lamiaceae*)

Akebia
ah-KEE-bee-uh
From Japanese *akebi*, the vernacular name for *A. quinata* (*Lardizabalaceae*)

alabamensis
al-uh-bam-EN-sis
alabamensis, alabamense
—

alabamicus
al-a-BAM-ih-kus
alabamica, alabamicum
From or of Alabama, USA, as in *Rhododendron alabamense*

Alangium
al-ANJ-ee-um
From Malayalam *alangi*, the vernacular name used in Kerala, India, for *A. salviifolium* (*Cornaceae*)

alaternus
a-la-TER-nus
The Roman name for *Rhamnus alaternus*

alatus
a-LAH-tus
alata, alatum
Winged, as in *Euonymus alatus*

albanensis
al-ba-NEN-sis
albanensis, albanense
From St Albans, Hertfordshire, England, as in *Coelogyne* × *albanense*

alberti
al-BER-tee
—

albertianus
al-ber-tee-AH-nus
albertiana, albertianum
—

albertii
al-BER-tee-eye
Named after various people called Albert, such as Albert von Regel (1845–1908), plant collector, as in *Tulipa albertii*

albescens
al-BES-enz
Becoming white, as in *Kniphofia albescens*

3

Ajuga reptans,
bugle

4

Ajuga genevensis,
blue bugle

Iris albicans,
white flag iris

Alcea rosea,
hollyhock

Alchemilla fissa,
hairless lady's mantle

albicans [1]
AL-bih-kanz
Off-white, as in *Hebe albicans*

albicaulis
al-bih-KAW-lis
albicaulis, albicaule
With white stems, as in *Lupinus albicaulis*

albidus
AL-bi-dus
albida, albidum
White, as in *Trillium albidum*

albiflorus
al-BIH-flor-us
albiflora, albiflorum
With white flowers, as in *Buddleja albiflora*

albifrons
AL-by-fronz
With white fronds, as in *Cyathea albifrons*

Albizia
al-BITZ-ee-uh
Named after Filippo degli Albizzi (18th century, dates uncertain), Italian naturalist and nobleman (*Fabaceae*)

albomaculatus
al-boh-mak-yoo-LAH-tus
albomaculata, albomaculatum
With white spots, as in *Asarum albomaculatum*

albomarginatus
AL-bow-mar-gin-AH-tus
albomarginata, albomarginatum
With white margins, as in *Agave albomarginata*

albopictus
al-boh-PIK-tus
albopicta, albopictum
With white hairs, as in *Begonia albopicta*

albosinensis
al-bo-sy-NEN-sis
albosinensis, albosinense
Meaning white and from China, as in *Betula albosinensis*

albovariegatus
al-bo-var-ee-GAH-tus
albovariegata, albovariegatum
Variegated with white, as in *Holcus mollis* 'Albovariegatus'

Albuca
all-BOO-ka
From Latin *albicans* meaning 'becoming white' in reference to the flower colour, though most species have yellow flowers (*Asparagaceae*)

albulus
ALB-yoo-lus
albula, albulum
Whitish in colour, as in *Carex albula*

albus
AL-bus
alba, album
White, as in *Veratrum album*

Alcea [2]
al-SEE-uh
From Greek *alkea* meaning 'mallow' (*Malvaceae*)

Alchemilla [3]
all-ke-MILL-uh
From Arabic *al-kemelih* meaning 'alchemy', as the hairy leaves repel water in an almost miraculous fashion (*Rosaceae*)

alcicornis
al-kee-KOR-nis
alcicornis, alcicorne
Palmate leaves that resemble the horns of the European elk (North American moose), as in *Platycerium alcicorne*

aleppensis
a-le-PEN-sis
aleppensis aleppense
—

aleppicus
a-LEP-ih-kus
aleppica, aleppicum
From Aleppo, Syria, as in *Adonis aleppica*

aleuticus

a-LEW-tih-kus

aleutica, aleuticum

Connected with the Aleutian Islands, Alaska, as in *Adiantum aleuticum*

alexandrae

al-ex-AN-dry

Named after Queen Alexandra (1844–1925), wife of Edward VII of England, as in *Archontophoenix alexandrae*

alexandrinus

al-ex-an-DREE-nus

alexandrina, alexandrinum

Connected with Alexandria, Egypt, as in *Senna alexandrina*

algeriensis

al-jir-ee-EN-sis

algeriensis, algeriense

From Algeria, as in *Ornithogalum algeriense*

algidus

AL-gee-dus

algida, algidum

Cold; of high mountain regions, as in *Olearia algida*

alienus

a-LY-en-us

aliena, alienum

A plant of foreign origin, as in *Heterolepis aliena*

Alisma

ah-LIZ-mah

From the ancient Greek name for a water plant (*Alismataceae*)

Alkanna

al-KA-na

From Arabic *al-hinna* meaning 'henna', as the plant produces a dye (*Boraginaceae*)

alkekengi

al-KEK-en-jee

From the Arabic for bladder cherry, as in *Physalis alkekengi*

Allamanda [4]

al-ah-MAN-duh

Named after Jean Frédéric-Louis Allamand (1736–1803), Swiss botanist (*Apocynaceae*)

alleghaniensis

al-leh-gay-nee-EN-sis

alleghaniensis, alleghaniense

From the Allegheny Mountains, USA, as in *Betula alleghaniensis*

alliaceus

al-lee-AY-see-us

alliacea, alliaceum

Like *Allium* (onion or garlic), as in *Tulbaghia alliacea*

Alliaria

al-ee-AIR-ee-uh

From Latin *allium* meaning 'garlic', due to the scent of crushed leaves (*Brassicaceae*)

alliariifolius

al-ee-ar-ee-FOH-lee-us

alliariifolia, alliariifolium

With leaves like *Alliaria*, as in *Valeriana alliariifolia*

allionii

al-ee-OH-nee-eye

Named after Carlo Allioni (1728–1804), Italian botanist, as in *Primula allionii*

Allium [5]

al-EE-um

From Latin *allium* meaning 'garlic', as in *A. sativum* (*Amaryllidaceae*)

Alluaudia

al-AWED-ee-uh

Named after François Alluaud (1778–1866), French scientist (*Didiereaceae*)

alnifolius

al-nee-FOH-lee-us

alnifolia, alnifolium

With leaves like alder (*Alnus*), as in *Sorbus alnifolia*

Alnus [6] (also alnus)

ALL-noos

From Latin name for alder tree (*Betulaceae*)

4

Allamanda cathartica,
golden trumpet

5

Allium caeruleum,
blue-flowered garlic

6

Alnus incana,
grey alder

Alpinia nutans,
cinnamon ginger

Alocasia
al-oh-KAY-see-uh
From Greek *a* meaning 'without' and
Colocasia, a related genus (*Araceae*)

Aloe
A-loh-ee
From Arabic *alloeh*, referring to the bitter
juice extracted from the leaves
(*Asphodelaceae*)

aloides
al-OY-deez
Resembling *Aloe*, as in *Lachenalia aloides*

aloifolius
al-oh-ih-FOH-lee-us
aloifolia, aloifolium
With leaves like *Aloe*, as in *Yucca aloifolia*

Aloinopsis
a-loh-in-OP-sis
Resembling the genus *Aloe* (*Aizoaceae*)

Alonsoa
al-ON-so-uh
Named after Zenón de Alonso Acosta (dates
unknown), Spanish soldier in Bogotá,
Colombia (*Scrophulariaceae*)

alopecuroides
al-oh-pek-yur-OY-deez
Like the genus *Alopecurus* (foxtail), as in
Pennisetum alopecuroides

Alopecurus
al-oh-pek-URE-us
From Greek *alopex* meaning 'fox' and *oura*
meaning 'tail', referring to the shape of the
inflorescence (*Poaceae*)

Aloysia
al-OY-see-uh
Named after Maria Luisa of Parma (1751–
1819), wife of King Charles IV of Spain
(*Verbenaceae*)

alpestris
al-PES-tris
alpestris, alpestre
Of lower, usually wooded, mountain
habitats, as in *Narcissus alpestris*

alpicola
al-PIH-koh-luh
Of high mountain habitats, as in *Primula
alpicola*

alpigenus
AL-pi-GEE-nus
alpigena, alpigenum
Of a mountainous region, as in *Saxifraga
alpigena*

Alpinia
al-PIN-ee-uh
Named after Prospero Alpini (1553–1617),
Italian physician and botanist
(*Zingiberaceae*)

alpinus
al-PEE-nus
alpina, alpinum
Of high, often rocky regions; from the Alps
region of Europe, as in *Pulsatilla alpina*

Alsobia
al-SOH-bee-uh
From Greek *alsos* meaning 'forest' and *bios*
meaning 'life', alluding to the epiphytic habit
(*Gesneriaceae*)

Alstroemeria
al-stro-MEE-ree-uh
Named after Clas Alströmer (1736–94),
Swedish nobleman (*Alstroemeriaceae*)

altaclerensis
al-ta-cler-EN-sis
altaclerensis, altaclerense
From Highclere Castle, Hampshire,
England, as in *Ilex × altaclerensis*

altaicus
al-TAY-ih-kus
altaica, altaicum
Connected with the Altai Mountains,
Central Asia, as in *Tulipa altaica*

alternans
al-TER-nans
Alternating, as in *Chamaedorea alternans*

Alternanthera
awl-ter-NAN-thu-rah
From Latin *alternans* and *anthera*, as the
anthers alternate with staminodes in the
flowers (*Amaranthaceae*)

alternifolius
al-tern-ee-FOH-lee-us
alternifolia, alternifolium
With leaves that grow from alternating
points of a stem, rather than opposite each
other, as in *Buddleja alternifolia*

Althaea
al-THEE-uh
From Greek *althos* meaning 'healing'; also
Althaea, Queen of Calydon in Greek
mythology (*Malvaceae*)

althaeoides
al-thay-OY-deez
Resembling hollyhock (formerly *Althaea*), as
in *Convolvulus althaeoides*

altissimus
al-TISS-ih-mus
altissima, altissimum
Very tall; the tallest, as in *Ailanthus altissima*

altus
AHL-tus
alta, altum
Tall, as in *Sempervivum altum*

MIXING IT UP

When creating a new genus,
the usual route is to choose a
name that describes the plant,
or failing that, name it after
someone. But with so many
names already in use, it can be
hard to come up with
something new. A novel
approach is to create an
anagram of an existing genus,
as in *Tellima* (from *Mitella*),
Docynia (from *Cydonia*),
Leymus (from *Elymus*) and
Saruma (from *Asarum*). Using
similar names not only makes
them easier to remember, but
also helps to reinforce the
familial relationship between
the pair.

Alyogyne
al-ee-oh-GY-nee
From Greek *alytos* meaning 'undivided' and *gyne* meaning 'female', as the styles are undivided (*Malvaceae*)

Alyssum
A-liss-um
From Greek *a* meaning 'without' and *lyssa* meaning 'rabies' or 'madness', a medicinal herb (*Brassicaceae*)

amabilis
am-AH-bih-lis
amabilis, amabile
Lovely, as in *Cynoglossum amabile*

amanus
a-MAH-nus
amana, amanum
Of the Amanus Mountains, Turkey, as in *Origanum amanum*

amaranthoides
am-ar-anth-OY-deez
Resembling amaranth (*Amaranthus*), as in *Calomeria amaranthoides*

Amaranthus
am-uh-RANTH-us
From Greek *amarantos* meaning 'unfading', as flowers are long-lasting (*Amaranthaceae*)

amarellus
a-mar-ELL-us
amarella, amarellum
—

amarus
a-MAH-rus
amara, amarum
Bitter, as in *Ribes amarum*

amaricaulis
am-ar-ee-KAW-lis
amaricaulis, amaricaule
With a bitter-tasting stem, as in *Hyophorbe amaricaulis*

Amaryllis
am-uh-RIL-us
From Greek *amarysso* meaning 'to sparkle', the name of a shepherdess in Virgil's *Eclogues* (*Amaryllidaceae*)

amazonicus
am-uh-ZOH-nih-kus
amazonica, amazonicum
Connected with the Amazon River, South America, as in *Victoria amazonica*

ambi-
Used in compound words to denote around

ambiguus
am-big-YOO-us
ambigua, ambiguum
Uncertain or doubtful, as in *Digitalis ambigua*

amblyanthus
am-blee-AN-thus
amblyantha, amblyanthum
With a blunt flower, as in *Indigofera amblyantha*

Ambrosia
am-BRO-zee-uh
From Greek *ambrosia* meaning 'food of the gods', though the allusion to this often weedy genus is unclear (*Asteraceae*)

GENUS SPOTLIGHT

Alyssum

For many gardeners, alyssum is a white-flowered bedding plant, often grown together with blue lobelia in containers and park bedding displays. However, that plant is now classified as *Lobularia maritima*; true *Alyssum* species are often known as 'madworts', as they are supposedly endowed with medicinal properties. In particular, they are said to fend off rabies, the Latin name *Alyssum* meaning 'without madness'. Another popular alyssum is no longer in *Alyssum* (*A. saxatile* =*Aurinia saxatilis*), but several species remain and they are often useful for growing in rock or crevice gardens.

Aurinia (formerly *Alyssum*) *saxatilis*, gold dust

ambrosioides

am-bro-zhee-OY-deez

Resembling *Ambrosia*, as in *Cephalaria ambrosioides*

Amelanchier

am-uh-LANG-kee-uh

From Provençal (France) *amalenquièr*, the vernacular name for *A. ovalis* (*Rosaceae*)

amelloides

am-el-OY-deez

Resembling *Aster amellus* (from its Roman name), as in *Felicia amelloides*

americanus

a-mer-ih-KAH-nus

americana, americanum

Connected with North or South America, as in *Lysichiton americanus*

amesianus

ame-see-AH-nus

amesiana, amesianum

Named after Frederick Lothrop Ames (1835–93), horticulturist and orchid grower, and Oakes Ames (1874–1950), supervisor of the Arnold Arboretum and professor of botany, Harvard, USA, as in *Cirrhopetalum amesianum*

amethystinus

am-eth-ih-STEE-nus

amethystina, amethystinum

Violet, as in *Brimeura amethystina*

Amherstia [1]

am-HURR-stee-ah

Named after Sarah, Countess Amherst (1762–1838), British naturalist and botanist (*Fabaceae*)

Amicia

am-ISS-ee-uh

Named after Giovanni Battista Amici (1786–1863), Italian astronomer and botanist (*Fabaceae*)

Ammi

AM-ee

Ancient name for a related plant, possibly derived from Greek *ammos*, meaning 'sand', an allusion to habitat (*Apiaceae*)

Ammobium

am-MOW-bee-um

From Greek *ammo* meaning 'sand' and *bio* meaning 'to live'; plants prefer a sandy habitat (*Asteraceae*)

1

Amherstia nobilis,
pride of Burma

Ammophila

ah-MOFF-il-uh

From Greek *ammo* meaning 'sand' and *philos* meaning 'loving'; these are dune grasses (*Poaceae*)

ammophilus

am-oh-FIL-us

ammophila, ammophilum

Of sandy places, as in *Oenothera ammophila*

amoenus

am-oh-EN-us

amoena, amoenum

Pleasant; delightful, as in *Lilium amoenum*

Amomyrtus

AM-oh-mer-tus

A combination of the names of two related genera, *Amomis* (*Pimenta*) and *Myrtus* (*Myrtaceae*)

Amorpha

a-MOR-fuh

From Greek *amorphos* meaning 'shapeless', as each flower only has a single petal (*Fabaceae*)

Amorphophallus

ah-mor-foh-FA-loos

From Greek *amorphos* meaning 'shapeless' or 'misshapen' and *phallos* meaning 'penis', referring to the shape of the floral spadix (*Araceae*)

Ampelopsis

am-pel-OP-sis

From Greek *ampelos* meaning 'a vine' and *opsis*, meaning 'resembling' (*Vitaceae*)

amphibius

am-FIB-ee-us

amphibia, amphibium

Growing both on land and in water, as in *Persicaria amphibia*

amplexicaulis

am-pleks-ih-KAW-lis

amplexicaulis, amplexicaule

Clasping the stem, as in *Persicaria amplexicaulis*

amplexifolius

am-pleks-ih-FOH-lee-us

amplexifolia, amplexifolium

Clasping the leaf, as in *Streptopus amplexifolius*

ampliatus

am-pli-AH-tus

ampliata, ampliatum

Enlarged, as in *Oncidium ampliatum*

amplissimus

am-PLIS-ih-mus

amplissima, amplissimum

Very large, as in *Chelonistele amplissima*

amplus

AMP-lus

ampla, amplum

Large, as in *Epigeneium amplum*

Amsonia

am-SOW-nee-uh

Named after John Amson (1698–1765?), British physician, botanist and alderman in Colonial Virginia (*Apocynaceae*)

amurensis

am-or-EN-sis

amurensis, amurense

From the Amur River region, Asia, as in *Sorbus amurensis*

amygdaliformis

am-mig-dal-ih-FOR-mis

amygdaliformis, amygdaliforme

Shaped like an almond, as in *Pyrus amygdaliformis*

amygdalinus

am-mig-duh-LEE-nus

amygdalina, amygdalinum

Relating to almond, as in *Eucalyptus amygdalina*

amygdaloides

am-ig-duh-LOY-deez

Resembling almond, as in *Euphorbia amygdaloides*

Anacampseros

ah-nah-KAMP-sir-os

From Greek *anakampseros*, the name for a herb that restores passion (*Anacampserotaceae*)

Anacardium

ah-nah-KAR-dee-um

From Greek *ana* meaning 'upwards' and *kardia* or 'heart', referring to the cashew seed, which is not at the heart of the fruit, but on its tip (*Anacardiaceae*)

Anacyclus

ah-nah-SIKE-loos

From Greek *a* ('without'), *anthos* ('flower') and *kyklos* ('ring'), as the outer flowers in the capitulae lack petals in the type species (*Asteraceae*)

Anagallis [1]

an-uh-GAH-lis

From Greek *ana* meaning 'again' and *agallo* 'to bloom', as the flowers open and close depending on the weather (*Primulaceae*)

Ananas [2]

ah-NAN-oos

From indigenous South American name for the pineapple (*Bromeliaceae*)

1

Anagallis arvensis,
scarlet pimpernel

2

Ananas comosus,
pineapple

ananassa

a-NAN-ass-uh

—

ananassae

a-NAN-ass-uh-ee

With a fragrance like pineapple, as in *Fragaria × ananassa*

Anaphalis

ah-NA-fah-lus

From the classical Greek name for this or a closely related plant (*Asteraceae*)

anatolicus

an-ah-TOH-lih-kus

anatolica, anatolicum

Connected with Anatolia, Turkey, as in *Muscari anatolicum*

anceps

AN-seps

Two-sided, ambiguous, as in *Laelia anceps*

3

Anemone obtusiloba,
Himalayan thimbleweed

Anchusa

an-CHOO-sah

From Greek *ankousa*, 'cosmetic paint', as the roots contain dye (*Boraginaceae*)

ancyrensis

an-syr-EN-sis

ancyrensis, ancyrense

From Ankara, Turkey, as in *Crocus ancyrensis*

andersonianus

an-der-soh-nee-AH-nus

andersoniana, andersonianum

—

andersonii

an-der-SON-ee-eye

Named after Dr Charles Lewis Anderson (1827–1910), American botanist, as in *Arctostaphylos andersonii*

andicola

an-DIH-koh-luh

—

andinus

an-DEE-nus

andina, andinum

Connected with the Andes, South America, as in *Calceolaria andina*

andrachne

an-DRAK-nee

—

andrachnoides

an-drak-NOY-deez

From the Greek *andrachne* (strawberry tree), as in *Arbutus × andrachnoides*

andraeanus

an-dree-AH-nus

andraeana, andraeanum

—

andreanus

an-dree-AH-nus

andreana, andreanum

Named after Édouard François André (1840–1911), French explorer, as in *Anthurium andraeanum*

androgynus

an-DROG-in-us

androgyna, androgynum

With separate male and female flowers growing on the same spike, as in *Semele androgyna*

Andromeda

an-DRAW-mee-dah

From Greek mythology, Andromeda was the daughter of Aethiopian king Cepheus and his wife Cassiopeia, rescued from a sea monster by Perseus (*Ericaceae*)

Andropogon

an-DRO-poh-gon

From Greek *andros* meaning 'man' and *pogon* meaning 'beard', to which the flower clusters resemble (*Poaceae*)

Androsace

an-DROS-uh-see

From Greek *andros* ('man') and *sakos* ('shield'), referring to the shape of the leaves or stamens (*Primulaceae*)

androsaemifolius

an-dro-say-MEE-fol-ee-us

androsaemifolia, androsaemifolium

With leaves like *Androsaemum*, as in *Apocynum androsaemifolium* (*Androsaemum* is now listed under *Hypericum*)

androsaemus

an-dro-SAY-mus

androsaema, androsaemum

With sap the colour of blood, as in *Hypericum androsaemum*

Anemanthele

ah-nem-AN-thuh-lee

From Greek *anemos* meaning 'wind' and *anthele* meaning 'plume', from the vernacular name wind plume-grass (*Poaceae*)

Anemone [3]

ah-NEM-oh-nee

From Greek *anemos* meaning 'wind' as the seeds are blown in the wind; also, in Greek mythology, Aphrodite's lover, Adonis, was killed by a boar and scarlet anemones sprang up from each drop of blood that was shed, though the flowers may have been from the related genus *Adonis* (*Ranunculaceae*)

Anemonopsis

ah-nem-uh-NOP-sis

Resembling the related genus *Anemone* (*Ranunculaceae*)

Anemopaegma

ah-nem-oh-PEG-mah

From Greek *anemos* meaning 'wind' and *paigma* meaning 'play'; these climbers are said to play in the wind (*Bignoniaceae*)

Anemopsis
ah-nem-OP-sis
Resembling the genus *Anemone*
(*Saururaceae*)

Anethum
ah-NEE-thum
From Greek *anethon* meaning 'anise' or 'dill'
(*Apiaceae*)

Angelica
an-JEL-ih-kuh
From Greek *angelos*, a 'messanger' or 'angel',
referring to its medicinal properties
(*Apiaceae*)

Angelonia
an-je-LOH-nee-uh
From indigenous South American name
(*Plantaginaceae*)

anglicus
AN-glih-kus
anglica, anglicum
Connected with England, as in *Sedum
anglicum*

Angophora
an-go-FOUR-uh
From Greek *angos* meaning a 'vessel' and
phero meaning 'to bear', as the vessel-like
fruits bear seeds (*Myrtaceae*)

Angraecum
an-GREE-koom
From Malay *angrek*, the name of a similar
epiphytic orchid (*Orchidaceae*)

angularis
ang-yoo-LAH-ris
angularis, angulare
—

angulatus
ang-yoo-LAH-tus
angulata, angulatum
Angular in shape or form, as in *Jasminum
angulare*

Anguloa
an-goo-LOW-uh
Named after Francisco de Angulo (?–1815),
Spanish director-general of mines and
botany student (*Orchidaceae*)

angulosus
an-gew-LOH-sus
angulosa, angulosum
With several corners or angles, as in
Bupleurum angulosum

angustatus
an-gus-TAH-tus
angustata, angustatum
Narrow, as in *Arisaema angustatum*

angustifolius
an-gus-tee-FOH-lee-us
angustifolia, angustifolium
With narrow leaves, as in *Pulmonaria
angustifolia*

angustus
an-GUS-tus
angusta, angustum
Narrow, as in *Rhodiola angusta*

Anigozanthos
an-ig-oh-ZAN-thoos
From Greek *anisos* meaning 'unequal' and
anthos meaning 'flower', as the petals are of
differing sizes (*Haemodoraceae*)

anisatus
an-ee-SAH-tus
anisata, anisatum
—

Anisodontea
an-iss-oh-DON-tee-uh
From Greek *anisos* meaning 'unequal' and
odontos meaning 'tooth', as the leaf edges are
irregularly toothed (*Malvaceae*)

anisodorus
an-ee-so-DOR-us
anisodora, anisodorum
With the scent of anise (*Pimpinella anisum*),
as in *Illicium anisatum*

anisophyllus
an-ee-so-FIL-us
anisophylla, anisophyllum
With leaves of unequal size, as in
Strobilanthes anisophylla

Anisotome
an-iss-oh-TOE-mee
From Greek *anisos* meaning 'unequal' and
tome meaning 'division', as the leaves are
irregularly divided (*Apiaceae*)

annamensis
an-a-MEN-sis
annamensis, annamense
From Annam, Asia (part of modern-day
Vietnam), as in *Viburnum annamensis*

Annona
ah-NOH-na
From Taíno *annon*, a Caribbean indigenous
name, or from Latin *annona* meaning 'yearly
produce' (*Annonaceae*)

annulatus
an-yoo-LAH-tus
annulata, annulatum
With rings, as in *Begonia annulata*

annuus
AN-yoo-us
annua, annuum
Annual, as in *Helianthus annuus*

anomalus
ah-NOM-uh-lus
anomala, anomalum
Unlike the norm found in a genus, as in
Hydrangea anomala

Anopterus
ah-NOP-ter-oos
From Greek *ano* meaning 'upwards' and
pteron meaning 'wing' as the seeds have
wings at their tips (*Escalloniaceae*)

anosmus
an-OS-mus
anosma, anosmum
Without scent, as in *Dendrobium anosmum*

Anredera
an-RED-er-uh
Possibly from Spanish *enredadera* meaning
'climbing plant' (*Basellaceae*)

antarcticus
ant-ARK-tih-kus
antarctica, antarcticum
Connected with the Antarctic region, as in
Dicksonia antarctica

Antennaria
an-ten-AIR-ree-uh
From Latin *antenna*, as the pappus bristles
resemble insect antennae (*Asteraceae*)

Anthemis
AN-tha-miss
From Greek *anthemis* meaning 'flower'
(*Asteraceae*)

anthemoides
an-them-OY-deez
Resembling chamomile (Greek *anthemis*), as
in *Rhodanthe anthemoides*

Chamaenerion angustifolium,
rosebay willowherb

Anthericum
an-ther-i-koom
From the Greek *antherikos*, a name for the flowering stem of asphodel (*Asparagaceae*)

Anthoxanthum
an-thox-ANTH-um
From Greek *anthos* meaning 'flower' and *xanthos* meaning 'yellow' (*Poaceae*)

Anthriscus
an-THRIS-koos
From Greek *anthriskon*, the classical name for a similar plant (*Apiaceae*)

Anthurium [1]
an-THOO-ree-um
From Greek *anthos* meaning 'flower' and *oura* meaning 'tail', as the inflorescence has a tail-like spadix (*Araceae*)

Anthyllis
an-THIL-us
From Greek *anthyllis*, the classical name for a similar plant (*Fabaceae*)

Antigonon
an-tee-GOH-non
From Greek *anti* meaning 'against' and *gonia* meaning 'knee', in reference to the flexible stems; alternatively, could combine Greek *anti* with related genus *Polygonum* (*Polygonaceae*)

antipodus
an-te-PO-dus
antipoda, antipodum
—
antipodeum
an-te-PO-dee-um
Connected with the Antipodes, as in *Gaultheria antipoda*

antiquorum
an-ti-KWOR-um
Of the ancients, as in *Helleborus antiquorum*

antiquus
an-TIK-yoo-us
antiqua, antiquum
Ancient; antique, as in *Asplenium antiquum*

antirrhiniflorus
an-tee-rin-IF-lor-us
antirrhiniflora, antirrhiniflorum
With flowers like snapdragon (*Antirrhinum*), as in *Maurandella antirrhiniflora*

Anthurium × crombezianum, flamingo flower

antirrhinoides
an-tee-ry-NOY-deez
Resembling snapdragon (*Antirrhinum*), as in *Keckiella antirrhinoides*

Antirrhinum [2]
an-tee-RYE-num
From Greek *antirrhinon* meaning 'calf's snout', perhaps referring to the shape of the petals or fruit (*Plantaginaceae*)

apenninus
ap-en-NEE-nus
apennina, apenninum
Connected with the Apennine Mountains, Italy, as in *Anemone apennina*

apertus
AP-ert-us
aperta, apertum
Open; exposed, as in *Nomocharis aperta*

apetalus
a-PET-uh-lus
apetala, apetalum
Without petals, as in *Sagina apetala*

Aphanes
A-fan-ees
From Greek *aphanes* meaning 'inconspicuous', as is this plant (*Rosaceae*)

Antirrhinum majus, snapdragon

Aphelandra
aff-ell-AND-rah
From Greek *apheles* meaning 'simple' and *andros* meaning 'male', as the anthers are only one-celled (*Acanthaceae*)

aphyllus
a-FIL-us
aphylla, aphyllum
Having, or appearing to have, no leaves, as in *Asparagus aphyllus*

apiculatus
uh-pik-yoo-LAH-tus
apiculata, apiculatum
With a short, sharp point, as in *Luma apiculata*

apiferus
a-PIH-fer-us
apifera, apiferum
Bearing bees, as in *Ophrys apifera*

apiifolius
ap-ee-FOH-lee-us
apiifolia, apiifolium
With leaves like celery (*Apium*), as in *Clematis apiifolia*

Apios
A-pee-oss
From Greek *apios* meaning 'pear', a reference to the shape of the tubers (*Fabaceae*)

Apium
A-pee-um
From Latin *apium*, the classical name for celery (*Apiaceae*)

Apocynum
ah-poh-SINE-um
From Greek *apokynon* meaning 'away from dogs', in reference to its toxicity; commonly known as 'dogbane' (*Apocynaceae*)

apodus
a-POH-dus
apoda, apodum
Without stalks, as in *Selaginella apoda*

Aponogeton
ap-oh-no-GEE-ton
Combines the Latin name of a healing spring *Aquae Aponi* with the Greek *geiton* meaning 'neighbour', a reference to its aquatic habitat (*Aponogetonaceae*)

appendiculatus
ap-pen-dik-yoo-LAH-tus
appendiculata, appendiculatum
With appendages such as hairs, as in *Caltha appendiculata*

applanatus
ap-PLAN-a-tus
applanata, applanatum
Flattened, as in *Sanguisorba applanata*

appressus
a-PRESS-us
appressa, appressum
Pressed close against, as in *Carex appressa*

apricus
AP-rih-kus
aprica, apricum
Open to the sun, as in *Silene aprica*

Aptenia
ap-TEE-nee-uh
From Greek *a* meaning 'without' and *pteron* meaning 'wing', as the fruits lack the wings characteristic of some related genera (*Aizoaceae*)

apterus
AP-ter-us
aptera, apterum
Without wings, as in *Odontoglossum apterum*

aquaticus
a-KWA-tih-kus
aquatica, aquaticum
—

aquatalis
ak-wa-TIL-is
aquatalis, aquatale
Growing in or near water, as in *Mentha aquatica*

aquifolius
a-kwee-FOH-lee-us
aquifolia, aquifolium
Holly-leaved (from the Latin name for holly, *aquifolium*), as in *Mahonia aquifolium*

Aquilegia [3]
ak-wi-LEE-juh
From Latin *aquila* meaning 'eagle', in reference to the clawed petals; the common name 'columbine' is from the Latin *columba* meaning 'dove', as each flower resembles five doves clustered together head-to-head (*Ranunculaceae*)

aquilegiifolius
ak-wil-egg-ee-ee-FOH-lee-us
aquilegiifolia, aquilegiifolium
With leaves like columbine (*Aquilegia*), as in *Thalictrum aquilegiifolium*

aquilinus
ak-will-LEE-nus
aquilina, aquilinum
Like an eagle; aquiline, as in *Pteridium aquilinum*

arabicus
a-RAB-ih-kus
arabica, arabicum
Connected with Arabia, as in *Coffea arabica*

Arabidopsis
ar-ab-ih-DOP-sis
Resembling the related genus *Arabis* (*Brassicaeae*)

3

Aquilegia alpina,
alpine columbine

Arachis hypogaea,
peanut

Araucaria araucana,
monkey puzzle

Arabis
A-ruh-bis
From Greek *arabis* meaning 'Arabian'
(*Brassicaceae*)

Arachis [1]
ah-RAH-kis
From Greek *arakhos* meaning 'chickling
vetch' (*Lathyrus sativus*), a legume with
edible seeds; this is the peanut or monkey-
nut (*Fabaceae*)

Arachniodes
ah-RAK-nee-oh-deez
From Greek *arachnion* meaning 'spider' and
odes meaning 'resembling', perhaps as some
species have web-like dissected fronds
(*Dryopteridaceae*)

arachnoides
a-rak-NOY-deez
—
arachnoideus
a-rak-NOY-dee-us
arachnoidea, arachnoideum
Like a spider's web, as in *Sempervivum
arachnoideum*

Aralia
uh-RAY-lee-uh
From French Canadian *aralie*, the name for
a North American species, possibly derived
from an indigenous name (*Araliaceae*)

aralioides
a-ray-lee-OY-deez
Like *Aralia*, as in *Trochodendron aralioides*

araucana
air-ah-KAY-nuh
Relating to the Arauco region in Chile, as in
Araucaria araucana

Araucaria [2]
a-raw-KAH-ree-uh
Named for the Mapuche, an indigenous
people of Chile, referred to by the Spanish as
araucanos; also, the Araucanía Region of
Chile, inhabited by *Araucaria araucana*
(*Araucariaceae*)

Araujia
ah-ROW-jee-uh
Named after António de Araújo e Azevedo
(1754–1817), Portuguese statesman and
botanist (*Apocynaceae*)

arbor-tristis
ar-bor-TRIS-tis
Latin for sad tree, as in *Nyctanthes arbor-
tristis*

arborescens
ar-bo-RES-senz
—
arboreus
ar-BOR-ee-us
arborea, arboreum
A woody or tree-like plant, as in *Erica
arborea*

arboricola
ar-bor-IH-koh-luh
Living on trees, as in *Schefflera arboricola*

arbusculus
ar-BUS-kyoo-lus
arbuscula, arbusculum
Like a small tree, as in *Daphne arbuscula*

arbutifolius
ar-bew-tih-FOH-lee-us
arbutifolia, arbutifolium
With leaves like strawberry tree (*Arbutus*), as
in *Aronia arbutifolia*

Arbutus

ar-BEW-tus

From classical Latin name for *A. unedo*
(*Ericaceae*)

archangelica

ark-an-JEL-ih-kuh

In reference to the Archangel Raphael, as in
Angelica archangelica

archeri

ARCH-er-eye

Named after William Archer (1820–74),
Australian botanist, as in *Eucalyptus archeri*

Archontophoenix

are-KON-to-fee-nix

From Greek *archon* meaning 'ruler' and
Phoenix, a related genus, in reference to its
stature (*Arecaceae*)

arcticus

ARK-tih-kus

arctica, arcticum
Connected with the Arctic region, as in
Lupinus arcticus

Arctium

ARK-tee-um

From Greek *arktos* meaning 'bear', perhaps
in reference to the spiny bracts surrounding
the flowers, which are shaggy like a bear
(*Asteraceae*)

Arctostaphylos

ark-toh-STAF-ih-loss

From Greek *arktos* meaning 'bear' and
staphyle, a 'bunch of grapes', as bears feed on
the berries, especially those of *A. uva-ursi*
(*Ericaceae*)

Arctotheca

ark-toh-THEE-kuh

From Greek *arktos* meaning 'bear' and *theke*
meaning 'capsule', as the fruits of some
species are covered in woolly hairs
(*Asteraceae*)

Arctotis

ark-TOH-tiss

From Greek *arktos* meaning 'bear' and *otos*
meaning 'ear', as the overlapping floral bracts
resemble bear ears (*Asteraceae*)

arcuatus

ark-yoo-AH-tus

arcuata, arcuatum
In the shape of a bow or arc, as in *Blechnum
arcuatum*

Ardisia

arr-DIZ-ee-uh

From Greek *ardis*, the point of a spear or
arrow, as the anthers are pointed
(*Primulaceae*)

Areca

ah-REE-kuh

From the Malabar (India) name for betel
nuts (from *A. catechu*) (*Arecaceae*)

Arenaria

a-ruh-NAIR-ee-uh

From Latin *arena* meaning 'sand', a common
habitat for sandworts (*Caryophyllaceae*)

arenarius

ar-en-AH-ree-us

arenaria, arenarium
—

Arenga

ah-REN-guh

From Javanese *aren*, the name for *A. pinnata*
(*Arecaceae*)

arendsii

ar-END-see-eye

Named after Georg Arends (1862–1952),
German nurseryman, as in *Astilbe × arendsii*

arenicola

ar-en-IH-koh-luh

—

arenosus

ar-en-OH-sus

arenosa, arenosum
Growing in sandy places, as in *Stapelia
arenosa*

areolatus

ar-ee-oh-LAH-tus

areolata, areolatum
Areolate, with surface divided into small
areas, as in *Coprosma areolata*

Argemone

ar-GEM-oh-nee

From the classical Greek name for a
poppy-like plant (*Papaveraceae*)

argent-

Used in compound words to denote silver

argentatus

ar-jen-TAH-tus

argentata, argentatum
—

argenteus

ar-JEN-tee-us

argentea, argenteum
Silver in colour, as in *Salvia argentea*

argenteomarginatus

ar-gent-eoh-mar-gin-AH-tus

argenteomarginata, argenteomarginatum
With silver edges, as in *Begonia
argenteomarginata*

argentinus

ar-jen-TEE-nus

argentina, argentinum
Connected with Argentina, as in *Tillandsia
argentina*

THE GENDER OF TREES

As in Spanish and French,
Latin nouns are attributed
to gender: masculine,
feminine or neuter.
Botanical Latin names also
follow this pattern;
masculine genera often end
in *-us*, e.g. *Acorus*, feminine
genera typically end in *-a*,
e.g. *Hosta*, while neuter
genera often end in *-um*,
e.g. *Delphinium*. The species
name that follows must
agree in gender, so *Acorus
gramineus*, *Hosta lancifolia*
and *Delphinium elatum*. A
major exception is trees,
many of which have
masculine genera (*Pinus,
Quercus, Malus, Prunus*), but
are treated as feminine
(*Pinus nigra, Quercus alba*),
a quirk of history as
fruit-bearing trees were
considered feminine by
the Romans.

argophyllus

ar-go-FIL-us

argophylla, argophyllum

With silver leaves, as in *Eriogonum argophyllum*

argutifolius

ar-gew-tih-FOH-lee-us

argutifolia, argutifolium

With sharp-toothed leaves, as in *Helleborus argutifolius*

argutus

ar-GOO-tus

arguta, argutum

With notched edges, as in *Rubus argutus*

argyraeus

ar-jy-RAY-us

argyraea, argyraeum

—

argyreus

ar-JY-ree-us

argyrea, argyreum

Silvery in colour, as in *Dierama argyreum*

Argyranthemum

ar-gi-RAN-thu-mum

From Greek *argyros* meaning 'silver' and *anthemis* meaning 'flower' (*Asteraceae*)

argyro-

Used in compound words to denote silver

argyrocomus

ar-gy-roh-KOH-mus

argyrocoma, argyrocomum

With silver hairs, as in *Astelia argyrocoma*

Argyrocytisus

ar-GYRO-sigh-tiss-us

From Greek *argyros* meaning 'silver' and *Cytisus,* a related genus (*Fabaceae*)

Argyroderma

ar-GYRO-der-muh

From Greek *argyros* meaning 'silver' and *dermis* meaning 'skin' as these succulents have silvery-grey foliage (*Aizoaceae*)

argyroneurus

ar-ji-roh-NOOR-us

argyroneura, argyroneurum

With silver veins, as in *Fittonia argyroneura*

argyrophyllus

ar-ger-o-FIL-us

argyrophylla, argyrophyllum

With silver leaves, as in *Rhododendron argyrophyllum*

aria

AR-ee-a

From the Greek *aria*, probably whitebeam, as in *Sorbus aria*

aridus

AR-id-us

arida, aridum

Growing in dry places, as in *Mimulus aridus*

arietinus

ar-ee-eh-TEEN-us

arietina, arietinum

In the shape of a ram's head; horned, as in *Cypripedium arietinum*

arifolius

air-ih-FOH-lee-us

arifolia, arifolium

With leaves like *Arum*, as in *Persicaria arifolia*

Ariocarpus

a-ree-oh-CAR-pus

From the genus *Aria* (=*Sorbus aria*) and Greek *karpos* meaning 'fruit', as their fruits are said to be similar (*Cactaceae*)

Arisaema [1]

a-ri-SEE-muh

From Greek *aris*, a type of arum, and *haema* meaning 'blood', as some species have red-spotted leaves (*Araceae*)

Arisarum

a-ri-SAR-um

From Greek *arisaron*, the classical name for *A. vulgare* (*Araceae*)

aristatus

a-ris-TAH-tus

aristata, aristatum

Bearded, as in *Aloe aristata*

Aristea

a-RIS-tee-uh

From Greek *arista* meaning 'awn', in reference to the pointed bracts (*Iridaceae*)

Arisaema triphyllum,
Jack-in-the-pulpit

Aristolochia

a-ris-tuh-LOKE-ee-uh

From Greek *aristos* meaning 'best' and *lochia* meaning 'delivery', in reference to the medicinal use of this plant in childbirth (*Aristolochiaceae*)

aristolochioides

a-ris-toh-loh-kee-OY-deez

Resembling *Aristolochia*, as in *Nepenthes aristolochioides*

Aristotelia

a-ris-toe-TEE-lee-uh

Named after Aristotle (384–322 BC), Greek philosopher and scientist (*Elaeocarpaceae*)

arizonicus

ar-ih-ZON-ih-kus

arizonica, arizonicum

Connected with Arizona, USA, as in *Yucca arizonica*

armandii

ar-MOND-ee-eye

Named after Armand David (1826–1900), French naturalist and missionary, as in *Pinus armandii*

armatus
arm-AH-tus

armata, armatum

With thorns, spines or spikes, as in *Dryandra armata*

armeniacus
ar-men-ee-AH-kus

armeniaca, armeniacum

Connected with Armenia, as in *Muscari armeniacum*

armenus
ar-MEE-nus

armena, armenum

Connected with Armenia, as in *Fritillaria armena*

Armeria (also armeria)
ar-MEER-ree-uh

From Celtic *arm or* meaning 'by the sea', in reference to their coastal habitat; also Latin for outwardly similar carnation, as in *Dianthus armeria* (*Plumbaginaceae*)

armillaris
arm-il-LAH-ris

armillaris, armillare

Like a bracelet, as in *Melaleuca armillaris*

Armoracia
ar-mo-RAY-see-uh

From the classical Greek name for horseradish (*A. rusticana*) (*Brassicaceae*)

Arnebia
ar-NEE-bee-uh

From Arabic *shajaret el arneb*, the name for the plant (*Boraginaceae*)

Arnica
AR-ni-kuh

From Greek *arni* meaning 'lamb', due to the soft, silky leaves (*Asteraceae*)

arnoldianus
ar-nold-ee-AH-nus

arnoldiana, arnoldianum

Connected with the Arnold Arboretum in Boston, Massachusetts, USA, as in *Abies × arnoldiana*

aromaticus
ar-oh-MAT-ih-kus

aromatica, aromaticum

With a fragrant, aromatic scent, as in *Lycaste aromatica*

Aronia
uh-ROH-nee-uh

From the genus *Aria* (=*Sorbus aria*), due to the similar fruits (*Rosaceae*)

Arrhenatherum
a-ruh-NATH-uh-room

From Greek *arrhen* meaning 'male' and *ather* meaning 'barb', as there are awns on the male flowers (*Poaceae*)

Artemisia
ar-te-MIZ-ee-uh

Named after Artemis, the Greek goddess of the hunt, or her namesake, Artemisia II of Caria, sister/wife of King Mausolus, and a botanist (*Asteraceae*)

artemisioides
ar-tem-iss-ee-OY-deez

Resembling *Artemisia*, as in *Senna artemisioides*

Arthropodium
arth-ro-POH-dee-um

From Greek *arthron*, meaning 'joint' and *podion*, meaning 'foot' as the pedicels (flower stalks) are jointed (*Asparagaceae*)

articulatus
ar-tik-oo-LAH-tus

articulata, articulatum

With a jointed stem, as in *Senecio articulatus*

Arum [2]
AIR-um

From Greek *aron*, the classical name for the plant (*Araceae*)

Aruncus
ah-RUN-kus

From Greek *aryngos*, the classical name for the plant (*Rosaceae*)

arundinaceus
a-run-din-uh-KEE-us

arundinacea, arundinaceum

Like a reed, as in *Phalaris arundinacea*

Arundinaria
ah-run-di-NAIR-ree-uh

From Latin *arundo* meaning 'reed' and *aria*, 'pertaining to' (*Poaceae*)

Arum maculatum,
Lords and ladies

Arundo
ah-RUN-doh
From Latin *arundo* meaning 'reed' (*Poaceae*)

arvensis
ar-VEN-sis
arvensis, arvense
Growing in cultivated fields, as in *Rosa arvensis*

asarifolius
as-ah-rih-FOH-lee-us
asarifolia, asarifolium
With leaves like wild ginger (*Asarum*), as in *Cardamine asarifolia*

Asarina
ah-suh-REE-nuh
From Spanish *asarina*, vernacular name for related *Antirrhinum* (*Plantaginaceae*)

Asarum
ah-SAR-um
From Greek *asaron*, classical name of unknown plant (*Aristolochiaceae*)

ascendens
as-SEN-denz
Rising upwards, as in *Calamintha ascendens*

asclepiadeus
ass-cle-pee-AD-ee-us
asclepiadea, asclepiadeum
Like milkweed (*Asclepias*), as in *Gentiana asclepiadea*

Asclepias [1]
ah-SKLEE-pee-uhs
Named after Asklepios, the Greek god of medicine, as some species have medicinal properties (*Apocynaceae*)

aselliformis
ass-el-ee-FOR-mis
aselliformis, aselliforme
Shaped like a woodlouse, as in *Pelecyphora aselliformis*

asiaticus
a-see-AT-ih-kus
asiatica, asiaticum
Connected with Asia, as in *Trachelospermum asiaticum*

Asimina
ah-si-MEE-nuh
From the Native American name for the plant, *assimin* (*Annonaceae*)

asparagoides
as-par-a-GOY-deez
Like asparagus, as in *Acacia asparagoides*

Asparagus
ah-SPA-ra-gus
From Greek *asparasso* meaning 'to rip', as some species bear spines (*Asparagaceae*)

asper
AS-per
aspera, asperum
—

asperatus
as-per-AH-tus
asperata, asperatum
With a rough texture, as in *Hydrangea aspera*

asperifolius
as-per-ih-FOH-lee-us
asperifolia, asperifolium
With rough leaves, as in *Cornus asperifolia*

asperrimus
as-PER-rih-mus
asperrima, asperrimum
With a very rough texture, as in *Agave asperrima*

Asperula
ah-speh-ROO-lah
From Latin *asper* meaning 'rough', as many species have coarse stems (*Rubiaceae*)

Asphodeline
as-fod-ah-LEE-nee
A modified version of the related genus *Asphodelus* (*Asphodelaceae*)

1

Asclepias curassavica,
bloodflower

2

Astrantia major,
masterwort

asphodeloides
ass-FOD-el-oy-deez
Like *Asphodelus*, as in *Geranium asphodeloides*

Asphodelus
as-FOD-uh-lus
The classical Greek name for *A. ramosus* (*Asphodelaceae*)

asplenifolius
ass-plee-ni-FOH-lee-us
asplenifolia, asplenifolium
—

aspleniifolius
ass-plee-ni-eye-FOH-lee-us
aspleniifolia, aspleniifolium
With fine, feathery, fern-like leaves, as in *Phyllocladus aspleniifolia*

Aspidistra
as-pi-DIS-truh
From Greek *aspidion* meaning 'shield', an allusion to the shield-like stigma (*Asparagaceae*)

Asplenium
as-PLEE-nee-um
From Greek *splen* meaning 'spleen', as spleenworts were used medicinally to treat ailments of this organ (*Aspleniaceae*)

assa-foetida
ass-uh-FET-uh-duh
From the Persian *aza*, 'mastic', and Latin *foetidus*, 'stinking', as in *Ferula assa-foetida*

assimilis
as-SIM-il-is
assimilis, assimile
Similar; alike, as in *Camellia assimilis*

assurgentiflorus
as-sur-jen-tih-FLOR-us
assurgentiflora, assurgentiflorum
With flowers in ascending clusters, as in *Lavatera assurgentiflora*

assyriacus
ass-see-re-AH-kus
assyriaca, assyriacum
Connected with Assyria, as in *Fritillaria assyriaca*

Astelia
ah-STEE-lee-uh
From Greek *a* meaning 'without' and *steli* meaning 'column', referencing the lack of a trunk (*Asteliaceae*)

Aster
A-stur
From Greek *aster* meaning 'star', as the capitulae are star-like (*Asteraceae*)

Asteranthera
a-stur-ANTH-er-uh
From Greek *aster* meaning 'star' and *anthera* meaning 'anther', as the anthers are fused together forming a star shape (*Gesneriaceae*)

asteroides
ass-ter-OY-deez
Resembling *Aster*, as in *Amellus asteroides*

Astilbe
ah-STIL-bee
From Greek *a* meaning 'without' and *stilbe* meaning 'shine' or 'gloss', as some species have dull, matte leaves (*Saxifragaceae*)

Astilboides
ah-stil-BOY-deez
Resembling the related genus *Astilbe* (*Saxifragaceae*)

Astragalus
ah-STRA-ga-loos
From Greek *astragalos*, an ankle or vertebra, perhaps alluding to the knotted roots that are said to resemble bones (*Fabaceae*)

Astrantia [2]
ah-STRAN-tee-uh
From Greek *aster* meaning 'star', as the flower heads are star-like, or from Latin *magister* or 'master', a common name being masterwort (*Apiaceae*)

Astrophytum
as-tro-FIE-toom
From Greek *aster* meaning 'star' and *phyton* meaning 'plant', as some of these cacti have a star-shaped body in outline (*Cactaceae*)

asturiensis
ass-tur-ee-EN-sis
asturiensis, asturiense
From the province of Asturias, Spain, as in *Narcissus asturiensis*

Asyneuma
a-sin-OOM-ah
From Greek *a* meaning 'without' and *syn* meaning 'together', referencing the divided petals (*Campanulaceae*)

Atherosperma
ah-ther-oh-SPER-muh
From Greek *ather* meaning 'barb' and *spermum* meaning 'seed', as the seeds are furnished with awns (*Atherospermataceae*)

Athrotaxis
ah-thro-TAX-iss
From Greek *athros* meaning 'crowded' and *taxis* meaning 'arrangement', as the scale-like leaves are densely arranged (*Cupressaceae*)

Athyrium
ah-THI-ree-um
From Greek *a* meaning 'without' and *thyra* meaning 'door', as the sporangia do not appear to open (*Athyriaceae*)

atkinsianus
at-kin-see-AH-nus
atkinsiana, atkinsianum
—

atkinsii
at-KIN-see-eye
Named after James Atkins (1802–84), British nurseryman, as in *Petunia × atkinsiana*

atlanticus
at-LAN-tih-kus
atlantica, atlanticum
Connected with the Atlantic shoreline, or from the Atlas Mountains, as in *Cedrus atlantica*

Atriplex
A-tree-plex
The classical Latin name for *A. hortensis* (*Amaranthaceae*)

atriplicifolius
at-ry-pliss-ih-FOH-lee-us
atriplicifolia, atriplicifolium
With leaves like orache or salt-bush (*Atriplex*), as in *Perovskia atriplicifolia*

atro-
Used in compound words to denote dark

atrocarpus
at-ro-KAR-pus
atrocarpa, atrocarpum
With black or very dark fruit, as in *Berberis atrocarpa*

Atropa [1]
AH-tro-pah
Named after Atropos, one of the three Greek goddesses of destiny. Atropos ended life by cutting the mortal thread; deadly nightshade is of course toxic (*Solanaceae*)

atropurpureus
at-ro-pur-PURR-ee-us
atropurpurea, atropurpureum
Dark purple, as in *Scabiosa atropurpurea*

atrorubens
at-roh-ROO-benz
Dark red, as in *Helleborus atrorubens*

atrosanguineus
at-ro-san-GWIN-ee-us
atrosanguinea, atrosanguineum
Dark blood red, as in *Rhodochiton atrosanguineus*

atroviolaceus
at-roh-vy-oh-LAH-see-us
atroviolacea, atroviolaceum
Dark violet, as in *Dendrobium atroviolaceum*

atrovirens
at-ro-VY-renz
Dark green, as in *Chamaedorea atrovirens*

attenuatus
at-ten-yoo-AH-tus
attenuata, attenuatum
With a narrow point, as in *Haworthia attenuata*

atticus
AT-tih-kus
attica, atticum
Connected with Attica, Greece, as in *Ornithogalum atticum*

Aubrieta
awe-BREE-shuh
Named for Claude Aubriet (1665–1742), French botanical artist (*Brassicaceae*)

aubrietioides
au-bre-teh-OY-deez
aubrietiodes
Resembling *Aubrieta*, as in *Arabis aubrietiodes*

aucheri
aw-CHER-ee
Named after Pierre Martin Rémi Aucher-Éloy (1792–1838), French pharmacist and botanist, as in *Iris aucheri*

Aucuba
awe-KOO-bah
From Japanese *aokiba*, the vernacular name (*Garryaceae*)

aucuparius
awk-yoo-PAH-ree-us
aucuparia, aucuparium
Of bird-catching, as in *Sorbus aucuparia*

augustinii
aw-gus-TIN-ee-eye
augustinei
Named after the Irish plantsman and botanist Dr Augustine Henry (1857–1930), as in *Rhododendron augustinii*

augustissimus
aw-gus-TIS-sih-mus
augustissima, augustissimum
—

augustus
aw-GUS-tus
augusta, augustum
Majestic, noteworthy, as in *Abroma augusta*

aurantiacus
aw-ran-ti-AH-kus
aurantiaca, aurantiacum
—

aurantius
aw-RAN-tee-us
aurantia, aurantium
Orange, as in *Pilosella aurantiaca*

aurantiifolius
aw-ran-tee-FOH-lee-us
aurantiifolia, aurantiifolium
With leaves like an orange tree (*Citrus aurantium*), as in *Citrus aurantiifolia*

auratus
aw-RAH-tus
aurata, auratum
With golden rays, as in *Lilium auratum*

aureo-
Used in compound words to denote golden

aureosulcatus
aw-ree-oh-sul-KAH-tus
aureosulcata, aureosulcatum
With yellow furrows, as in *Phyllostachys aureosulcata*

aureus
AW-re-us
aurea, aureum
Golden yellow, as in *Phyllostachys aurea*

auricomus
aw-RIK-oh-mus
auricoma, auricomum
With golden hair, as in *Ranunculus auricomus*

auriculatus
aw-rik-yoo-LAH-tus
auriculata, auriculatum
—

auriculus
aw-RIK-yoo-lus
auricula, auriculum
—

auritus
aw-RY-tus
aurita, auritum
With ears or ear-shaped appendages, as in *Plumbago auriculata*

Aurinia
awe-RIN-ee-uh
From Latin *aurum* meaning 'gold' and *inia* meaning 'coloured', as most species have yellow flowers (*Brassicaceae*)

australiensis
aw-stra-li-EN-sis
australiensis, australiense
From Australia, as in *Idiospermum autraliense*

australis
aw-STRAH-lis
australis, australe
Southern, as in *Cordyline australis*

austriacus
oss-tree-AH-kus
austriaca, austriacum
Connected with Austria, as in *Doronicum austriacum*

austrinus
oss-TREE-nus
austrina, austrinum
Southern, as in *Rhododendron austrinum*

Austrocedrus
os-troh-SEED-rus
From Latin *australis* meaning 'southern' and Greek *kedros* meaning 'cedar', as this conifer occurs only in the Southern Hemisphere (*Cupressaceae*)

Austrocylindropuntia
os-troh-sil-in-droh-PUN-tee-uh
From Latin *australis* meaning 'southern' and *Cylindropuntia*, a related genus (*Cactaceae*)

1

2

Atropa belladonna,
deadly nightshade

Anchusa azurea,
Italian alkanet

Austroderia
os-troh-DEER-ee-uh
From Latin *australis* meaning 'southern' and
Cortaderia, a related genus (*Poaceae*)

autumnalis
aw-tum-NAH-lis
autumnalis, autumnale
Relating to autumn, as in *Colchicum
autumnale*

avellanus
av-el-AH-nus
avellana, avellanum
Connected with Avella, Italy, as in *Corylus
avellana*

Avena
ah-VEE-nuh
The classical Latin name for oats (*A. sativa*)
(*Poaceae*)

avenaceus
a-vee-NAY-see-us
avenacea, avenaceum
Like *Avena* (oats), as in *Agrostis avenacea*

Averrhoa
ah-vuh-ROH-ah
Named after Ibn Rushd (1126–98),
Andalusian Muslim philosopher, whose
name was Latinised as Averroes
(*Oxalidaceae*)

avium
AY-ve-um
Relating to birds, as in *Prunus avium*

axillaris
ax-ILL-ah-ris
axillaris, axillare
Growing in the axil, as in *Petunia axillaris*

Azara
a-ZAR-uh
Named after Félix Manuel de Azara
(1742–1821), Spanish military officer and
naturalist, or perhaps his brother José
Nicolás de Azara (1730–1804), Spanish
diplomat and patron of science (*Salicaceae*)

azedarach
a-ZED-ur-ack
From the Persian for noble tree, as in *Melia
azedarach*

Azolla
ah-ZOLL-uh
From Greek *azo* meaning 'to dry' and *ollyo*
meaning 'to kill', as these aquatic ferns are
intolerant of drought (*Salviniaceae*)

Azorella
ah-zaw-RELL-uh
From the Azores, plus Latin diminutive *ella*,
indicating small stature (*Apiaceae*)

azoricus
a-ZOR-ih-kus
azorica, azoricum
Connected with the Azores Islands, as in
Jasminum azoricum

Azorina
ah-zaw-REE-nuh
From the Azores (*Campanulaceae*)

Aztekium
azz-TEE-kee-um
Named after the Aztec people of present-day
Mexico (*Cactaceae*)

azureus [2]
a-ZOOR-ee-us
azurea, azureum
Azure; sky blue, as in *Muscari azureum*

Babiana

ba-bee-AH-nah

From Dutch *baviaan* meaning 'baboon', monkeys that consume the corms (*Iridaceae*)

babylonicus

bab-il-LON-ih-kus

babylonica, babylonicum

Connected with Babylonia, Mesopotamia (Iraq), as in *Salix babylonica*, which Linnaeus mistakenly believed to be from southwest Asia

baccans

BAK-kanz

—

bacciferus

bak-IH-fer-us

baccifera, bacciferum

With berries, as in *Erica baccans*

baccatus

BAK-ah-tus

baccata, baccatum

With fleshy berries, as in *Malus baccata*

Baccharis

BAK-uh-riss

Named after Bacchus, Roman god of wine, for reasons unknown (*Asteraceae*)

bacillaris

bak-ILL-ah-ris

bacillaris, bacillare

Like a stick, as in *Cotoneaster bacillaris*

backhousia

bak-how-zee-AH

backhouseanus, backhouseana, backhouseanum

—

backhousianus

bak-how-zee-AH-nus

backhousiana, backhousianum

—

backhousei

bak-HOW-zee-eye

Named after James Backhouse (1794–1869), British nurseryman, as in *Correa backhouseana*

badius

bad-ee-AH-nus

badia, badium

Chestnut brown, as in *Trifolium badium*

Baeckea

BEK-ee-uh

Named after Abraham Bäck (1713–95), Swedish physician and naturalist (*Myrtaceae*)

baicalensis

by-kol-EN-sis

baicalensis, baicalense

From Lake Baikal, eastern Siberia, as in *Anemone baicalensis*

baileyi

BAY-lee-eye

—

baileyanus

bay-lee-AH-nus

baileyana, baileyanum

Named after one of the following: Frederick Manson Bailey (1827–1915), Australian botanist; Lt Colonel Frederick Marshman Bailey (1882–1967), Indian Army soldier who collected plants on the Tibetan borders from 1913; Major Vernon Bailey (1864–1942), American Army soldier who collected cacti from 1900; Liberty Hyde Bailey (1858–1954), author and professor of horticulture at Cornell University, USA, as in *Rhododendron baileyi* (named after Lt Colonel Frederick Marshman Bailey)

bakeri

BAY-ker-eye

—

bakerianus

bay-ker-ee-AH-nus

bakeriana, bakerianum

Usually honouring John Gilbert Baker (1834–1920) of Kew, as in *Aloe bakeri*, but also George Percival Baker (1856–1951), British plant collector

baldensis [1]

bald-EN-sis

baldensis, baldense

—

baldianus

bald-ee-AN-ee-us

baldiana, baldianum

From or of Monte Baldo, Italy, as in *Hieracium baldense*

baldschuanicus

bald-SHWAN-ih-kus

baldschuanica, baldschuanicum

Connected with Baljuan, Turkistan, as in *Fallopia baldschuanica*

balearicus

bal-AIR-ih-kus

balearica, balearicum

Connected with the Balearic Islands, Spain, as in *Buxus balearica*

1

Anemone baldensis,
Mount Baldo windrose

Bambusa bambos,
common bamboo

Banksia squarrosa,
pingle

Ballota
bah-LOT-uh
The classical Greek name for *B. nigra* (*Lamiaceae*)

balsameus
bal-SAM-ee-us
balsamea, balsameum
Like balsam, as in *Abies balsamea*

balsamiferus
bal-sam-IH-fer-us
balsamifera, balsamiferum
Producing balsam, as in *Aeonium balsamiferum*

Balsamorhiza
bal-SAM-oh-rye-zuh
From Greek *balsamon*, a fragrant gum, and *rhiza* meaning 'root', as the crushed roots are resinous (*Asteraceae*)

balticus
BOL-tih-kus
baltica, balticum
Connected with the Baltic Sea region, as in *Cotoneaster balticus*

Bambusa [1]
bam-BOO-suh
Original source unknown, but could be Malay *bambu* or Kannada (India) *bambu*; also source of English word 'bamboo' (*Poaceae*)

bambusoides
bam-BOO-soy-deez
Resembling bamboo (*Bambusa*), as in *Phyllostachys bambusoides*

banaticus
ba-NAT-ih-kus
banatica, banaticum
Connected with the Banat region of Central Europe, as in *Crocus banaticus*

Banksia [2]
BANK-see-uh
Named after Sir Joseph Banks (1743–1820), British botanist and explorer, founding member of the RHS (*Proteaceae*)

banksianus
banks-ee-AH-nus
banksiana, banksianum
—

banksii
BANK-see-eye
Named after Sir Joseph Banks (1743–1820), British botanist and plant collector, as in *Cordyline banksii*; *banksiae* commemorates his wife, Lady Dorothea Banks (1758–1828)

bannaticus
ban-AT-ih-kus
bannatica, bannaticum
Connected with Banat, Central Europe, as in *Echinops bannaticus*

Baptisia tinctoria,
wild indigo

Barleria recurva

Baptisia [3]
bap-TIZ-ee-uh
From Greek *bapto* meaning 'to dye', as plants were used as a substitute for *Indigofera*, the source of indigo dye (*Fabaceae*)

Barbarea
bar-BUH-ree-uh
Named after Saint Barbara, perhaps because this plant is one of the few edibles available on her feast day, 4th December (*Brassicaceae*)

barbarus
BAR-bar-rus
barbara, barbarum
Foreign, as in *Lycium barbarum*

barbatulus
bar-BAT-yoo-lus
barbatula, barbatulum
—

barbatus
bar-BAH-tus
barbata, barbatum
Bearded; with long, weak hairs, as in *Hypericum barbatum*

barbigerus
bar-BEE-ger-us
barbigera, barbigerum
With beards or barbs, as in *Bulbophyllum barbigerum*

barbinervis
bar-bih-NER-vis
barbinervis, barbinerve
With bearded or barbed veins, as in *Clethra barbinervis*

barbinodis
bar-bin-OH-dis
barbinodis, barbinode
With beards at the nodes or joints, as in *Bothriochloa barbinodis*

barbulatus
bar-bul-AH-tus
barbulata, barbulatum
With a short or less significant beard, as in *Anemone barbulata*

barcinonensis
bar-sin-oh-NEN-sis
barcinonensis, barcinonense
From Barcelona, Spain, as in *Galium × barcinonense*

Barleria [4]
bar-LEER-ee-uh
Named after Jacques Barrelier (1606–73), French botanist and monk (*Acanthaceae*)

baselloides
bar-sell-OY-deez
Resembling *Basella*, as in *Boussangaultia baselloides*

Begonia diadema,
diadem begonia

basilaris

bas-il-LAH-ris

basilaris, basilare

Relating to the base or bottom, as in *Opuntia basilaris*

basilicus

bass-IL-ih-kus

basilica, basilicum

With princely or royal properties, as in *Ocimum basilicum*

Bassia

BAH-see-uh

Named after Ferdinando Bassi (1710–74), Italian naturalist (*Amaranthaceae*)

Bauera

BOW-er-ah

Named after brothers Ferdinand (1760–1826) and Franz Bauer (1758–1840), Austrian botanical illustrators (*Cunoniaceae*)

baueri

baw-WARE-eye

—

bauerianus

baw-ware-ee-AH-nus

baueriana, bauerianum

Named after Ferdinand Bauer (1760–1826), Austrian botanical artist to Flinders' Australian expedition, as in *Eucalyptus baueriana*

Bauhinia

bau-EEN-ee-uh

Named after brothers Gaspard (1560–1624) and Jean Bauhin (1541–1613), Swiss physicians and botanists (*Fabaceae*)

baurii

BOUR-ee-eye

Named after Dr Georg Herman Carl Ludwig Baur (1859–98), German plant collector, as in *Rhodohypoxis baurii*

Beaucarnea

bow-CAR-nee-uh

Named after Jean-Baptiste Beaucarne (dates unknown), Belgian plant collector (*Asparagaceae*)

Beaufortia

bow-FOR-tee-uh

Named for Mary Somerset, Duchess of Beaufort (1630–1715), British gardener and botanist (*Myrtaceae*)

Beaumontia

bow-MON-tee-uh

Named after Lady Diana Beaumont (1765–1831), British patron of horticulture (*Apocynaceae*)

Beesia

BEE-zee-uh

Named after Bees Nursery (est. 1903/4), now Ness Botanic Garden, which sponsored plant-hunting trips by George Forrest, Reginald Farrer and Frank Kingdon-Ward (*Ranunculaceae*)

beesianus

bee-zee-AH-nus

beesiana, beesianum

Named after Bees Nursery, Chester, England, as in *Allium beesianum*

Begonia

beh-GO-nee-uh

Named after Michel Bégon (1638–1710), French Intendant of Saint-Domingue (now Haiti) and patron of botany (*Begoniaceae*)

belladonna

bel-uh-DON-nuh

Beautiful lady, as in *Amaryllis belladonna*

Bellevalia

bel-VAL-ee-uh

Named after Pierre Richer de Belleval (1564–1632), French physician and botanist (*Asparagaceae*)

bellidifolius

bel-lid-ee-FOH-lee-us

bellidifolia, bellidifolium

With leaves like a daisy (*Bellis*), as in *Ageratina bellidifolia*

bellidiformis

bel-id-EE-for-mis

bellidiformis, bellidiforme

Like a daisy (*Bellis*), as in *Dorotheanthus bellidiformis*

bellidioides

bell-id-ee-OY-deez

Resembling *Bellium*, as in *Silene bellidioides*

Bellis

BEH-liss

From Latin *bellus* meaning 'pretty' (*Asteraceae*)

bellus

BELL-us

bella, bellum

Beautiful; handsome, as in *Graptopetalum bellum*

benedictus

ben-uh-DICK-tus

benedicta, benedictum

A blessed plant; spoken of favourably, as in *Centaurea benedicta*

benghalensis

ben-gal-EN-sis

benghalensis, benghalense

Also *bengalensis*; from Bengal, India, as in *Ficus benghalensis*

Berberidopsis

bur-beh-ri-DOP-sis

Resembling the genus *Berberis* (*Berberidopsidaceae*)

Berberis

BUR-beh-riss

From Latin *barbaris*, itself derived from the Arabic word for North Africa, the Barbary Coast inhabited by the Berber people (*Berberidaceae*)

Berchemia

bur-SHEE-mee-uh

Named after Jacob Pierre Berthoud van Berchem (1763–1832), Dutch mineralogist and naturalist (*Rhamnaceae*)

Bergenia

bur-JEE-nee-uh

Named after Karl August von Bergen (1704–1759), German anatomist and botanist (*Saxifragaceae*)

Berkheya

bur-KAY-uh

Named after Johannes le Francq van Berkhey (1729–1812), Dutch painter, poet and scientist (*Asteraceae*)

bermudianus

ber-myoo-dee-AH-nus

bermudiana, bermudianum

Connected with Bermuda, as in *Juniperus bermudiana*

berolinensis

ber-oh-lin-EN-sis

berolinensis, berolinense

From Berlin, Germany, as in *Populus × berolinensis*

berthelotii
berth-eh-LOT-ee-eye
Named after Sabin Berthelot (1794–1880), French naturalist, as in *Lotus berthelotii*

Bertolonia
bur-tah-LOW-nee-uh
Named after Antonio Bertoloni (1775–1869), Italian physician and botanist (*Melastomataceae*)

Beschorneria
besh-or-NEAR-ee-uh
Named after Friedrich Beschorner (1806–1873), German botanist (*Asparagaceae*)

Bessera
BES-uh-ruh
Named after Wilibald von Besser (1784–1842), Austrian botanist (*Asparagaceae*)

Beta [1]
BEE-tuh
From Latin *beta*, meaning 'beet', as in beetroot (*Amaranthaceae*)

betaceus
bet-uh-KEE-us
betacea, betaceum
Like a beet (*Beta*), as in *Solanum betaceum*

betonicifolius
bet-on-ih-see-FOH-lee-us
betonicifolia, betonicifolium
Like betony (*Stachys*), as in *Meconopsis betonicifolia*

Betula [2]
BET-you-luh
From classical Latin name for birch; Pliny used *betula* as a word for pitch, which is extracted from birch bark (*Betulaceae*)

betulifolius
bet-yoo-lee-FOH-lee-us
betulifolia, betulifolium
With leaves like a birch (*Betula*), as in *Pyrus betulifolia*

betulinus
bet-yoo-LEE-nus
betulina, betulinum
—

betuloides
bet-yoo-LOY-deez
Resembling or like a birch (*Betula*), as in *Carpinus betulinus*

Biarum
BYE-air-oom
From Latin *bis* meaning 'two' plus *Arum*, a related genus, though the exact reason for this name is unclear (*Araceae*)

bicolor
BY-kul-ur
With two colours, as in *Caladium bicolor*

bicornis
BY-korn-is
bicornis, bicorne
—

bicornutus
by-kor-NOO-tus
bicornuta, bicornutum
With two horns or horn-like spurs, as in *Passiflora bicornis*

Bidens
BYE-denz
From Latis *bis* meaning 'two' and *dens* meaning 'tooth' as some species have fruit tipped with two teeth (*Asteraceae*)

bidentatus
by-den-TAH-tus
bidentata, bidentatum
With two teeth, as in *Allium bidentatum*

biennis
by-EN-is
biennis, bienne
Biennial, as in *Oenothera biennis*

bifidus
BIF-id-us
bifida, bifidum
Cleft in two parts, as in *Rhodophila bifida*

biflorus
BY-flo-rus
biflora, biflorum
With twin flowers, as in *Geranium biflorum*

1

Beta vulgaris,
common beet

2

Betula pendula,
silver birch

Bismarckia

The Bismarck palm (*Bismarckia nobilis*) is widely grown in tropical countries, primarily for the beauty of its large, silvery leaves. Native to Madagascar, it was first described by German botanists Johann Hildebrandt (1847–81) and Hermann Wendland (1825–1903), honouring the first German Chancellor, Otto von Bismarck. It's unusual for plants to be named after politicians and perhaps this choice of name didn't sit well with France, who colonised Madagascar. Two attempts were made to transfer the palm to a related (and less political) genus, as *Medemia nobilis*, but current taxonomic opinion is that *Bismarckia* and *Medemia* are separate and distinct.

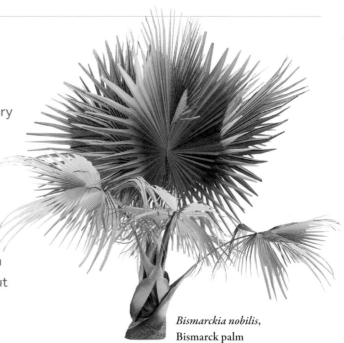

Bismarckia nobilis,
Bismarck palm

bifolius
by-FOH-lee-us
bifolia, bifolium
With twin leaves, as in *Scilla bifolia*

bifurcatus
by-fur-KAH-tus
bifurcata, bifurcatum
Divided into equal stems or branches, as in *Platycerium bifurcatum*

Bignonia
big-NOH-nee-uh
Named after Jean-Paul Bignon (1662–1743), French preacher, statesman and librarian (*Bignoniaceae*)

bignonioides
big-non-YOY-deez
Resembling crossvine (*Bignonia*), as in *Catalpa bignonioides*

bijugus
bih-JOO-gus
bijuga, bijugum
Two pairs joined together, as in *Pelargonium bijugum*

Billardiera
bil-ar-dee-AIR-uh
Named after Jacques-Julien Houtou de Labillardière (1755-1834), French botanist (*Pittosporaceae*)

Billbergia
bil-BUR-gee-uh
Named after Gustaf Johann Billberg (1772–1844), Swedish botanist (*Bromeliaceae*)

bilobatus
by-low-BAH-tus
bilobata, bilobatum
—

bilobus
by-LOW-bus
biloba, bilobum
With two lobes, as in *Ginkgo biloba*

Biophytum
bye-oh-FY-toom
From Greek *bios* meaning 'life' and *phyton* meaning 'plant', probably an allusion to the leaves, which can rapidly move giving the plant the appearance of springing back to life (*Oxalidaceae*)

bipinnatus
by-pin-NAH-tus
bipinnata, bipinnatum
A leaf that is doubly pinnate, as in *Cosmos bipinnatus*

biserratus
by-ser-AH-tus
biserrata, biserratum
A leaf that is double-toothed, as in *Nephrolepis biserrata*

Bismarckia
biz-MAR-kee-uh
Named after Otto von Bismarck (1815–98), Prussian/German politician (*Arecaceae*)

biternatus
by-ter-NAH-tus
biternata, biternatum
A leaf that is twice ternate, as in *Actaea biternata*

bituminosus
by-tu-min-OH-sus
bituminosa, bituminosum
Like bitumen, sticky, as in *Bituminaria bituminosa*

bivalvis
by-VAL-vis
bivalvis, bivalve
With two valves, as in *Ipheion bivalve*

Bixa
BICKS-uh
From indigenous Carib name *biché* or *bija* (*Bixaceae*)

Blandfordia
bland-FOR-dee-uh
Named after George Spencer-Churchill, Marquess of Blandford (1766–1840), British politician and collector (*Blandfordiaceae*)

blandus
BLAN-dus
blanda, blandum
Mild or charming, as in *Anemone blanda*

Blechnum
BLEK-noom
From Greek *blechnon*, a generic name for ferns (*Blechnaceae*)

blepharophyllus
blef-ar-oh-FIL-us
blepharophylla, blepharophyllum
With leaves that are fringed like eyelashes, as in *Arabis blepharophylla*

Bletilla
bleh-TILL-uh
From Latin *Bletia*, a related genus, plus diminutive *ella* implying a resemblance; *Bletia* is named after Luis Blet (dates unknown), Spanish apothecary (*Orchidaceae*)

LANGUAGE BIAS
The system of taxonomy used to classify plants has its origins in Europe and a bias towards Europe is noticeable when surveying plant names. Genera named after people most often venerate Europeans, though this has begun to change and many newly described genera honour botanists and collectors from around the globe. A handful of generic names are based on native names for the plant, rather than using a purely Latin moniker. *Catalpa* derives from Muscogee, a Native American language, while *Luma* originates in the Mapuche language of Chile. *Manihot*, *Ananas*, *Luffa*, *Puya* and *Nelumbo* are all based on local languages.

Blossfeldia
blow-FEL-tee-uh
Named after Harry Blossfeld (1913–1986), German botanist (*Cactaceae*)

bodinieri
boh-din-ee-ER-ee
Named after Émile-Marie Bodinier (1842–1901), French missionary who collected plants in China, as in *Callicarpa bodinieri*

bodnantense
bod-nan-TEN-see
Named after Bodnant Gardens, Wales, as in *Viburnum × bodnantense*

Boehmeria
bow-MEER-ee-uh
Named after Georg Rudolf Böhmer (1723–1803), German botanist (*Urticaceae*)

Boenninghausenia
bur-ning-how-ZEN-ee-uh
Named after Clemens Maria Franz von Bönninghausen (1785–1864), Dutch lawyer and botanist (*Rutaceae*)

Bolax
BOH-lax
From Greek *bolax* meaning 'lump', possibly in reference to its mounded habit or the shape of the flower clusters (*Apiaceae*)

Boltonia
bowl-TOH-nee-uh
Named after James Bolton (1735–99), British naturalist and illustrator (*Asteraceae*)

Bolusanthus
boh-lus-ANTH-us
Named for Harry Bolus (1834–1911), South African botanist and philanthropist (*Fabaceae*)

Bomarea
boh-MA-ree-uh
Named for Jacques-Christophe Valmont de Bomare (1731–1807), French botanist and naturalist (*Alstroemeriaceae*)

Bombax [1]
BOM-backs
From Greek *bombyx* meaning 'silkworm', as the seeds are covered in silky hairs (*Malvaceae*)

bonariensis
bon-ar-ee-EN-sis
bonariensis, bonariense
From Buenos Aires, as in *Verbena bonariensis*

Bongardia
bon-GAR-dee-uh
Named after Gustav Heinrich von Bongard (1786–1839), German botanist (*Berberidaceae*)

1

Bombax ceiba, silk cotton tree

Borago officinalis,
borage

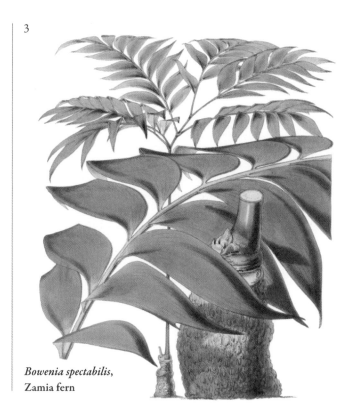

Bowenia spectabilis,
Zamia fern

bonus
BOW-nus
bona, bonum
In compound words, good, as in
Chenopodium bonus-henricus, good (King)
Henry

Borago [2]
buh-RAY-go
From Latin *burra* meaning a 'shaggy
garment' and *ago* meaning 'like', referring to
the hairy foliage (*Boraginaceae*)

borbonicus
bor-BON-ih-kus
borbonica, borbonicum
Connected with Réunion Island in the
Indian Ocean, formerly known as Île
Bourbon. Also refers to the French Bourbon
kings, as in *Watsonia borbonica*

borealis
bor-ee-AH-lis
borealis, boreale
Northern, as in *Erigeron borealis*

Borinda
buh-RIN-duh
Named after Norman Loftus Bor
(1893–1972), Irish taxonomist (*Poaceae*)

borinquenus
bor-in-KAH-nus
borinquena, borinquenum
From Borinquen, local name for Puerto
Rico, as in *Roystonea borinquena*

borneensis
bor-nee-EN-sis
borneensis, borneense
From Borneo, as in *Gaultheria borneensis*

Boronia
buh-ROW-nee-uh
Named after Francesco Borone (1769–94),
Italian naturalist (*Rutaceae*)

Bothriochloa
BOTH-ree-oh-klo-ah
From Greek *bothros*, meaning 'pit' and *chloa*,
'a blade of grass'; some species have glumes
(floral bracts) that are pitted (*Poaceae*)

botryoides
bot-ROY-deez
Resembling a bunch of grapes, as in *Muscari
botryoides*

Bougainvillea
boo-gun-VILL-ee-uh
Named after Louis-Antoine, Comte de
Bougainville (1729–1811), French admiral
and explorer (*Nyctaginaceae*)

Bouteloua
boo-tuh-LOO-ah
Named after brothers Claudio (1774–1842)
and Esteban Boutelou (1776–1813),
Spanish botanists (*Poaceae*)

Bouvardia
boo-VAR-dee-uh
Named after Charles Bouvard (1572–1658),
French chemist and physician (*Rubiaceae*)

bowdenii
bow-DEN-ee-eye
Named after plantsman Athelstan Cornish-
Bowden (1871–1942), as in *Nerine
bowdenii*

Bowenia [3]
boh-WEE-nee-uh
Named for George Ferguson Bowen
(1821–99), British colonial administrator
and first governor of Queensland
(*Zamiaceae*)

Bowiea
BOH-wee-uh
Named after James Bowie (1789–1869),
British botanist (*Asparagaceae*)

Boykinia
boy-KIN-ee-uh
Named after Samuel Boykin (1786–1848),
American physician and naturalist
(*Saxifragaceae*)

brachiatus

brak-ee-AH-tus

brachiata, brachiatum

With branches at right angles; like arms, as in *Clematis brachiata*

brachy-

Used in compound words to denote short

brachybotrys

brak-ee-BOT-rees

With short clusters, as in *Wisteria brachybotrys*

brachycerus

brak-ee-SER-us

brachycera, brachycerum

With short horns, as in *Gaylussacia brachycera*

Brachychiton

bra-kee-KY-tun

From Greek *brachys* meaning 'short' and *chiton*, 'tunic', in reference to the coating of shorts hairs on the seeds (*Malvaceae*)

Brachyglottis

bra-kee-GLOT-iss

From Greek *brachys* meaning 'short' and *glottis* meaning 'tongue' as the ray florets are short (*Asteraceae*)

brachypetalus

brak-ee-PET-uh-lus

brachypetala, brachypetalum

With short petals, as in *Cerastium brachypetalum*

brachyphyllus

brak-ee-FIL-us

brachyphylla, brachyphyllum

With short leaves, as in *Colchicum brachyphyllum*

Brachypodium

bra-kee-POH-dee-um

From Greek *brachys* meaning 'short' and *podion* meaning 'foot' as the flower stalks (pedicels) are short (*Poaceae*)

Brachyscome

bra-kee-SKO-mee

From Greek *brachys* meaning 'short' and *kome* meaning 'hair' as the pappus hairs are short (*Asteraceae*)

Brachystelma

bra-kee-STEL-muh

From Greek *brachys* meaning 'short' and *stelma* meaning 'crown' referring to the short corona (*Apocynaceae*)

bracteatus

brak-tee-AH-tus

bracteata, bracteatum

—

bracteosus

brak-tee-OO-tus

bracteosa, bracteosum

—

bractescens

brak-TES-senz

With bracts, as in *Veltheimia bracteata*

Brahea

bra-HEE-uh

Named after Tycho Brahe (1546–1601), Danish astronomer (*Arecaceae*)

brasilianus

bra-sill-ee-AHN-us

brasiliana, brasilianum

—

brasiliensis

bra-sill-ee-EN-sis

brasiliensis, brasiliense

From or of Brazil, as in *Begonia brasiliensis*

Brassavola

BRAS-ah-voh-lah

Named after Antonio Musa Brassavola (1500–55), Italian physician and botanist (*Orchidaceae*)

Brassia

BRAS-ee-uh

Named after William Brass (?–1783), British botanist (*Orchidaceae*)

Brassica

BRAS-i-kuh

The classical Latin name for cabbage (*Brassicaceae*)

brevifolius

brev-ee-FOH-lee-us

brevifolia, brevifolium

With short leaves, as in *Gladiolus brevifolius*

brevipedunculatus

brev-ee-ped-un-kew-LAH-tus

brevipedunculata, brevipedunculatum

With a short flower stalk, as in *Olearia brevipedunculata*

brevis

BREV-is

brevis, breve

Short, as in *Androsace brevis*

breviscapus

brev-ee-SKAY-pus

breviscapa, breviscapum

With a short scape, as in *Lupinus breviscapus*

Breynia

BRY-nee-uh

Named after Jacob Breyne (1637–97) and his son Johann Philipp Breyne (1680–1764), Polish botanists (*Phyllanthaceae*)

Brickellia

bri-KEH-lee-uh

Named after John Brickell (1748–1809), Irish physician and naturalist (*Asteraceae*)

Briggsia

BRIG-zee-uh

Named after Munro Briggs Scot (1887–1917), Scottish botanist (*Gesneriaceae*)

Briza

BREE-zuh

From Greek *brizo*, meaning 'to nod, sleep', in reference to the drooping flower spikes (*Poaceae*)

Brodiaea

broh-dee-IE-uh

Named after James Brodie (1744–1824), Scottish politician and botanist (*Asparagaceae*)

Bromelia

bruh-MEE-lee-uh

Named after Olaf Bromel (1629–1705), Swedish botanist (*Bromeliaceae*)

bromoides

brom-OY-deez

Resembling brome grass (*Bromus*), as in *Stipa bromoides*

Bromus

BROH-muss

From Greek *bromos* meaning fodder (*Poaceae*)

bronchialis

bron-kee-AL-lis

bronchialis, bronchiale

Used in the past as a treatment for bronchitis, as in *Saxifraga bronchialis*

Brassica oleracea,
cabbage

Broussonetia

broo-son-ET-ee-uh

Named after Pierre Marie Auguste Broussonet (1761–1807), French naturalist (*Moraceae*)

Browallia

bro-WAH-lee-uh

Named after Johann Browall (1707–55), Swedish botanist and cleric (*Solanaceae*)

Brownea

BROW-nee-uh

Named after Patrick Browne (1720–90), Irish physician and historian (*Fabaceae*)

Browningia

brow-NIN-gee-uh

Named after Webster Browning (1869–1942), Director of the Instituto Inglés, Santiago, Chile (*Cactaceae*)

Brugmansia

broog-MAN-zee-uh

Named after Sebald Justinus Brugmans (1763–1819), Dutch physician and botanist (*Solanaceae*)

Brunfelsia

broon-FELL-zee-uh

Named after Otto Brunfels (1488–1534), German theologian and botanist (*Solanaceae*)

Brunnera

BRUN-uh-ruh

Named after Samuel Brunner (1790–1844), Swiss botanist (*Boraginaceae*)

brunneus

BROO-nee-us

brunnea, brunneum

Deep brown, as in *Coprosma brunnea*

Brunsvigia

broonz-VIG-gee-uh

Named after Karl Wilhelm Ferdinand (1713–80), Duke of Brunswick-Lunenburg, patron of arts and sciences (*Amaryllidaceae*)

bryoides

bri-ROY-deez

Resembling moss, as in *Dionysia bryoides*

Bryonia

bry-OH-nee-uh

From Greek *bruein* meaning 'to swell' or 'grow', as these herbaceous climbers regrow each year from the roots (*Cucurbitaceae*)

buckleyi

BUK-lee-eye

For those named Buckley, such as William Buckley, American geologist, as in *Schlumbergera × buckleyi*

Buddleja [1]

BUD-lee-uh

Named after Adam Buddle (1660–1715), British botanist and cleric (*Scrophulariaceae*)

bufonius

buf-OH-nee-us

bufonia, bufonium

Relating to toads; grows in damp places, as in *Juncus bufonius*

Buglossoides

boo-glos-OY-deez

Resembling the related genus *Buglossum* (=*Anchusa*) (*Boraginaceae*)

bulbiferus

bulb-IH-fer-us

bulbifera, bulbiferum

—

bulbiliferus

bulb-il-IH-fer-us

bulbilifera, bulbiliferum

With bulbs, often referring to bulbils, as in *Lachenalia bulbifera*

Bulbine

bul-BYE-nee

From Greek *bolbos* meaning 'bulb' (*Asphodelaceae*)

Bulbinella

bul-bi-NEL-uh

From *Bulbine*, a related genus, plus diminutive *ella* implying a resemblance (*Asphodelaceae*)

bulbocodium

bulb-oh-KOD-ee-um

With a woolly bulb, as in *Narcissus bulbocodium*

1

Buddleja colvilei,
Colvile's butterfly bush

Bulbophyllum [2]
bul-boh-FIL-um
From Greek *bolbos* meaning 'bulb' and *phyllon* meaning 'leaf', as each pseudobulb has one leaf (*Orchidaceae*)

bulbosus
bul-BOH-sus
bulbosa, bulbosum
A bulbous, swollen stem that grows underground; resembling a bulb, as in *Ranunculus bulbosus*

bulgaricus
bul-GAR-ih-kus
bulgarica, bulgaricum
Connected with Bulgaria, as in *Cerastium bulgaricum*

bullatus
bul-LAH-tus
bullata, bullatum
With blistered or puckered leaves, as in *Cotoneaster bullatus*

bulleyanus
bul-ee-YAH-nus
bulleyana, bulleyanum
—

bulleyi
bul-ee-YAH-eye
Named after Arthur Bulley (1861–1942), founder of Ness Botanic Gardens, Cheshire, England, as in *Primula bulleyana*

bungeanus
bun-jee-AH-nus
bungeana, bungeanum
Named after Dr Alexander von Bunge (1803–90), Russian botanist, as in *Pinus bungeana*

Buphthalmum
boof-THAL-mum
From Greek *bous*, meaning 'ox' and *opthalmos* meaning 'eye' to which the inflorescence resembles (*Asteraceae*)

Bupleurum
boo-PLUR-um
From classical Greek name, which means 'ox-rib' (*Apiaceae*)

Burbidgea
bur-BIJ-ee-uh
Named after Frederick William Burbidge (1847–1905), British botanist and explorer (*Zingiberaceae*)

Burchellia
bur-CHEE-lee-uh
Named after William John Burchell (1781–1863), British explorer (*Rubiaceae*)

burkwoodii
berk-WOOD-ee-eye
Named after brothers Arthur and Albert Burkwood, 19th-century hybridisers, as in *Viburnum* × *burkwoodii*

2

Bulbophyllum anceps,
two-sided bulbophyllum

Bursera
BER-suh-ruh
Named after Joachim Burser (1583–1639), German botanist (*Burseraceae*)

Butia
BOO-tee-uh
From indigenous South American name *mbotiá* meaning 'to make teeth', probably referring to the spines on the petiole (*Arecaceae*)

Butomus
boo-TOH-mus
From Greek *bous* meaning 'cow' and *temno* meaning 'to cut' as the sharp leaves were said to damage the mouths of grazing cattle (*Butomaceae*)

buxifolius
buks-ih-FOH-lee-us
buxifolia, buxifolium
With leaves like box (*Buxus*), as in *Cantua buxifolia*

Buxus
BUK-sus
The classical Latin name for this plant (*Buxaceae*)

byzantinus
biz-an-TEE-nus
byzantina, byzantinum
Connected with Istanbul, Turkey, as in *Colchicum byzantinum*

Cabomba

kah-BOM-buh

From the Guyanese vernacular name for *C. aquatica* (*Cabombaceae*)

cacaliifolius

ka-KAY-see-eye-FOH-lee-us

cacaliifolia, cacaliifolium

With leaves like *Cacalia*, as in *Salvia cacaliifolia*

cachemiricus

kash-MI-rih-kus

cachemirica, cachemiricum

Connected with Kashmir, as in *Gentiana cachemirica*

cadierei

kad-ee-AIR-eye

Named after R.P. Cadière, 20th-century plant collector in Vietnam, as in *Pilea cadierei*

cadmicus

KAD-mih-kus

cadmica, cadmicum

Metallic; like tin, as in *Ranunculus cadmicus*

caerulescens

see-roo-LES-enz

Turning blue, as in *Euphorbia caerulescens*

caeruleus

see-ROO-lee-us

caerulea, caeruleum

Dark blue, as in *Passiflora caerulea*

Caesalpinia

sees-al-PIN-ee-uh

Named after Andrea Caesalpino (1519–1603), Italian physician, philosopher and botanist (*Fabaceae*)

caesius

KESS-ee-us

caesia, caesium

Bluish grey, as in *Allium caesium*

caespitosus

kess-pi-TOH-sus

caespitosa, caespitosum

Growing in a dense clump, as in *Eschscholzia caespitosa*

caffer

KAF-er

caffra, caffrum

—

caffrorum

kaf-ROR-um

Connected with South Africa, as in *Erica caffra*

Cakile

ka-KY-lee

From the Arabic name *qaqulleh* (*Brassicaceae*)

calabricus

ka-LA-brih-kus

calabrica, calabricum

Connected with the Calabria region of Italy, as in *Thalictrum calabricum*

Caladium

kuh-LAY-dee-um

From indigenous Indian name *kaladi*, for this or a related plant (*Araceae*)

Calamagrostis

kal-uh-muh-GROS-tis

From Greek *kalamos* meaning 'reed' and *agrostis* meaning 'grass' (*Poaceae*)

Calamintha

kah-luh-MIN-thuh

From Greek *kallos* meaning 'beautiful' and *Mentha*, a related genus (*Lamiaceae*)

Calamus

KAL-uh-mus

From Greek *kalamos* meaning 'reed', as rattan palms have long reed-like stems (*Arecaceae*)

GENUS SPOTLIGHT

Calceolaria

Slipper flower gets its name from its pouch-like lower petal. The genus name, too, has similar origins in the Greek word *calceolus*, meaning 'little shoe'. Slipper-like flowers occur throughout *Calceolaria*, but also in the orchid family, as in *Cypripedium calceolus*. *Calceolaria* floral pouches contain oil-secreting hairs that attract bees, which use the oils to charm their mates. *Calceolaria uniflora* is an exception, as it does not produce oils. Instead, it develops a large white food body on the pouch, which is pecked away by hungry birds, inadvertently pollinating the flowers.

Calceolaria diffusa,
slipper flower

69

1

Callicarpa dichotoma,
beauty berry

2

Callistemon speciosus,
Albany bottlebrush

Calandrinia
kah-lan-DRI-nee-uh
Named after Jean-Louis Calandrini
(1703–58), Swiss scientist (*Portulacaceae*)

calandrinioides
ka-lan-DREEN-ee-oy-deez
Resembling *Calandrinia*, as in *Ranunculus calandrinioides*

Calanthe
kah-LAN-thee
From Greek *kallos* meaning 'beautiful' and *anthos* meaning 'flower' (*Orchidaceae*)

Calathea
kah-LA-thee-uh
From Greek *kalathos* meaning 'basket', as the flowers are enclosed within bracts (*Marantaceae*)

calcaratus
kal-ka-RAH-tus
calcarata, calcaratum
With spurs, as in *Viola calcarata*

calcareus
kal-KAH-ree-us
calcarea, calcareum
Relating to lime, as in *Titanopsis calcarea*

Calceolaria
kal-see-oh-LAIR-ee-uh
From Latin *calceolus*, 'a slipper', in reference to the pouched petal (*Calceolariaceae*)

Calendula
kah-LEN-dew-luh
From Latin *calendae* meaning 'first day of the month', an allusion to the marigold's long flowering period (*Asteraceae*)

calendulaceus
kal-en-dew-LAY-see-us
calendulacea, calendulaceum
The colour of the yellow-flowered marigold (*Calendula officinalis*), as in *Rhododendron calendulaceum*

Calibrachoa
kah-lee-bra-KOH-uh
Named after Antonio de la Cal y Bracho (1766–1833), Mexican botanist and pharmacologist (*Solanaceae*)

californicus
kal-ih-FOR-nih-kus
californica, californicum
Connected with California, USA, as in *Zauschneria californica*

Calla
KAH-luh
From Greek *kallos* meaning 'beautiful' (*Araceae*)

calleryanus
kal-lee-ree-AH-nus
calleryana, calleryanum
Named after Joseph-Marie Callery (1810–62), 19th-century French missionary who plant-hunted in France, as in *Pyrus calleryana*

Calliandra
ka-lee-AN-druh
From Greek *kallos* meaning 'beautiful' and *andros* meaning 'stamen' (*Fabaceae*)

callianthus
kal-lee-AN-thus
calliantha, callianthum
With beautiful flowers, as in *Berberis calliantha*

Callicarpa [1]
ka-lee-KAR-puh
From Greek *kallos* meaning 'beautiful' and *karpos*, 'fruit' (*Lamiaceae*)

callicarpus
kal-ee-KAR-pus
callicarpa, callicarpum
With beautiful fruit, as in *Sambucus callicarpa*

Calochortus clavatus,
golden bowl

Calystegia sepium,
hedge bindweed

Callirhoe
ka-lee-ROW-ee
From Greek *kallos* meaning 'beautiful' and *rhoias*, a corn poppy, or after the daughter of the Greek river god Achelous (*Malvaceae*)

Callisia
ka-LIZ-ee-uh
From Greek *kallos* meaning 'beautiful' (*Commelinaceae*)

Callistemon [2]
ka-lis-STEM-on
From Greek *kallos* meaning 'beautiful' and *stemon* meaning 'stamen' (*Myrtaceae*)

Callistephus
ka-lee-STEF-us
From Greek *kallos* meaning 'beautiful' and *stephos* meaning 'crown', a reference to the shape of the inflorescence (*Asteraceae*)

Callitriche
ka-li-TREE-kee
From Greek *kallos* meaning 'beautiful' and *thrix* meaning 'hair', perhaps an allusion to the hair-like leaves (*Plantaginaceae*)

Callitris
ka-LEE-triss
From Greek *kallos* meaning 'beautiful', referring to the tree (*Cupressaceae*)

callizonus
kal-ih-ZOH-nus
callizona, callizonum
With beautiful bands or zones, as in *Dianthus callizonus*

callosus
kal-OH-sus
callosa, callosum
With thick skin; with calluses, as in *Saxifraga callosa*

Calluna
ka-LOO-nuh
From Greek *kallyno* meaning 'to sweep' as their stems were traditionally used as brooms (*Ericaceae*)

Calocedrus
kal-oh-SEED-rus
From Greek *kallos* meaning 'beautiful' and *Cedrus*, another conifer genus (*Cupressaceae*)

Calochortus [3]
kal-oh-KOR-tus
From Greek *kallos* meaning 'beautiful' and *chortus* meaning 'grass' (*Liliaceae*)

calophyllus
kal-ee-FIL-us
calophylla, calophyllum
With beautiful leaves, as in *Dracocephalum calophyllum*

Calothamnus
cal-oh-THAM-nus
From Greek *kallos* meaning 'beautiful' and *thamnos* meaning 'shrub' (*Myrtaceae*)

Caltha
KAL-thuh
From Greek *kalathos* meaning 'goblet', in reference to the cup-shaped flowers; in Latin, the name for a marigold (*Ranunculaceae*)

calvus
KAL-vus
calva, calvum
Without hair; naked, as in *Viburnum calvum*

Calycanthus
ca-lee-CAN-thus
From Greek *kalyx* ('calyx') and *anthos* ('flower') referring to the blooms in which the sepals and petals are similar (*Calycanthaceae*)

calycinus
ka-lih-KEE-nus
calycina, calycinum
Like a calyx, as in *Halimium calycinum*

Calypso
ka-LIP-soh
From Greek mythology, Calypso was a nymph and the daughter of Atlas, who entertained Odysseus (*Orchidaceae*)

calyptratus
kal-lip-TRA-tus
calyptrata, calyptratum
With a calyptra, a cap-like covering of a flower or fruit, as in *Podalyria calyptrata*

Calystegia [4]
ka-lee-STEE-jee-uh
From Greek *kalux* meaning 'cup' and *stegos* meaning 'covering', perhaps referring to the bracts that surround the flower (*Convolvulaceae*)

Calytrix
ka-LEE-tricks
From Greek *kalyx* meaning 'calyx' and *thrix* meaning 'hair', as the sepals have elongated tips (*Myrtaceae*)

Camassia
ka-MAS-see-uh
From the Shoshone name *camas* or *quamash* (*Asparagaceae*)

cambricus

KAM-brih-kus

cambrica, cambricum

Connected with Wales, as in *Papaver cambricum*

Camellia [1]

kuh-MEE-lee-uh

Named after Georg Josef Kamel (1661–1706), Moravian/Czech missionary and botanist (*Theaceae*)

Campanula (also campanula)

kam-PAN-yu-luh

From Latin *campana*, meaning 'bell', plus diminutive *ella*, as the small flowers are bell-shaped (*Campanulaceae*)

campanularius

kam-pan-yoo-LAH-ri-us

campanularia, campanularium

With bell-shaped flowers, as in *Phacelia campanularia*

campanulatus

kam-pan-yoo-LAH-tus

campanulata, campanulatum

In the shape of a bell, as in *Enkianthus campanulatus*

campbellii

kam-BEL-ee-eye

Named after Dr Archibald Campbell (1805–74), Superintendent of Darjeeling, who accompanied Hooker to the Himalayas, as in *Magnolia campbellii*

campestris

kam-PES-tris

campestris, campestre

Of fields or open plains, as in *Acer campestre*

camphoratus

kam-for-AH-tus

camphorata, camphoratum

—

camphora

kam-for-AH

Like camphor, as in *Thymus camphoratus*

Campsis

KAMP-siss

From Greek *kampe*, meaning 'bent' as the stamens curve (*Bignoniaceae*)

campylocarpus

kam-plo-KAR-pus

campylocarpa, campylocarpum

With curved fruit, as in *Rhododendron campylocarpum*

camtschatcensis

kam-shat-KEN-sis

camtschatcensis, camtschatcense

—

camtschaticus

kam-SHAY-tih-kus

camtschatica, camtschaticum

From or of the Kamchatka Peninsula, Russia, as in *Lysichiton camtschatcensis*

canadensis

ka-na-DEN-sis

canadensis, canadense

From Canada, though once also applied to north-eastern parts of the USA, as in *Cornus canadensis*

canaliculatus

kan-uh-lik-yoo-LAH-tus

canaliculata, canaliculatum

With channels or grooves, as in *Erica canaliculata*

Cananga

kuh-NAN-guh

From Tagalog *ilang-ilang*, the name for *C. odorata*; the vernacular name 'ylang-ylang' has the same origin (*Annonaceae*)

canariensis

kuh-nair-ee-EN-sis

canariensis, canariense

From the Canary Islands, Spain, as in *Phoenix canariensis*

Canarina

cah-nair-EE-nuh

Named for the Canary Islands, where one species (*C. canariensis*) is native (*Campanulaceae*)

canbyi

KAN-bee-eye

Named after William Marriott Canby (1831–1904), American botanist, as in *Quercus canbyi*

cancellatus

kan-sell-AH-tus

cancellata, cancellatum

With cross bars, as in *Phlomis cancellata*

1

Camellia japonica, common camellia

Rosa canina,
dog rose

candelabrum

kan-del-AH-brum
Branched like a candelabra as in *Salvia
candelabrum*

candicans

KAN-dee-kanz
—

candidus

KAN-dee-dus
candida, candidum
Shining white, as in *Echium candicans*

canescens

kan-ESS-kenz
With off-white or grey hairs, as in *Populus ×
canescens*

caninus [2]

kay-NEE-nus
canina, caninum
Relating to dogs, often meaning inferior, as
in *Rosa canina*

Canistrum

kah-NISS-trum
From Greek *kanistron*, a type of basket,
perhaps alluding to the rosette shape of the
foliage or the inflorescence (*Bromeliaceae*)

Canna

KA-nuh
From Greek *kanna*, a reed-like plant
(*Cannaceae*)

Cannabis

KA-nuh-biss
From Greek *kannabis* meaning 'hemp'
(*Cannabaceae*)

cannabinus

kan-na-BEE-nus
cannabina, cannabinum
Like hemp (*Cannabis*), as in *Eupatorium
cannabinum*

Cannomois

KAH-no-moys
From Greek *kanna* meaning 'reed' and
omoios meaning 'similar' (*Restionaceae*)

cantabricus

kan-TAB-rih-kus
cantabrica, cantabricum
Connected with the Cantabria region of
Spain, as in *Narcissus cantabricus*

Cantua

KAN-too-uh
From the indigenous Peruvian name for the
plant (*Polemoniaceae*)

canus

kan-nus
cana, canum
Off-white; ash-coloured, as in *Calceolaria
cana*

capensis

ka-PEN-sis
capensis, capense
From the Cape of Good Hope, South
Africa, as in *Phygelius capensis*

capillaris

kap-ill-AH-ris
capillaris, capillare
Very slender, like fine hair, as in *Tillandsia
capillaris*

capillatus

kap-ill-AH-tus
capillata, capillatum
With fine hairs, as in *Stipa capillata*

capillifolius

kap-ill-ih-FOH-lee-us
capillifolia, capillifolium
With hairy leaves, as in *Eupatorium
capillifolium*

capilliformis

kap-il-ih-FOR-mis
capilliformis, capilliforme
Like hair, as in *Carex capilliformis*

capillipes

cap-ILL-ih-peez
With slender feet, as in *Acer capillipes*

capillus-veneris

KAP-il-is VEN-er-is
Venus's hair, as in *Adiantum capillus-veneris*

capitatus

kap-ih-TAH-tus
capitata, capitatum
Flowers, fruit or whole plant growing in a
dense head, as in *Cornus capitata*

capitellatus
kap-ih-tel-AH-tus
capitellata, capitellatum
—

capitellus
kap-ih-TELL-us
capitella, capitellum
—

capitulatus
kap-ih-tu-LAH-tus
capitulata, capitulatum
With a small head, as in *Primula capitellata*

cappadocicus
kap-puh-doh-SIH-kus
cappadocica, cappadocicum
Connected with the ancient province of
Cappadocia, Asia Minor, as *Omphalodes
cappadocica*

Capparis
KAH-par-iss
From Arabic *kabar* meaning 'caper',
C. spinosa (*Capparidaceae*)

capreolatus
kap-ree-oh-LAH-tus
capreolata, capreolatum
With tendrils, as in *Bignonia capreolata*

capreus
KAP-ray-us
caprea, capreum
Relating to goats, as in *Salix caprea*

capricornis
kap-ree-KOR-nis
capricornis, capricorne
Of or below the Tropic of Capricorn in the
Southern Hemisphere; shaped like a goat's
horn, as in *Astrophytum capricorne*

caprifolius
kap-rih-FOH-lee-us
caprifolia, caprifolium
With leaves having some characteristic of
goats, as in *Lonicera caprifolium*

Capsicum
KAP-sih-kum
From Greek *kapto* meaning 'to bite', referring
to the pepper's bitter taste (*Solanaceae*)

capsularis
kap-SYOO-lah-ris
capsularis, capsulare
With capsules, as in *Corchorus capsularis*

caracasanus
kar-ah-ka-SAH-nus
caracasana, caracasanum
Connected with Caracas, Venezuela, as in
Serjania caracasana

Caragana
ka-ruh-GAH-nuh
From Mongolian *caragan*, the name for
C. arborescens (*Fabaceae*)

Caralluma
ka-ruh-LOO-muh
Possibly from Telugu (India) name *car-allam*
(*Apocynaceae*)

Cardamine
kar-DA-mi-nee
From Greek *kardamon*, meaning 'cress'
(*Brassicaceae*)

cardinalis
kar-dih-NAH-lis
cardinalis, cardinale
Bright scarlet; cardinal red, as in *Lobelia
cardinalis*

Cardiocrinum
kar-dee-oh-KRY-num
From Greek *kardia* meaning 'heart' and
krinon meaning 'lily' as this lily relative has
heart-shaped leaves (*Liliaceae*)

cardiopetalus
kar-dee-oh-PET-uh-lus
cardiopetala, cardiopetalum
With heart-shaped petals, as in *Silene
cardiopetala*

Cardiospermum
kar-dee-oh-SPER-mum
From Greek *kardia* meaning 'heart' and
spermum meaning 'seed' as the black seeds
each have a white, heart-shaped mark
(*Sapindaceae*)

carduaceus
kard-yoo-AY-see-us
carduacea, carduaceum
Like a thistle, as in *Salvia carduacea*

cardunculus
kar-DUNK-yoo-lus
carduncula, cardunculum
Like a small thistle, as in *Cynara cardunculus*

Carduus
KAR-doo-us
From classical Greek name for thistle
(*Asteraceae*)

Carex
KAIR-ex
From classical Latin name for a sedge
(*Cyperaceae*)

caribaeus
kuh-RIB-ee-us
caribaea, caribaeum
Connected with the Caribbean, as in
Pinus caribaea

Carica
KA-ri-kuh
From Latin for dried fig (*Ficus carica*), to
which the fruit (pawpaw) may resemble, or
from their similar leaves, or possibly due to
the mistaken belief that these plants hailed
from ancient Caria in modern-day Turkey
(*Caricaceae*)

caricinus
kar-ih-KEE-nus
caricina, caricinum
—

caricosus
kar-ee-KOH-sus
caricosa, caricosum
Like sedge (*Carex*), as in *Dichanthium
caricosum*

carinatus
kar-IN-uh-tus
carinata, carinatum
—

cariniferus
kar-in-IH-fer-us
carinifera, cariniferum
With a keel, as in *Allium carinatum*

carinthiacus
kar-in-thee-AH-kus
carinthiaca, carinthiacum
Connected with the Carinthia region of
Austria, as in *Wulfenia carinthiaca*

Carissa
kuh-RIS-uh
Possibly from Sanskrit *krishnapakphula*,
the name for *C. carandas* (*Apocynaceae*)

Carduus crispa,
welted thistle

carlesii

KARLS-ee-eye

Named after William Richard Carles (1848–1929) of the British consular service in China, who collected plants in Korea, as in *Viburnum carlesii*

Carlina

kar-LIE-nuh

Named after Charlemagne (742–814), Holy Roman Emperor, after he supposedly cured a plague amongst his soldiers using this plant (*Asteraceae*)

Carludovica

car-loo-doh-VEE-kuh

Named after Charles IV of Spain (1748–1819) and his wife Maria Luisa (1751–1819) (*Cyclanthaceae*)

Carmichaelia

kar-my-KEE-lee-uh

Named after Dugald Carmichael (1772–1827), Scottish surgeon and naturalist (*Fabaceae*)

carminatus

kar-MIN-uh-tus

carminata, carminatum

—

carmineus

kar-MIN-ee-us

carminea, carmineum

Carmine; bright crimson, as in *Metrosideros carminea*

Carnegiea

kar-NEE-gee-uh

Named after Andrew Carnegie (1835–1919), Scottish industrialist and philanthropist (*Cactaceae*)

carneus

KAR-nee-us

carnea, carneum

Flesh colour; deep pink, as in *Androsace carnea*

carnicus

KAR-nih-kus

carnica, carnicum

Like flesh, as in *Campanula carnica*

carniolicus

kar-nee-OH-lih-kus

carniolica, carniolicum

Connected with the historical region of Carniola, now in Slovenia, as in *Centaurea carniolica*

Hoya carnosa,
wax plant

carnosulus

karn-OH-syoo-lus

carnosula, carnosulum

Rather fleshy, as in *Hebe carnosula*

carnosus [1]

kar-NOH-sus

carnosa, carnosum

Fleshy, as in *Hoya carnosa*

carolinianus

kair-oh-lin-ee-AH-nus

caroliniana, carolinianum

—

carolinensis

kair-oh-lin-ee-EN-sis

carolinensis, carolinense

—

carolinus

kar-oh-LEE-nus

carolina, carolinum

From or of North or South Carolina, USA, as in *Halesia carolina*

carota

kar-OH-tuh

Carrot, as in *Daucus carota*

carpaticus

kar-PAT-ih-kus

carpatica, carpaticum

Connected with the Carpathian Mountains, as in *Campanula carpatica*

Carpinus betulus,
common hornbeam

Carpenteria

kar-pen-TEE-ree-uh

Named after William Marbury Carpenter (1811–48), American physician (*Hydrangeaceae*)

carpinifolius

kar-pine-ih-FOH-lee-us

carpinifolia, carpinifolium

With leaves like hornbeam (*Carpinus*), as in *Zelkova carpinifolia*

Carpinus [2]

kar-PIE-noos

From classical Latin name for hornbeam, *C. betulus* (*Betulaceae*)

Carpobrotus

kar-poh-BRO-tus

From Greek *karpos* meaning 'fruit' and *brota* meaning 'edible' (*Aizoaceae*)

Carrierea

kah-ree-AIR-ee-uh

Named after Élie-Abel Carrière (1818–96), French botanist (*Salicaceae*)

Carthamus

KAR-thu-mus

From Arabic *qartam*, the name for safflower (*C. tinctorius*), deriving from the verb 'to paint', as the flowers yield a brilliant dye (*Asteraceae*)

carthusianorum

kar-thoo-see-an-OR-um
Of Grande Chartreuse, Carthusian monastery near Grenoble, France, as in *Dianthus carthusianorum*

cartilagineus

kart-ill-uh-GIN-ee-us
cartilaginea, cartilagineum
Like cartilage, as in *Blechnum cartilagineum*

cartwrightianus

kart-RITE-ee-AH-nus
Named after John Cartwright, 19th-century British consul to Constantinople (now Istanbul, Turkey) , as in *Crocus cartwrightianus*

Carum

KA-room
Both Latin and common name (caraway) originate with the Arabic *karawya*, the vernacular name, though Pliny suggested the name derives from Caria (now part of Turkey), its native country (*Apiaceae*)

Carya

KA-ree-uh
From Greek *karyon* meaning 'nut', these trees produce pecans (*Juglandaceae*)

caryophyllus [3]

kar-ee-oh-FIL-us
caryophylla, caryophyllum
Walnut-leaved (from Greek *karya*); likened to clove for their smell, and thence to clove pink, as in *Dianthus caryophyllus*

caryopteridifolius

kar-ee-op-ter-id-ih-FOH-lee-us
caryopteridifolia, caryopteridifolium
With leaves like *Caryopteris*, as in *Buddleja caryopteridifolia*

Caryopteris

ka-ree-OP-tuh-ris
From Greek *karyon* meaning 'nut' and *pteron* meaning 'wing' as the fruits are winged (*Lamiaceae*)

Caryota

ka-ree-OH-tah
From Greek *karyon* meaning 'nut', as the fruits are vaguely nut-like (*Arecaceae*)

caryotideus

kar-ee-oh-TID-ee-us
caryotidea, caryotideum
Like fishtail palms (*Caryota*), as in *Cyrtomium caryotideum*

cashmerianus

kash-meer-ee-AH-nus
cashmeriana, cashmerianum

cashmirianus

kash-meer-ee-AH-nus
cashmiriana, cashmirianum
—

cashmiriensis

kash-meer-ee-EN-sis
cashmiriensis, cashmiriense
From or of Kashmir, as in *Cupressus cashmeriana*

caspicus

KAS-pih-kus
caspica, caspicum
—

caspius

KAS-pee-us
caspia, caspium
Connected with the Caspian Sea, as in *Ferula caspica*

Cassia

KA-see-uh
From classical Greek name for the plant that produces medicinal senna pods (*Fabaceae*)

Cassinia

ka-SIN-ee-uh
Named after Alexandre Henri Gabriel de Cassini (1781–1832), French botanist (*Asteraceae*)

Cassiope

ka-SEE-oh-pee
From Greek mythology, the wife of Cepheus, King of Aethiopia, and mother to Andromeda (*Ericaceae*)

3

Dianthus caryophyllus,
border carnation

Catalpa bignonioides,
Indian bean tree

Catasetum purum,
one-coloured catasetum

Castanea

kas-TAN-ee-uh

From Greek *kastanaion karuon*, or 'nut from Castania', probably referring either to Kastanaia in Pontus (NE Turkey) or Castana in Thessaly (Greece) (*Fagaceae*)

Castanopsis

kas-tan-OP-sis

Resembling the related genus *Castanea* (*Fagaceae*)

Castanospermum

kas-tan-oh-SPER-mum

A combination of Latin *castanea* meaning 'chestnut' and Greek *spermum* meaning 'seed', in reference to their large seeds (*Fabaceae*)

Castilleja

kah-stee-LAY-uh

Named after Domingo Castillejo (18th century, dates uncertain), Spanish botanist (*Orobanchaceae*)

Casuarina

kah-shoo-ah-REE-nuh

Named after the Australian cassowary (*Casuarius*) as the thin, pendulous stems resemble its plumage (*Casuarinaceae*)

Catalpa [1]

kah-TAL-puh

From the indigenous North American name (*Bignoniaceae*)

catalpifolius

ka-tal-pih-FOH-lee-us

catalpifolia, catalpifolium

With leaves like *Catalpa*, as in *Paulownia catalpifolia*

Catananche

kat-uh-NAN-kee

From Greek *katananke* meaning 'strong force' as it was a common ingredient in love potions (*Asteraceae*)

cataria

kat-AR-ee-uh

Relating to cats, as in *Nepeta cataria*

catarractae

kat-uh-RAK-tay

Of waterfalls, as in *Parahebe catarractae*

Catasetum [2]

kat-uh-SEE-toom

From Greek *kata* meaning 'downwards' and *seta* meaning 'bristle', as the male flowers have hanging bristles that act as triggers, launching the pollen when touched (*Orchidaceae*)

catawbiensis

ka-taw-bee-EN-sis

catawbiensis, catawbiense

From the Catawba River, North Carolina, USA, as in *Rhododendron catawbiense*

catesbyi

KAYTS-bee-eye

Named after Mark Catesby (1682–1749), British naturalist, as in *Sarracenia × catesbyi*

Catharanthus

kath-uh-RAN-thus

From Greek *katharos* meaning 'pure' and *anthos* meaning 'flower' (*Apocynaceae*)

catharticus

kat-AR-tih-kus

carthartica, catharticum

Cathartic; purgative, as in *Rhamnus cathartica*

cathayanus

kat-ay-YAH-nus

cathayana, cathayanum

—

cathayensis

kat-ay-YEN-sis

cathayensis, cathayense

From or of China, as in *Cardiocrinum cathayana*

Cattleya

KAT-lay-uh

Named after William Cattley (1788–1835), British merchant and horticulturist (*Orchidaceae*)

caucasicus

kaw-KAS-ih-kus

caucasica, caucasicum

Connected with the Caucasus, as in *Symphytum caucasicum*

caudatus

kaw-DAH-tus

caudata, caudatum

With a tail, as in *Asarum caudatum*

caulescens

kawl-ESS-kenz

With a stem, as in *Kniphofia caulescens*

cauliflorus

kaw-lih-FLOR-us

cauliflora, cauliflorum

With flowers on the stem or trunk, as in *Saraca cauliflora*

Caulophyllum

kaw-low-FIL-um

From Greek *kaulon* meaning 'stem' and *phyllon* meaning 'leaf', as these plants typically have a single stem with one divided leaf on top (*Berberidaceae*)

causticus

KAWS-tih-kus

caustica, causticum

With a caustic or burning taste, as in *Lithraea caustica*

cauticola

kaw-TIH-koh-luh

Growing on cliffs, as in *Sedum cauticola*

Cautleya

KAWT-ley-uh

Named after Sir Proby Thomas Cautley (1802–71), British engineer and palaeontologist (*Zingiberaceae*)

cautleyoides

kawt-ley-OY-deez

Resembling *Cautleya*, as in *Roscoea cautleyoides*

Cavendishia

kav-un-DISH-ee-uh

Named after William George Spencer Cavendish (1790–1858), 6th Duke of Devonshire, politician and horticulturist (*Ericaceae*)

cavus

KA-vus

cava, cavum

Hollow, as in *Corydalis cava*

Ceanothus

see-uh-NOH-thoos

From Greek *keanothus*, the classical name for a spiny plant, but not this one (*Rhamnaceae*)

cebennensis

kae-ben-EN-sis

cebennensis, cebennense

From Cévennes, France, as in *Saxifraga cebennensis*

Cedronella

see-dro-NEL-luh

From the genus *Cedrus* (cedar), plus Latin diminutive *ella*, indicating small stature; fragrant herbaceous perennials (*Lamiaceae*)

Cedrus (also cedrus)

SEE-druss

The classical Latin name for cedar (*Pinaceae*)

Ceiba

SEE-buh

From indigenous South American name (*Malvaceae*)

celastrinus

seh-lass-TREE-nus

celastrina, celastrinum

Like the staff vine (*Celastrus*), as in *Azara celastrina*

Celastrus

sel-AS-trus

From Greek *kelastros* meaning 'evergreen tree', possibly holly (*Celastraceae*)

Celmisia

sel-MIZ-ee-uh

Named after Celmisios, son of Alciope in Greek mythology; this genus was so named because a related genus in South Africa already bore the name *Alciope* (now *Capelio*) (*Asteraceae*)

Celosia [3]

sel-OH-see-uh

From Greek *kelos* meaning 'burned', a reference to flower colour (*Amaranthaceae*)

Celtis

KEL-tis

The classical Greek name for a tree with sweet fruits (*Cannabaceae*)

Centaurea

sen-TAW-ree-uh

After the centaurs of Greek mythology, who are said to have discovered the medicinal properties of this plant (*Asteraceae*)

Centaurium

sen-TAW-ree-um

For the centaur Chiron, an expert in medicinal herbs (*Gentianaceae*)

centifolius

sen-tih-FOH-lee-us

centifolia, centifolium

With many leaves; with a hundred leaves, as in *Rosa* × *centifolia*

Centradenia

sen-tra-DEE-nee-uh

From Greek *kentron* meaning 'spur' and *aden* meaning 'gland' as the anthers have a spur-like gland (*Melastomataceae*)

centralis

sen-tr-AH-lis

centralis, centrale

Central (for instance in distribution), as in *Diplocaulobium centrale*

centranthifolius

sen-tran-thih-FOH-lee-us

centranthifolia, centranthifolium

With leaves like valerian (*Centranthus*), as in *Penstemon centranthifolius*

Centranthus

sen-TRAN-thus

From Greek *kentron* meaning 'spur' and *anthos* meaning 'flower' as the flowers are spurred (*Caprifoliaceae*)

Celosia argentea, **cockscomb**

Ceratostigma willmottianum,
Chinese plumbago

cepa

KEP-uh

The Roman name for an onion, as in *Allium cepa*

Cephalanthus

kef-uh-LAN-thus

From Greek *kephale* meaning 'head' and *anthos* meaning 'flower' as the flowers are arranged in a globe-shaped inflorescence (*Rubiaceae*)

Cephalaria

kef-uh-LAIR-ee-uh

From Greek *kephale* meaning 'head', as the flowers are in circular clusters (*Caprifoliaceae*)

Cephalocereus

kef-al-oh-SER-ee-us

From Greek *kephale* meaning 'head' and *Cereus*, a related genus, as this cactus forms a woolly head when flowering (*Cactaceae*)

cephalonicus

kef-al-OH-nih-kus

cephalonica, cephalonicum

Connected with Cephalonia, Greece, as in *Abies cephalonica*

Cephalotaxus

kef-al-oh-TAX-us

From Greek *kephale* meaning 'head' and *Taxus*, a related genus, as the pollen cones are spherical (*Taxaceae*)

cephalotes

sef-ah-LOH-tees

Like a small head, as in *Gypsophila cephalotes*

ceraceus

ke-ra-KEE-us

ceracea, ceraceum

With a waxy texture, as in *Wahlenbergia ceracea*

ceramicus

ke-RA-mih-kus

ceramica, ceramicum

Like pottery, as in *Rhopaloblaste ceramica*

cerasiferus

ke-ra-SIH-fer-us

cerasifera, cerasiferum

A plant that bears cherries or cherry-like fruit, as in *Prunus cerasifera*

cerasiformis

see-ras-if-FOR-mis

cerasiformis, cerasiforme

Shaped like a cherry, as in *Oemleria cerasiformis*

cerasinus

ker-ras-EE-nus

cerasina, cerasinum

Cherry-red, as in *Rhododendron cerasinum*

cerastiodes

ker-ras-tee-OY-deez

cerastioides

Resembling mouse-ear chickweed (*Cerastium*), as in *Arenaria cerastioides*

Cerastium

suh-RAS-tee-um

From Greek *keras* meaning 'horn', a reference to the shape of the fruit (*Caryophyllaceae*)

cerasus

KER-uh-sus

Latin for cherry, as in *Prunus cerasus*

Ceratopetalum

suh-rah-toh-PET-al-um

From Greek *keras* meaning 'horn' and *petalon* meaning 'petal', as one species has antler-like petals (*Cunoniaceae*)

Ceratophyllum

suh-rah-toh-FIL-um

From Greek *keras* meaning 'horn' and *phyllon* meaning 'leaf' as the leaves resemble antlers (*Ceratophyllaceae*)

Ceratopteris

suh-rah-TOP-ter-us

From Greek *keras* meaning 'horn' and *Pteris*, a related genus (*Pteridaceae*)

Ceratostigma

suh-rah-to-STIG-muh

From Greek *keras* meaning 'horn' as the stigma has a horn-like protrusion (*Plumbaginaceae*)

Ceratozamia

suh-rah-to-ZAY-mee-uh

From Greek *keras* meaning 'horn' and *Zamia*, a related genus, as the cones have horned scales (*Zamiaceae*)

cercidifolius

ser-uh-sid-ih-FOH-lee-us

cercidifolia, cercidifolium

With leaves like redbud tree (*Cercis*), as in *Disanthus cercidifolius*

Cercidiphyllum

sur-sid-i-FIL-um

From the genus *Cercis*, plus Greek *phyllon* meaning 'leaf', as the two genera have similarly-shaped foliage (*Cercidiphyllaceae*)

Cercis

SUR-sis

From Greek *kerkis*, meaning 'weaver's shuttle', to which the pods resemble (*Fabaceae*)

cerealis

ser-ee-AH-lis

cerealis, cereale

Relating to agriculture, derived from Ceres, the goddess of farming, as in *Secale cereale*

CLERICAL CLASSIFICATION

From Copernicus to Gregor Mendel, clergy have long held an important role in the development of science. Historically, they were some of the only members of society to receive a university education and while their clerical studies enabled them to care for the spiritual welfare of their respective flocks, scientific curiosity was far from uncommon. The ubiquitous genus *Buddleja* honours such a man, the Reverend Adam Buddle, vicar to a parish in Essex. He was an authority on bryophytes (mosses and liverworts) and wrote a Flora of England that alas was never published.

cerefolius
ker-ee-FOH-lee-us
cerefolia, cerefolium
With waxy leaves, as in *Anthriscus cerefolium*

Cereus
seh-REE-us
From Latin *cereus* meaning 'wax candle', a reference to the shape of this columnar cactus (*Cactaceae*)

Cerinthe
suh-RIN-thee
From Greek *keros* meaning 'wax' and *anthos* meaning 'flower', possibly due to the waxy texture of the flowers, or the mistaken belief that bees collected wax from the blooms (*Boraginaceae*)

ceriferus
ker-IH-fer-us
cerifera, ceriferum
Producing wax, as in *Morella cerifera*

cerinthoides
ser-in-THOY-deez
Resembling honeywort (*Cerinthe*), as in *Tradescantia cerinthoides*

cerinus
ker-REE-nus
cerina, cerinum
Waxy, as in *Narcissus cerinus*

cernuus
SER-new-us
cernua, cernuum
Drooping or nodding, as in *Enkianthus cernuus*

Ceropegia
seer-oh-PEE-gee-uh
From Greek *keros* meaning 'wax' and *pege* meaning 'fountain' as the flowers are waxy (*Apocynaceae*)

Cestrum
SES-trum
From Greek *kestron*, the name of a plant, or *kestrum*, a tool used for engraving, which the anthers supposedly resemble (*Solanaceae*)

ceterach
KET-er-ak
Derived from an Arabic word applied to spleenworts (*Asplenium*), as in *Asplenium ceterach*

Chaenomeles [2]
kah-NOM-uh-leez
From Greek *chaino* meaning 'to split' and *melon* meaning 'apple', as the fruits were thought to split open (*Rosaceae*)

Chaenostoma
kee-noh-STOW-muh
From Greek *chaino* meaning 'to split' and *stoma* meaning 'mouth' as these snapdragon-like flowers gape (*Scrophulariaceae*)

chaixii
kay-IKX-ee-eye
Named after Dominique Chaix (1730–99), French botanist, as in *Verbascum chaixii*

chalcedonicus
kalk-ee-DON-ih-kus
chalcedonica, chalcedonicum
Connected with Chalcedon, the ancient name for a district of Istanbul, Turkey, as in *Lychnis chalcedonica*

chamaebuxus
kam-ay-BUKS-us
Dwarf boxwood, as in *Polygala chamaebuxus*

Chamaecyparis [1]
kam-ee-SIP-uh-ris
From Greek *chamai* meaning 'on the ground' or 'low-growing' and *cyparissos* meaning 'cypress' (*Cupressaceae*)

chamaecyparissus
kam-ee-ky-pah-RIS-us
Like *Chamaecyparis*, as in *Santolina chamaecyparissus*

Chamaecytisus
kam-ee-sy-TIS-us
From Greek *chamai* meaning 'on the ground' or 'low-growing' and *Cytisus*, a related genus (*Fabaceae*)

Chamaedaphne
kam-ee-DAF-nee
From Greek *chamai* meaning 'on the ground' or 'low-growing' and *Daphne*, another genus, inappropriate for this upright plant (*Ericaceae*)

Chamaedorea
kam-ee-DORE-ee-uh
From Greek *chamai* meaning 'on the ground' or 'low-growing' and *dorea*, 'a gift', referencing the small stature of many of these pretty palms (*Arecaceae*)

chamaedrifolius
kam-ee-drih-FOH-lee-us
chamaedrifolia, chamaedrifolium, chamaedryfolius, chamaedryfolia, chamaedryfolium
With leaves like *Chamaedrys*, as in *Aloysia chamaedrifolia* (Note: *Chamaedrys* is now listed under *Teucrium*).

Chamaelirium
kam-ee-LI-ree-um
From Greek *chamai* meaning 'on the ground' or 'low-growing' and *lirion* meaning 'lily' (*Melanthiaceae*)

Chamaemelum
kam-ee-MEL-um
From Greek *chamai* meaning 'on the ground' or 'low-growing' and *melon* meaning 'apple', as the foliage is apple-scented (*Asteraceae*)

Chamaenerion
kam-ee-NEER-ee-on
From Greek *chamai* meaning 'on the ground' or 'low-growing' and *Nerium*, the oleander genus, on account of their similar leaves (*Onagraceae*)

Chamaerops
KAM-air-opps
From Greek *chamai* meaning 'on the ground' or 'low-growing' and *rhops*, 'a bush' (*Arecaceae*)

Chamelaucium
kam-ee-LAW-see-um
From Greek *chamai* meaning 'on the ground' or 'low-growing' and *leucos* meaning 'white', perhaps referencing flower colour (*Myrtaceae*)

chantrieri
shon-tree-ER-ee
Named after the French nursery Chantrier Frères, as in *Tacca chantrieri*

charianthus
kar-ee-AN-thus
chariantha, charianthum
With elegant flowers, as in *Ceratostema charianthum*

Chasmanthe
kas-MAN-thee
From Greek *chasme* meaning 'gaping' and *anthos* meaning 'flower' (*Iridaceae*)

Chamaecyparis obtusa,
hinoki cypress

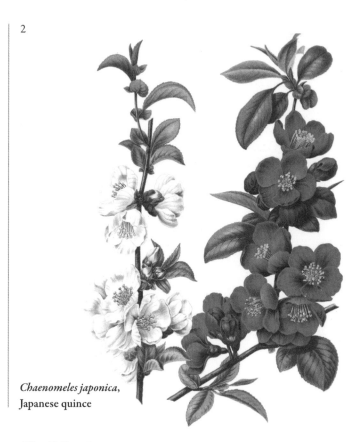

Chaenomeles japonica,
Japanese quince

Chasmanthium
kas-MAN-thee-um
Same derivation as *Chasmanthe* (*Poaceae*)

chathamicus
chath-AM-ih-kus
chathamica, chathamicum
Connected with the Chatham Islands, in the South Pacific, as in
Astelia chathamica

Cheilanthes
ky-LAN-theez
From Greek *cheilos* meaning 'lip' and *anthos* meaning 'flower' as the
sporangia are tucked under the leaf edges (*Pteridaceae*)

cheilanthus
kay-LAN-thus
cheilantha, cheilanthum
With flowers that have a lip, as in *Delphinium cheilanthum*

cheiri
kye-EE-ee
Perhaps from the Greek word *cheir*, 'a hand', as in *Erysimum cheiri*

chelidonioides
kye-li-don-OY-deez
Resembling greater celandine (*Chelidonium*), as in *Calceolaria
chelidonioides*

Chelidonium
kel-i-DOW-nee-um
From Greek *chelidon* meaning 'swallow' as plants bloom when the
swallows arrive in spring; a more fanciful derivation from Greek
mythology is that swallows bathe their chick's eyes in saliva and this
plant is used medicinally to treat ailments of the eye (*Papaveraceae*)

Chelone
kee-LOH-nee
From Greek *chelone* meaning 'tortoise', which the flowers resemble
(*Plantaginaceae*)

Chelonopsis
kee-loh-NOP-sis
Resembling the genus *Chelone* (*Lamiaceae*)

Chenopodium
kee-noh-POD-ee-um
From Greek *chen* meaning 'goose' and *podion* meaning 'foot', which
the leaves resemble (*Amaranthaceae*)

chilensis
chil-ee-EN-sis
chilensis, chilense
From Chile, as in *Blechnum chilense*

chiloensis
kye-loh-EN-sis
chiloensis, chiloense
From the island of Chiloe, Chile, as in *Fragaria chiloensis*

Chimaphila
ky-muh-FIL-uh
From Greek *cheima* meaning 'winter' and *philos* meaning 'loving' as these herbs are evergreen (*Ericaceae*)

Chimonanthus
kim-oh-NAN-thus
From Greek *cheima* meaning 'winter' and *anthos* meaning 'flower', referencing the bloom period (*Calycanthaceae*)

Chimonobambusa
kim-oh-no-bam-BOO-suh
From Greek *cheima* meaning 'winter' and *Bambusa*, a related genus, as some species shoot in winter (*Poaceae*)

chinensis
CHI-nen-sis
chinensis, chinense
From China, as in *Stachyurus chinensis*

Chionanthus
kee-oh-NAN-thus
From Greek *chion* meaning 'snow' and *anthos* meaning 'flower', as the blooms are white (*Oleaceae*)

Chionochloa
kee-on-oh-KLO-uh
From Greek *chion* meaning 'snow' and *chloa*, 'a blade of grass', as some species grow above the snow line (*Poaceae*)

Chionohebe
kee-on-oh-HE-bee
From Greek *chion* meaning 'snow' and *Hebe*, a related genus (*Plantaginaceae*)

Chirita
chi-REE-tuh
From vernacular name in India for a species of gentian (*Gesneriaceae*)

Chlidanthus
kli-DAN-thus
From Greek *chlide* meaning 'luxury' and *anthos* meaning 'flower' (*Amaryllidaceae*)

Chloranthus
klor-AN-thus
From Greek *chloros* meaning 'green' and *anthos* meaning 'flower' (*Chloranthaceae*)

Chloris
KLOR-iss
From Greek mythology, Khloris was the goddess of flowers (*Poaceae*)

chlorochilon
klor-oh-KY-lon
With a green lip, as in *Cycnoches chlorochilon*

Chlorogalum
klor-oh-GA-lum
From Greek *chloros* meaning 'green' and *gala* meaning 'milk', as crushed bulbs produce a green sap (*Asparagaceae*)

chloropetalus
klo-ro-PET-al-lus
chloropetala, chloropetalum
With green petals, as in *Trillium chloropetalum*

Chlorophytum
klor-oh-FY-tum
From Greek *chloros* meaning 'green' and *phyton* meaning 'plant' (*Asparagaceae*)

Choisya [1]
CHOI-see-uh
Named after Jacques Denis Choisy (1799–1859), Swiss cleric and botanist (*Rutaceae*)

Chorizema
kor-is-ZEE-muh
From Greek *chora* meaning 'place' and *zema* meaning 'drink' as the plant was discovered growing over a usable water source; alternatively, could derive from Greek *chorizo* meaning 'to separate' and *nema* meaning 'thread', for reasons unknown (*Fabaceae*)

Chrysanthemum
kri-SAN-thuh-mum
From Greek *khrysos* meaning 'gold' and *anthos* meaning 'flower' (*Asteraceae*)

chrysanthus
kris-AN-thus
chrysantha, chrysanthum
With golden flowers, as in *Crocus chrysanthus*

chryseus
KRIS-ee-us
chrysea, chryseum
Golden, as in *Dendrobium chryseum*

1

Choisya ternata,
Mexican orange blossom

Chrysosplenium oppositifolium,
opposite-leaved golden saxifrage

Cichorium intybus,
chicory

Erodium cicutarium,
common storksbill

chrysocarpus
kris-oh-KAR-pus
chrysocarpa, chrysocarpum
With golden fruit, as in *Crataegus chrysocarpa*

chrysocomus
kris-oh-KOH-mus
chrysocoma, chrysocomum
With golden hairs, as in *Clematis chrysocoma*

Chrysogonum
kry-soh-GOH-num
From Greek *khrysos* meaning 'gold' and *gonia* meaning 'knee', as the inflorescences develop at stem joints (*Asteraceae*)

chrysographes
kris-oh-GRAF-ees
With gold markings, as in *Iris chrysographes*

Chrysolepis
kry-soh-LEE-pis
From Greek *khrysos* meaning 'gold' and *lepis* meaning 'scale', as many parts of the plant have golden glands (*Fagaceae*)

chrysoleucus
kris-roh-LEW-kus
chrysoleuca, chrysoleucum
Gold and white, as in *Hedychium chrysoleucum*

chrysophyllus
kris-oh-FIL-us
chrysophylla, chrysophyllum
With golden leaves, as in *Phlomis chrysophylla*

Chrysosplenium [2]
kry-soh-SPLEE-nee-um
From Greek *khrysos* meaning 'gold' and *splen* meaning 'spleen' as this golden-flowered plant has alleged medicinal value (*Saxifragaceae*)

chrysostoma
kris-oh-STO-muh
With a golden mouth, as in *Lasthenia chrysostoma*

Chusquea
CHUS-kwee-uh
From indigenous South America name *chusque* (*Poaceae*)

Cibotium
si-BOH-tee-um
From Greek *kibotion* meaning 'box' as the sporangia are enclosed within the indusium (*Cibotiaceae*)

Cicer
SY-sur
The classical Latin name for chickpea (*Fabaceae*)

Cicerbita
sy-SUR-bi-tuh
From Italian name for related plant, either sow-thistle (*Sonchus*) or perhaps chicory (*Cichorium*) (*Asteraceae*)

Cichorium [3]
ki-CHOR-ee-um
From Arabic *chikouryeh*, the vernacular name for chicory (*Asteraceae*)

cicutarius [4]
kik-u-tah-ree-us
cicutaria, cicutarium
Like water hemlock (*Conium maculatum*, formerly *Cicuta*), as in *Erodium cicutarium*

ciliaris
sil-ee-AH-ris
ciliaris, ciliare
—

ciliatus
sil-ee-ATE-us
ciliata, ciliatum
With leaves and petals that are fringed with hairs, as in *Tropaeolum ciliatum*

cilicicus
kil-LEE-kih-kus
cilicica, cilicicum
Connected with Lesser Armenia (formerly Cilicia), as in *Colchicum cilicicum*

ciliicalyx
kil-LEE-kal-ux
With a fringed calyx, as in *Menziesia ciliicalyx*

ciliosus
sil-ee-OH-sus
ciliosa, ciliosum
With a small fringe, as in *Sempervivum ciliosum*

cinctus
SINK-tus
cincta, cinctum
With a girdle, as in *Angelica cincta*

Cineraria

sin-uh-RARE-ree-uh

From Latin *cinerea* meaning 'ash-coloured', due to the silvery leaves (*Asteraceae*)

cinerariifolius

sin-uh-rar-ee-ay-FOH-lee-us

cinerariifolia, cinerariifolium

With leaves like *Cineraria*, as in *Tanacetum cinerariifolium*

cinerarius

sin-uh-RAH-ree-us

cineraria, cinerarium

Ash-grey, as in *Centaurea cineraria*

cinerascens

sin-er-ASS-enz

Turning to ash-grey, as in *Senecio cinerascens*

cinereus

sin-EER-ee-us

cinerea, cinereum

The colour of ash, as in *Veronica cinerea*

cinnabarinus

sin-uh-bar-EE-nus

cinnabarina, cinnabarinum

Vermilion, as in *Echinopsis cinnabarina*

cinnamomeus

sin-uh-MOH-mee-us

cinnamomea, cinnamomeum

Cinnamon brown, as in *Osmunda cinnamomea*

cinnamomifolius

sin-uh-mom-ih-FOH-lee-us

cinnamomifolia, cinnamomifolium

With leaves like cinnamon (*Cinnamomum*), as in *Viburnum cinnamomifolium*

Cinnamomum

sin-uh-MOH-mum

From Greek *kinnamomon*, the vernacular name for cinnamon (*Lauraceae*)

circinalis

kir-KIN-ah-lis

circinalis, circinale

Coiled in form, as in *Cycas circinalis*

circum-

Used in compound words to denote around

cirratus

sir-RAH-tus

cirrata, cirratum

—

cirrhosus

sir-ROH-sus

cirrhosa, cirrhosum

With tendrils, as in *Clematis cirrhosa*

Cirsium

SUR-see-um

From Greek *kirsion*, a type of thistle (*Asteraceae*)

cissifolius

kiss-ih-FOH-lee-us

cissifolia, cissifolium

With leaves like ivy (from the Greek *kissos*), as in *Acer cissifolium*

Cissus

SIS-oos

From Greek *kissos* meaning 'ivy', as this is a climbing plant (*Vitaceae*)

cistena

sis-TEE-nuh

Of dwarf habit, from the Sioux word for baby, as in *Prunus* × *cistena*

Cistus [1]

SIS-toos

From Greek *kistos*, the name for a red-flowered shrub (*Cistaceae*)

citratus

sit-TRAH-tus

citrata, citratum

Like *Citrus*, as in *Mentha citrata*

citrinus

sit-REE-nus

citrina, citrinum

Lemon yellow or like *Citrus*, as in *Callistemon citrinus*

citriodorus

sit-ree-oh-DOR-us

citriodora, citriodorum

With the scent of lemons, as in *Thymus citriodorus*

citrodora

sit-roh-DOR-uh

With a lemon scent, as in *Aloysia citrodora*

Citrullus

si-TROO-lus

From genus *Citrus*, plus diminutive *ella*, suggesting a resemblance between a watermelon (*C. lanatus*) and citrus fruit, or their colour (*Cucurbitaceae*)

Citrus [2]

SI-troos

From classical Latin name for *C. medica*, though possibly derived from Greek *kedros* ('cedar') as they share a similar fragrance (*Rutaceae*)

Cladanthus

kla-DAN-thus

From Greek *klados* meaning 'branch' and *anthos* meaning 'flower' as the inflorescences are at the branch tips (*Asteraceae*)

cladocalyx

kla-do-KAL-iks

From the Greek *klados*, 'a branch', referring to flowers borne on leafless branches, as in *Eucalyptus cladocalyx*

Cladrastis

kla-DRAS-tis

From Greek *klados* meaning 'branch' and *thraustos* meaning 'fragile' as this tree's limbs are notoriously brittle (*Fabaceae*)

clandestinus

klan-des-TEE-nus

clandestina, clandestinum

Hidden; concealed, as in *Lathraea clandestina*

1

Cistus × *purpureus*, orchid rockrose

clandonensis

klan-don-EN-sis

From Clandon, England, as in *Caryopteris × clandonensis*

clarkei

KLAR-kee-eye

Commemorates various noteworthy people with the surname Clarke, including Charles Baron Clarke (1832–1906), Superintendent of the Calcutta Botanic Gardens and former president of the Linnean Society, as in *Geranium clarkei*

Clarkia

KLAR-kee-uh

Named after William Clark (1770–1838), American explorer (*Onagraceae*)

clausus

KLAW-sus

clausa, clausum

Closed; shut, as in *Pinus clausa*

clavatus

KLAV-ah-tus

clavata, clavatum

Shaped like a club, as in *Calochortus clavatus*

Claytonia

klay-TOW-nee-uh

Named after John Clayton (1694–1773), British-born American botanist (*Montiaceae*)

claytonianus

klay-ton-ee-AH-nus

claytoniana, claytonianum

Named after John Clayton (1694–1773), plant collector in Virginia, USA, as in *Osmunda claytoniana*

Cleistocactus

KLY-stoh-kak-tus

From Greek *cleistos* meaning 'closed', as the flowers of this cactus barely open (*Cactaceae*)

clematideus

klem-AH-tee-dus

clematidea, clematideum

Like *Clematis*, as in *Agdestis clematidea*

Clematis [3]

KLEM-uh-tis

From classical Greek name for a climbing plant (*Ranunculaceae*)

Cleome

KLEE-oh-mee

Derivation unknown, though perhaps from Greek *kleos* meaning 'glory' or after Kleo, a Greek muse (*Cleomaceae*)

Clerodendrum

kleh-roh-DEN-drum

From Greek *kleros* meaning 'chance' and *dendron* meaning 'tree', probably referencing medicinal properties (*Lamiaceae*)

2

Citrus trifoliata,
Japanese bitter orange

3

Clematis 'Jackmanii',
Jackman's clematis

1

Clivia miniata,
Natal lily

2

Cocos nucifera,
coconut

Clethra

KLETH-ruh

From Greek *klethra*, a name for alder (*Alnus*), which has similar leaves (*Clethraceae*)

clethroides

klee-THROY-deez

Resembling white alder (*Clethra*), as in *Lysimachia clethroides*

clevelandii

kleev-LAN-dee-eye

Named after Daniel Cleveland, 19th-century American collector and fern expert, as in *Bloomeria clevelandii*

Cleyera

klay-AIR-uh

Named after Andreas Cleyer (1634–98), German physician and botanist (*Pentaphylacaceae*)

Clianthus

klee-ANTH-us

From Greek *kleios* meaning 'glory' and *anthos* meaning 'flower' (*Fabaceae*)

Clintonia

klin-TOW-nee-uh

Named after De Witt Clinton (1769–1828), American politician and naturalist, sixth Governor of New York State (*Liliaceae*)

Clitoria

kly-TOR-ee-uh

From Latin *clitoris*, as the flowers resemble this part of the female anatomy (*Fabaceae*)

Clivia [1]

KLI-vee-uh

Named after Charlotte Florentia Clive (1787–1866), Duchess of Northumberland (*Amaryllidaceae*)

Clusia

KLOO-see-uh

Named after Charles de l'Écluse (1526–1609), Flemish botanist (*Clusiaceae*)

clusianus

kloo-zee-AH-nus

clusiana, clusianum

Named after Charles de l'Écluse (1526–1609), Flemish botanist, as in *Tulipa clusiana*

clypeatus

klye-pee-AH-tus

clypeata, clypeatum

Like the round Roman shield, as in *Fibigia clypeata*

clypeolatus

klye-pee-OH-la-tus

clypeolata, clypeolatum

Shaped rather like a shield, as in *Achillea clypeolata*

Clytostoma

kly-toh-STO-muh

From Greek *klytos* meaning 'beautiful' and *stoma* meaning 'mouth', in reference to the tubular flowers (*Bignoniaceae*)

cneorum

suh-NOR-um

From the Greek for a small shrub like olive, possibly a kind of *Daphne*; as in *Convolvulus cneorum*

coarctatus

koh-ARK-tah-tus

coarctata, coarctatum

Pressed or crowded together, as in *Achillea coarctata*

Cobaea
KOH-bee-uh
Named after Bernabé Cobo (1582–1657), Spanish missionary (*Polemoniaceae*)

cocciferus
koh-KIH-fer-us
coccifera, cocciferum
—

coccigerus
koh-KEE-ger-us
coccigera, coccigerum
Producing berries, as in *Eucalyptus coccifera*

coccineus
kok-SIN-ee-us
coccinea, coccineum
Scarlet, as in *Musa coccinea*

Coccoloba
ko-koh-LOW-buh
From Greek *kokkos* meaning 'berry' and *lobos* meaning 'pod', as the dry fruit has a fleshy covering (*Polygonaceae*)

Coccothrinax
ko-koh-THRI-nax
From Greek *kokkos* meaning 'berry' and *Thrinax*, a related genus (*Arecaceae*)

Cochlearia
kok-LEER-ee-uh
From Greek *kokhliarion* meaning 'spoon', the shape of the leaves in some species (*Brassicaceae*)

cochlearis
kok-lee-AH-ris
cochlearis, cochleare
Shaped like a spoon, as in *Saxifraga cochlearis*

cochleatus
kok-lee-AH-tus
cochleata, cochleatum
Shaped like a spiral, as in *Lycaste cochleata*

cockburnianus
kok-burn-ee-AH-nus
cockburniana, cockburnianum
Named after the family Cockburn, residents of China, as in *Rubus cockburnianus*

Cocos [2]
KOH-koss
From Portuguese *coco* meaning 'ape', as coconut shells have a face-like appearance (*Arecaceae*)

Codiaeum
koh-die-EE-um
From Malay *kodiho*, the vernacular name (*Euphorbiaceae*)

Codonanthe
koh-duh-NAN-thee
From Greek *codon* meaning 'bell' and *anthe* meaning 'flower' (*Gesneriaceae*)

Codonopsis
koh-duh-NOP-sis
From Greek *codon* meaning 'bell' and *opsis* meaning 'like' (*Campanulaceae*)

coelestinus
koh-el-es-TEE-nus
coelestina, coelestinum
—

coelestis
koh-el-ES-tis
coelestis, coeleste
Sky-blue, as in *Phalocallis coelestis*

Coelia
SEE-lee-uh
From Greek *koilos* meaning 'hollow', due to the mistaken belief that the pollen masses (pollinia) are hollow (*Orchidaceae*)

Coelogyne
see-LOJ-uh-nee
From Greek *koilos* meaning 'hollow' and *gyne* meaning 'female' as the stigma is depressed (*Orchidaceae*)

coeruleus
ko-er-OO-lee-us
coerulea, coeruleum
Blue, as in *Satureja coerulea*

Coffea [3]
KOFF-ee-uh
From Dutch *koffie*, itself derived originally from Arabic *qah-wah*, the vernacular name for the drink (*Rubiaceae*)

3

Coffea arabica,
Arabian coffee

cognatus

kog-NAH-tus

cognata, cognatum

Closely related to, as in *Acacia cognata*

Coix

KOH-ix

The Greek name for the sub-Saharan palm *Hyphaene thebaica*, though it is unknown why this was applied to a grass (*Poaceae*)

Cola

KOH-luh

From indigenous African name *kola* (*Malvaceae*)

Colchicum

KOL-chi-kum

Named after Colchis, a state on the Black Sea in modern-day Georgia, where autumn-crocus is said to be plentiful (*Colchicaceae*)

colchicus

KOHL-chih-kus

colchica, colchicum

Connected with the coastal region of the Black Sea, Georgia, as in *Hedera colchica*

colensoi

co-len-SO-ee

Named after Revd William Colenso (1811–99), New Zealand plant collector, as in *Pittosporum colensoi*

Coleonema

koh-lee-oh-NEE-muh

From Greek *koleos* meaning 'sheath' and *nema* meaning 'thread' as some of the stamen filaments are enclosed within petal folds (*Rutaceae*)

Coleus

KOH-lee-us

From Greek *koleos* meaning 'sheath' as the stamen filaments fuse together, forming a tube around the style (*Lamiaceae*)

Colletia

ko-LEET-ee-uh

Named after Philibert Collet (1643–1718), French botanist (*Rhamnaceae*)

Collinsia

ko-LIN-see-uh

Named after Zaccheus Collins (1764–1831), American botanist (*Plantaginaceae*)

Collinsonia

ko-lin-SOH-nee-uh

Named after Peter Collinson (1694–1768), British merchant and horticulturist (*Lamiaceae*)

collinus

kol-EE-nus

collina, collinum

Relating to hills, as in *Geranium collinum*

Collomia

ko-LOH-mee-uh

From Greek *kolla* meaning 'glue', as the seeds become mucilaginous when wet (*Polemoniaceae*)

Colocasia

ko-loh-KAY-see-uh

From Greek *kolokasia*, the classical name for an edible root, possibly of *Nelumbo nucifera* (*Araceae*)

colorans

kol-LOR-anz

—

coloratus

kol-or-AH-tus

colorata, coloratum

Coloured, as in *Silene colorata*

Colquhounia

koh-HOON-ee-uh

Named after Robert David Colquhoun (1786–1838), British soldier and plant collector (*Lamiaceae*)

colubrinus

kol-oo-BREE-nus

colubrina, colubrinum

Like a snake, as in *Opuntia colubrina*

columbarius

kol-um-BAH-ree-us

columbaria, columbarium

Like a dove, as in *Scabiosa columbaria*

columbianus

kol-um-bee-AH-nus

columbiana, columbianum

Connected with British Columbia, Canada, as in *Aconitum columbianum*

columellaris

kol-um-EL-ah-ris

columellaris, columellare

Relating to a small pillar or pedestal, as in *Callitris columellaris*

columnaris

kol-um-nah-ris

columnaris, columnare

In the shape of a column, as in *Eryngium columnare*

Columnea

ko-LUM-nee-uh

Named after Fabio Colonna (1567–1640), Italian botanist (*Gesneriaceae*)

Colutea

ko-LOO-tee-uh

From Greek *kolutea*, the classical name for these plants (*Fabaceae*)

Coluteocarpus

ko-loo-tee-oh-KAR-pus

From Greek *karpos* meaning 'fruit', as this plant's capsules resemble those of *Colutea* (*Brassicaceae*)

Colvillea

kol-VILL-ee-uh

Named after Charles Colville (1770–1843), British soldier and third Governor of Mauritius (*Fabaceae*)

colvillei

koh-VIL-ee-eye

Named after either Sir James William Colville (1801–80), Scottish lawyer and judge in Calcutta, or James Colville, 19th-century nurseryman, as in *Gladiolus × colvillei* (after the latter)

comans

KO-manz

—

comatus

kom-MAH-tus

comata, comatum

Tufted, as in *Carex comans*

Comarum

koh-MAR-um

From Greek *komaros*, the name for the strawberry tree (*Arbutus unedo*), as the fruits are said to appear similar (*Rosaceae*)

Combretum

kom-BREE-tum

From Latin for climbing plant as used by Pliny, though referring to a different plant (*Combretaceae*)

Colchicum autumnale,
autumn crocus

Pyrus communis,
pear

Lycopodium complanatum,
ground cedar

Commelina
ko-muh-LEE-nuh
Named after brothers Jan (1629–92) and Caspar Commelijn (1668–1731), Dutch botanists, and a third unnamed brother who died young. The flowers have two large, showy petals and one that is small and inconspicuous (*Commelinaceae*)

commixtus
kom-MIKS-tus
commixta, commixtum
Mixed; mingled together, as in *Sorbus commixta*

communis [1]
KOM-yoo-nis
communis, commune
Growing in groups; common, as in *Myrtus communis*

commutatus
kom-yoo-TAH-tus
commutata, commutatum
Changed, for instance when formerly included in another species, as in *Papaver commutatum*

comosus
kom-OH-sus
comosa, comosum
With tufts, as in *Eucomis comosa*

compactus
kom-PAK-tus
compacta, compactum
Compact; dense, as in *Pleiospilos compactus*

complanatus [2]
kom-plan-NAH-tus
complanata, complanatum
Flat; level, as in *Lycopodium complanatum*

complexus
kom-PLEKS-us
complexa, complexum
Complex; encircled; as in *Muehlenbeckia complexa*

complicatus
kom-plih-KAH-tus
complicata, complicatum
Complicated; complex, as in *Adenocarpus complicatus*

compressus
kom-PRESS-us
compressa, compressum
Compressed, flattened, as in *Conophytum compressum*

Comptonia [3]
komp-TOW-nee-uh
Named after Henry Compton (1632–1713), Bishop of London and patron of botany (*Myricaceae*)

comptoniana
komp-toh-nee-AH-nuh
For various people with the surname Compton, as in *Hardenbergia comptoniana*

concavus
kon-KAV-us
concava, concavum
Hollowed out, as in *Conophytum concavum*

conchifolius

con-chee-FOH-lee-us

conchifolia, conchifolium

With leaves shaped like sea shells, as in *Begonia conchifolia*

concinnus

KON-kin-us

concinna, concinnum

With a neat or elegant form, as in *Parodia concinna*

concolor

KON-kol-or

All the same colour, as in *Abies concolor*

condensatus

kon-den-SAH-tus

condensata, condensatum

—

condensus

kon-DEN-sus

condensa, condensum

Crowded together, as in *Alyssum condensatum*

confertiflorus

kon-fer-tih-FLOR-us

confertiflora, confertiflorum

With flowers crowded together, as in *Salvia confertiflora*

confertus

KON-fer-tus

conferta, confertum

Crowded together, as in *Polemonium confertum*

confusus

kon-FEW-sus

confusa, confusum

Confused or uncertain, as in *Sarcococca confusa*

congestus

kon-JES-tus

congesta, congestum

Congested or crowded together, as in *Aciphylla congesta*

conglomeratus

kon-glom-er-AH-tus

conglomerata, conglomeratum

Crowded together, as in *Cyperus conglomeratus*

conicus

KON-ih-kus

conica, conicum

In the shape of a cone, as in *Carex conica*

coniferus

koh-NIH-fer-us

conifera, coniferum

With cones, as in *Magnolia conifera*

Coniogramme

koh-nee-oh-GRA-mee

From Greek *konion* meaning 'dust' and *gramme* meaning 'line' as the sporangia are arranged along the veins (*Pteridaceae*)

Conium [4]

KOH-nee-um

From Greek *koneion* meaning 'hemlock', perhaps originating in *konas* meaning 'to whorl', as dizziness is a common symptom of hemlock poisoning (*Apiaceae*)

3

Comptonia peregrina,
sweet fern

4

Conium maculatum,
hemlock

conjunctus

kon-JUNK-tus

conjuncta, conjunctum

Joined, as in *Alchemilla conjuncta*

connatus

kon-NAH-tus

connata, connatum

United; twin; opposite leaves joined together at the base, as in *Bidens connata*

conoideus

ko-NOY-dee-us

conoidea, conoideum

Resembling a cone, as in *Silene conoidea*

Conophytum

koh-no-FY-tum

From Greek *konos* meaning 'cone' and *phyton* meaning 'plant', as this succulent plant has conical leaves (*Aizoaceae*)

conopseus

kon-OP-see-us

conopsea, conopseum

Gnat-like, from Greek *konops*, as in *Gymnadenia conopsea*

consanguineus

kon-san-GWIN-ee-us

consanguinea, consanguineum

Related, as in *Vaccinium consanguineum*

Consolida

kon-SOL-i-duh

From Latin *consolidatus* meaning 'to become firm', from its reputed medicinal value (*Ranunculaceae*)

conspersus

kon-SPER-sus

conspersa, conspersum

Scattered, as in *Primula conspersa*

conspicuus

kon-SPIK-yoo-us

conspicua, conspicuum

Conspicuous, as in *Sinningia conspicua*

constrictus

kon-STRIK-tus

constricta, constrictum

Constricted, as in *Yucca constricta*

contaminatus

kon-tam-in-AH-tus

contaminata, contaminatum

Contaminated; defiled, as in *Lachenalia contaminata*

continentalis

kon-tin-en-TAH-lis

continentalis, continentale

Continental, as in *Aralia continentalis*

contortus

kon-TOR-tus

contorta, contortum

Twisted; contorted, as in *Pinus contorta*

contra-

Used in compound words to denote against

contractus

kon-TRAK-tus

contracta, contractum

Contracted; drawn together, as in *Fargesia contracta*

controversus

kon-troh-VER-sus

controversa, controversum

Controversial; doubtful, as in *Cornus contraversa*

Convallaria [1]

kon-val-AIR-ee-uh

From Latin *convallis* meaning 'valley', appropriate for lily-of-the-valley, *C. majalis* (*Asparagaceae*)

convallarioides

kon-va-lar-ee-OY-deez

Resembling lily-of-the-valley (*Convallaria*), as in *Speirantha convallarioides*

convolvulaceus

kon-vol-vu-la-SEE-us

convolvulacea, convolvulaceum

Rather like *Convolvulus*, as in *Codonopsis convolvulacea*

Convolvulus

kon-VOL-voo-lus

From Latin *convolvo* meaning 'to twine around', in reference to the manner of climbing employed by bindweeds (*Convolvulaceae*)

1

Convallaria majalis,
lily-of-the-valley

Cordia myxa,
Assyrian plum

Coreopsis verticillata,
whorled tickseed

Conyza
kuh-NY-zuh
The classical name for fleabane, perhaps from Greek *konops* meaning 'flea' or *konis* meaning 'dust', as powdered plant is used to repell insects (*Asteraceae*)

conyzoides
kon-ny-ZOY-deez
Resembling *Conyza*, as in *Ageratum conyzoides*

copallinus
kop-al-EE-nus
copallina, copallinum
With gum or resin, as in *Rhus copallinum*

Copernicia
kop-ur-NIS-ee-uh
Named after Nicolaus Copernicus (1473–1543), Polish astronomer (*Arecaceae*)

Copiapoa
koh-pee-uh-POH-uh
Named for the city of Copiapó in the Atacama Desert of Chile (*Cactaceae*)

Coprosma
kuh-PROZ-muh
From Greek *kopros* meaning 'dung' and *osme* meaning 'fragrance', relating to the foetid odour of the crushed foliage (*Rubiaceae*)

Coptis
KOP-tis
From Greek *kopto* meaning 'to cut', as the foliage is finely dissected (*Ranunculaceae*)

coralliflorus
kaw-llh-FLOR-us
coralliflora, coralliflorum
With coral-red flowers, as in *Lampranthus coralliflorus*

corallinus
kor-al-LEE-nus
corallina, corallinum
Coral-red, as in *Ilex corallina*

coralloides
kor-al-OY-deez
Resembling coral, as in *Ozothamnus coralloides*

cordatus
kor-DAH-tus
cordata, cordatum
In the shape of a heart, as in *Pontederia cordata*

Cordia [2]
KOR-dee-uh
Named after Enricus Cordus (1486–1535) and his son Valerius Cordus (1515–1544), German physicians and botanists (*Boraginaceae*)

cordifolius
kor-di-FOH-lee-us
cordifolia, cordifolium
With heart-shaped leaves, as in *Crambe cordifolia*

cordiformis
kord-ih-FOR-mis
cordiformis, cordiforme
Heart-shaped, as in *Carya cordiformis*

Cordyline
kor-di-LIE-nee
From Greek *cordyle* meaning 'club', in reference to the shape of the trunk (*Asparagaceae*)

coreanus
kor-ee-AH-nus
coreana, coreanum
Connected with Korea, as in *Hemerocallis coreana*

Coreopsis [3]
kor-ee-OP-sis
From Greek *korios* meaning 'bedbug' as the seeds resemble ticks (*Asteraceae*)

coriaceus
kor-ee-uh-KEE-us
coriacea, coriaceum
Thick, tough and leathery, as in *Paeonia coriacea*

Coriandrum
kor-ee-AN-drum
From Greek *korios,* meaning 'bedbug', to which the fragrance of the leaves and unripe fruits are supposed to resemble (*Apiaceae*)

Coriaria
kor-ee-AIR-ee-uh
From Latin *corium* meaning 'leather', as some species are used in the tanning process (*Coriariaceae*)

coriarius
kor-i-AH-ree-us
coriaria, coriarium
Like leather, as in *Caesalpinia coriaria*

coridifolius
kor-id-ee-FOH-lee-us
coridifolia, coridifolium
—

coriophyllus
kor-ee-uh-FIL-us
coriophylla, coriophyllum
With leaves like *Coris*, as in *Erica corifolia*

corifolius

kor-ee-FOH-lee-us

corifolia, corifolium

—

coriifolius

kor-ee-eye-FOH-lee-us

coriifolia, coriifolium

With leathery leaves, as in *Erica corifolia*

corniculatus

korn-ee-ku-LAH-tus

corniculata, corniculatum

With small horns, as in *Lotus corniculatus*

corniferus

korn-IH-fer-us

conifera, coniferum

—

corniger

korn-ee-ger

cornigera, cornigerum

With horns, as in *Coryphantha cornifera*

cornucopiae

korn-oo-KOP-ee-ay

Of a cornucopia or horn of plenty, as in *Fedia cornucopiae*

Cornus [1]

KOR-nus

From Latin *cornu* meaning 'hard', a reference to the wood; also, the classical name for cornelian cherry (*C. mas*) (*Cornaceae*)

cornutus

kor-NOO-tus

cornuta, cornutum

With horns or shaped like a horn, as in *Viola cornuta*

Corokia

kuh-ROH-kee-uh

From Maori (New Zealand) *korokio*, the vernacular name (*Argophyllaceae*)

corollatus

kor-uh-LAH-tus

corollata, corollatum

Like a corolla, as in *Fuchsia corollata*

coronans

kor-OH-nanz

—

coronatus

kor-oh-NAH-tus

coronata, coronatum

Crowned, as in *Lychnis coronata*

coronarius

kor-oh-NAH-ree-us

coronaria, coronarium

Used for garlands, as in *Anemone coronaria*

Coronilla

ko-roh-NIL-uh

From Latin *corona* meaning 'crown' plus diminutive *illa*, as the flowers are arranged in a small ring (*Fabaceae*)

coronopifolius

koh-ron-oh-pih-FOH-lee-us

coronopifolia, coronopifolium

With leaves like *Coronopus*, as in *Lobelia coronopifolia*

Correa

KOR-ee-uh

Named after José Francisco Correia da Serra (1750–1823), Portuguese abbot, politician and scientist (*Rutaceae*)

corrugatus

kor-yoo-GAH-tus

corrugata, corrugatum

Corrugated; wrinkled, as in *Salvia corrugata*

corsicus

KOR-sih-kus

corsica, corsicum

Connected with Corsica, France, as in *Crocus corsicus*

Cortaderia

kor-tuh-DEER-ee-uh

From Argentinian name for pampas grass, *cortadera*, derived from Spanish *cortar* meaning 'to cut', as the leaves have sharp edges (*Poaceae*)

Cortusa

kor-TOO-suh

Named after Jacobi Antonii Cortusi (1513–93), Italian botanist (*Primulaceae*)

cortusoides

kor-too-SOY-deez

Resembling *Cortusa*, as in *Primula cortusoides*

Corydalis

ko-RI-dah-lis

From Greek *korydallis* meaning 'crested lark' as the flower spurs resemble the bird's crest (*Papaveraceae*)

1

Cornus canadensis,
dwarf cornel

Corylus avellana,
hazel

Corypha taliera,
tali palm

Cotoneaster moupinensis,
Moupin cotoneaster

corylifolius
kor-ee-lee-FOH-lee-us
corylifolia, corylifolium
With leaves like hazelnut (*Corylus*), as in
Betula corylifolia

Corylopsis
ko-ri-LOP-sis
Resembling the genus *Corylus*
(*Hamamelidaceae*)

Corylus [2]
KO-ri-lus
From Greek *korus* meaning 'helmet', a
reference to the shape and strength of the
nuts (*Betulaceae*)

Corymbia
kuh-RIM-bee-uh
From Latin *corymbium* meaning 'cluster', as
the flowers are arranged in corymbs
(*Myrtaceae*)

corymbiferus
kor-im-BIH-fer-us
corymbifera, corymbiferum
With a corymb, as in *Linum corymbiferum*

corymbiflorus
kor-im-BEE-flor-us
corymbiflora, corymbiflorum
With flowers produced in a corymb, as in
Solanum corymbiflorum

corymbosus
kor-rim-BOH-sus
corymbosa, corymbosum
With corymbs, as in *Vaccinium corymbosum*

Corynocarpus
kuh-rye-noh-KAR-pus
From Greek *koryne* meaning 'club' and
karpos meaning 'fruit' (*Corynocarpaceae*)

Corypha [3]
kuh-RYE-fuh
From Greek *koryphe* meaning 'tip' or
'summit', as this palm produces a massive
inflorescence that terminates the trunk
(*Arecaceae*)

Coryphantha
ko-ree-FAN-thuh
From Greek *koryphe* meaning 'tip' and
anthos meaning 'flower', as the flowers
appear at the stem tip, unlike in the
closely-related *Mammillaria*, where they
develop in a ring around the stem
(*Cactaceae*)

cosmophyllus
kor-mo-FIL-us
cosmophylla, cosmophyllum
With leaves like *Cosmos*, as in *Eucalyptus
cosmophylla*

Cosmos
KOZ-moss
From Greek *kosmo* meaning 'ornamental'
(*Asteraceae*)

costatus
kos-TAH-tus
costata, costatum
With ribs, as in *Aglaonema costatum*

Costus (also costus)
KOS-toos
From Greek *kostos* meaning 'aromatic plant'
in reference to the fragrant root, though also
applied to *Saussurea costus* (*Costaceae*)

cotinifolius
kot-in-ih-FOH-lee-us
cotinifolia, cotinifolium
With leaves like smoke tree (*Cotinus*), as in
Euphorbia cotinifolia

Cotinus
KOT-i-nus
From Greek *kotinus* meaning 'olive'
(*Anacardiaceae*)

Cotoneaster [4]
(also cotoneaster)
kot-oh-nee-AS-ter
From Latin *cotoneum* meaning 'quince' and
aster meaning 'similar' (*Rosaceae*)

Cotula
KOT-ew-luh
From Greek *kotule* meaning 'small cup', alluding to the small capitulae (*Asteraceae*)

Cotyledon
kot-i-LEE-don
From Greek *kotyle* meaning 'cup-shaped hollow', as some species have concave leaves (*Crassulaceae*)

coulteri
kol-TER-ee-eye
Named after Dr Thomas Coulter (1793–1843), Irish botanist, as in *Romneya coulteri*

coum
KOO-um
Connected with Kos, Greece, as in *Cyclamen coum*

Crambe
KRAM-bee
From Greek *krambe* meaning 'cabbage' (*Brassicaceae*)

Craspedia
kras-PEE-dee-uh
From Greek *kraspedon* meaning 'hem' as some species have a woolly fringe to the leaves (*Asteraceae*)

crassicaulis
krass-ih-KAW-lis
crassicaulis, crassicaule
With a thick stem, as in *Begonia crassicaulis*

crassifolius
krass-ih-FOH-lee-us
crassifolia, crassifolium
With thick leaves, as in *Pittosporum crassifolium*

crassipes
KRASS-ih-peez
With thick feet or thick stems, as in *Quercus crassipes*

crassiusculus
krass-ih-US-kyoo-lus
crassiuscula, crassiusculum
Quite thick, as in *Acacia crassiuscula*

Crassula [1]
KRAS-ew-luh
From Greek *krassus* meaning 'thick', as many species have succulent leaves (*Crassulaceae*)

Crassula coccinea,
garden coral

crassus
KRASS-us
crassa, crassum
Thick; fleshy, as in *Asarum crassum*

crataegifolius
krah-tee-gi-FOH-lee-us
crataegifolia, crataegifolium
With leaves like hawthorn (*Crataegus*), as in *Acer crataegifolium*

Crataegus
kra-TEE-gus
From Greek *kratos* meaning 'strength' and *akis* meaning 'sharp tip', in reference to the thorns (*Rosaceae*)

crenatiflorus
kren-at-ih-FLOR-us
crenatiflora, crenatiflorum
With flowers cut into rounded scallops, as in *Calceolaria crenatiflora*

crenatus
kre-NAH-tus
crenata, crenatum
Scalloped, crenate, as in *Ilex crenata*

crenulatus
kren-yoo-LAH-tus
crenulata, crenulatum
Rather scalloped, as in *Boronia crenulata*

Crocus speciosus,
large autumn crocus

crepidatus
krep-id-AH-tus
crepidata, crepidatum
Shaped like a sandal or slipper, as in *Dendrobium crepidatum*

Crepis
KRE-pis
From Greek *krepis* meaning 'slipper', perhaps referring to the shape of the fruit (*Asteraceae*)

crepitans
KREP-ih-tanz
Rustling; crackling, as in *Hura crepitans*

cretaceus
kret-AY-see-us
cretacea, cretaceum
Relating to chalk, as in *Dianthus cretaceus*

creticus
KRET-ih-kus
cretica, creticum
Connected with Crete, Greece, as in *Pteris cretica*

crinitus
krin-EE-tus
crinita, crinitum
With long, weak hairs, as in *Acanthophoenix crinita*

Crinodendron

kry-noh-DEN-dron

From Greek *krinon* meaning 'lily' and *dendron* meaning 'tree' (*Elaeocarpaceae*)

Crinum

KRY-num

From Greek *krinon* meaning 'lily' (*Amaryllidaceae*)

crispatus

kriss-PAH-tus

crispata, crispatum

—

crispus

KRISP-us

crispa, crispum

Closely curled, as in *Mentha crispa*

cristatus

kris-TAH-tus

cristata, cristatum

With tassel-like tips, as in *Iris cristata*

crithmifolius

krith-mih-FOH-lee-us

crithmifolia, crithmifolium

With leaves like *Crithmum*, as in *Achillea crithmifolia*

—

Crithmum

KRITH-moom

From Greek *krithe* meaning 'barley' as the ribbed seeds resemble this grain

---

WOMEN IN BOTANY

While male botanists predominate in any list of eponymous genera, several women of note have been memorialised. Charlotte Percy (*née* Clive), Duchess of Northumberland, was an avid gardener and successfully grew several plants brought back from South Africa. She was the first person to flower a *Clivia*, which is named in her honour. Less is known of the Irish Fitton sisters, after whom *Fittonia* is named, though the elder sister Sarah did publish a botanical work. Mildred Mathias earned her namesake genus (*Mathiasella*) as a professional botanist who travelled around the world collecting. Other genera named after women include *Libertia*, *Lapageria*, *Strelitzia* and *Victoria*.

---

crocatus

kroh-KAH-tus

crocata, crocatum

—

croceus

KRO-kee-us

crocea, croceum

Saffron yellow, as in *Tritonia crocata*

Crocosmia

kro-KOZ-mee-uh

From Greek *krokos* meaning 'saffron' and *osme* meaning 'fragrance' as this *Crocus* relative has scented flowers (*Iridaceae*)

crocosmiiflorus

kroh-koz-mee-eye-FLOR-us

crocosmiiflora, crocosmiiflorum

With flowers like *Crocosmia*. The genus of *Crocosmia* × *crocosmiiflora* was originally *Montbretia*; the name therefore meant crocosmia-flowered montbretia

Crocus [2]

KRO-kus

From Greek *krokos* meaning 'saffron', extracted from *C. sativus* (*Iridaceae*)

Crossandra

kros-AND-ruh

From Greek *krossos* meaning 'fringe' and *andros* meaning 'male' as the anthers are fringed (*Acanthaceae*)

Crotalaria [3]

kro-tuh-LAIR-ee-uh

From Greek *krotalon* meaning a 'rattle' as the seeds rattle within the pods (*Fabaceae*)

3

Crotalaria juncea,
Bengal hemp

Croton

KRO-ton

From Greek *kroton* meaning a 'tick', as the seeds resemble these parasites (*Euphorbiaceae*)

Crowea

KROW-ee-uh

Named after James Crowe (1750–1807), British surgeon and botanist (*Fabaceae*)

cruciatus

kruks-ee-AH-tus

cruciata, crusiatum

In the shape of a cross, as in *Gentiana cruciata*

cruentus

kroo-EN-tus

cruenta, cruentum

Bloody, as in *Lycaste cruenta*

crus-galli

krus GAL-ee

Cockspur, as in *Crataegus crus-galli*

crustatus

krus-TAH-tus

crustata, crustatum

Encrusted, as in *Saxifraga crustata*

Cryptanthus

krip-TAN-thus

From Greek *krypte* meaning 'hidden' and *anthos* meaning 'flower' as the lower part of the flowers is concealed among bracts (*Bromeliaceae*)

Cryptocoryne

krip-toh-kor-AY-nee

From Greek *krypte* meaning 'hidden' and *koryne* meaning 'club' as the spadix is concealed within a tubular spathe (*Araceae*)

Cryptogramma

krip-toh-GRAM-uh

From Greek *krypte* meaning 'hidden' and *gramme* meaning 'line', as the line of sporangia are secreted within the curled leaf margin (*Pteridaceae*)

Cryptomeria [1]

krip-toh-MEER-ee-uh

From Greek *krypte* meaning 'hidden' and *meris* meaning 'part' as the fertile structures are hidden within cones (*Cupressaceae*)

crystallinus

kris-tal-EE-nus

crystallina, crystallinum

Crystalline, as in *Anthurium crystallinum*

Ctenanthe

ten-AN-thee

From Greek *ktenion* meaning 'comb' and *anthos* meaning 'flower', as the blooms emerge from parallel comb-like bracts (*Marantaceae*)

cucullatus

kuk-yoo-LAH-tus

cucullata, cucullatum

Like a hood, as in *Viola cucullata*

cucumerifolius

ku-ku-mer-ee-FOH-lee-us

cucumerifolia, cucumerifolium

With leaves like a cucumber, as in *Cissus cucumerifolia*

cucumerinus

ku-ku-mer-EE-nus

cucumerina, cucumerinum

Like a cucumber, as in *Trichosanthes cucumerina*

Cucumis [2]

koo-KEW-mis

From Latin *cucumis* meaning 'cucumber' (*Cucurbitaceae*)

Cucurbita

koo-KUR-bit-uh

From Latin *cucurbita* meaning 'gourd' (*Cucurbitaceae*)

cultorum

kult-OR-um

Relating to gardens, as in *Trollius* × *cultorum*

cultratus

kul-TRAH-tus

cultrata, cultratum

—

cultriformis

kul-tre-FOR-mis

cultriformis, cultriforme

Shaped like a knife, as in *Angraecum cultriforme*

Cuminum

koo-MINE-um

From Greek *kuminon*, the classical name for cumin (*Apiaceae*)

1

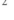

Cryptomeria japonica,
Japanese cedar

2

Cucumis melo,
musk melon

Helianthemum cupreum,
copper-coloured sun rose

cuneatus
kew-nee-AH-tus
cuneata, cuneatum
In the shape of a wedge, as in *Prostanthera cuneata*

cuneifolius
kew-nee-FOH-lee-us
cuneifolia, cuneifolium
With leaves shaped like a wedge, as in *Primula cuneifolia*

cuneiformis
kew-nee-FOR-mis
cuneiformis, cuneiforme
In the form of a wedge, as in *Hibbertia cuneiformis*

Cunninghamia
kuh-ning-HAY-mee-uh
Named after James Cunningham (dates unknown), British surgeon with East India Company (*Cupressaceae*)

cunninghamianus
kun-ing-ham-ee-AH-nus
cunninghamiana, cunninghamianum
—

cunninghamii
kuh-ning-HAY-mee-eye
May commemorate various people called Cunningham, including Alan Cunningham (1791–1839), British plant collector and botanist, as in *Archontophoenix cunninghamiana*

Cunonia
koo-NOH-nee-uh
Named after Johann Christian Cuno (1708–83), German poet, merchant and botanist (*Cunoniaceae*)

Cuphea
KOO-fee-uh
From Greek *kyphos* meaning 'curved' or 'humped', in reference to the shape of the fruit or the protuberance on the calyx (*Lythraceae*)

cupreatus
kew-pree-AH-tus
cupreata, cupreatum
—

cupreus [3]
kew-pree-US
cuprea, cupreum
The colour of copper, as in *Alocasia cuprea*

cupressinus
koo-pres-EE-nus
cupressina, cupressinum
—

cupressoides
koo-press-OY-deez
Resembling cypress, as in *Fitzroya cupressoides*

Cupressus
koo-PRES-us
From Greek *kuparissos*, the classical name for a cypress tree, probably *C. sempervirens* (*Cupressaceae*)

curassavicus
ku-ra-SAV-ih-kus
curassavica, curassavicum
From Curaçao, Lesser Antilles, as in *Asclepias curassavica*

Curcuma
kur-KOO-muh
From Arabic *kurkum* meaning 'turmeric', extracted from *C. longa* (*Zingiberaceae*)

curtus
KUR-tus
curta, curtum
Shortened, as in *Ixia curta*

curvatus
KUR-va-tus
curvata, curvatum
Curved, as in *Adiantum curvatum*

curvifolius
kur-vi-FOH-lee-us
curvifolia, curvifolium
With curved leaves, as in *Ascocentrum curvifolium*

cuspidatus
kus-pi-DAH-tus
cuspidata, cuspidatum
With a stiff point, as in *Taxus cuspidata*

cuspidifolius
kus-pi-di-FOH-lee-us
cuspidifolia, cuspidifolium
With leaves with a stiff point, as in *Passiflora cuspidifolia*

Cyananthus
sy-uh-NAN-thus
From Greek *cyanos* meaning 'blue' and *anthos* meaning 'flower' (*Campanulaceae*)

cyaneus
sy-AN-ee-us
cyanea, cyaneum
—

cyanus
sy-AH-nus
Blue, as in *Allium cyaneum*

cyanocarpus
sy-an-o-KAR-pus
cyanocarpa, cyanocarpum
Bearing blue fruit, as in *Rhododendron cyanocarpum*

Cyanotis

sy-uh-NO-tis

From Greek *cyanos* meaning 'blue' and *otos* meaning 'ear', to which the petals resemble (*Commelinaceae*)

Cyathea

sy-ATH-ee-uh

From Greek *kyathios* meaning 'little cup', as the membrane covering the sporangia is cup-like in some species (*Cyatheaceae*)

cyatheoides

sigh-ath-ee-OY-deez

Resembling *Cyathea*, as in *Sadleria cyatheoides*

Cycas

SY-cass

From Greek *kykas*, probably a spelling error from *koikas*, meaning 'palm tree', which these gymnosperms resemble (*Cycadaceae*)

Cyclamen [1]

SIK-luh-min

From Greek *kyklos* meaning 'circle', in reference to the circular tubers, the coiling stem holding the fruit, or perhaps the use of leaves in garlands (*Primulaceae*)

cyclamineus

SIGH-kluh-min-ee-us

cyclaminea, cyclamineum

Like *Cyclamen*, as in *Narcissus cyclamineus*

cyclocarpus

sigh-klo-KAR-pus

cyclocarpa, cyclocarpum

With fruit arranged in a circle, as in *Enterolobium cyclocarpum*

Cycnoches

sik-NOH-kees

From Greek *kykneios* meaning 'swan', referring to the gracefully arching column in male flowers (*Orchidaceae*)

Cydonia

sy-DOH-nee-uh

Named for the city of Kydonia (now Chania) in Crete, Greece (*Rosaceae*)

cylindraceus

sil-in-DRA-see-us

cylindracea, cylindraceum

—

cylindricus

sil-IN-drih-kus

cylindrica, cylindricum

Long and cylindrical, as in *Vaccinium cylindraceum*

Cylindropuntia

sil-in-droh-PUN-tee-uh

From Latin *cylindrus* meaning 'cylindrical' and *Opuntia*, a related genus; unlike *Opuntia*, which has flat, pad-like stems, these cacti have cylindrical stems (*Cactaceae*)

cylindrostachyus

sil-in-dro-STAK-ee-us

cylindrostachya, cylindrostachyum

With a cylindrical spike, as in *Betula cylindrostachya*

Cymbalaria

sim-buh-LAIR-ee-uh

From Greek *kymbalon* meaning 'cymbal', an allusion to leaf shape in some species (*Plantaginaceae*)

Cymbidium

sim-BID-ee-um

From Greek *kymbe* meaning 'boat', as the lip of the flower is concave (*Orchidaceae*)

cymbiformis

sim-BIH-for-mis

cymbiformis, cymbiforme

Shaped like a boat, as in *Haworthia cymbiformis*

GENUS SPOTLIGHT

Cyperus

The genus *Cyperus* is found on all continents but Antarctica, and these grass-like plants are especially common in wet areas, so not surprisingly the genus name derives from a Greek word for marsh plant. The name does not appear connected with Cyprus (the island), which is thought to derive from the Greek word for cypress (*Cupressus sempervirens*) or an older word for copper. *Cyperus* plants are harvested for their edible tubers (e.g. *C. esculentus*), are troublesome weeds (e.g. *C. rotundus*) or houseplants (e.g. *C. alternifolius*). Papyrus paper was manufactured using the stems of *Cyperus papyrus*.

Cyperus alternifolius, **umbrella plant**

Cymbopogon

sim-boh-POH-gon

From Greek *kymbe* meaning 'boat' and *pogon* meaning 'beard', as the flower spikelets have numerous bristle-like awns and boat-shaped glumes (*Poaceae*)

cymosus

sy-MOH-sus

cymosa, cymosum

With flower clusters that flower from the centre outwards, as in *Rosa cymosa*

Cynanchum

sy-NAN-kum

From Greek *kynos* meaning 'dog' and *anchein* meaning 'to choke' in reference to the many poisonous species (*Apocynaceae*)

Cynara

sy-NAR-uh

From Greek *kynara* meaning 'artichoke' (harvested from *C. cardunculus*), perhaps derived from *kynos* meaning 'dog', as the stiff involucral bracts are tooth-like (*Asteraceae*)

cynaroides

sin-nar-OY-deez

Resembling *Cynara*, as in *Protea cynaroides*

Cynodon

SY-noh-don

From Greek *kynos* meaning 'dog' and *odontos* meaning 'tooth', though the object of this description is uncertain (*Poaceae*)

Cynoglossum

sy-noh-GLOS-um

From Greek *kynos* meaning 'dog' and *glossa* meaning 'tongue' as the coarsely-textured leaves are tongue-like (*Boraginaceae*)

Cynosurus

sy-noh-SOOR-us

From Greek *kynos* meaning 'dog' and *oura* meaning 'tail', as the inflorescence is so shaped (*Poaceae*)

cyparissias

sy-pah-RIS-ee-as

Latin name for a kind of spurge, as in *Euphorbia cyparissias*

Cypella

sy-PEL-uh

From Greek *kyphella* meaning the 'hollow of the ear', as the innermost petals are cupped (*Iridaceae*)

1

Cyclamen hederifolium, ivy-leaved cyclamen

Cyperus

SY-per-us

From Greek *kypeiros*, the classical name for an aromatic marsh plant, probably *C. longus* (*Cyperaceae*)

Cyphostemma

sy-foh-STEM-uh

From Greek *kyphos* meaning 'hump' and *stemma* meaning 'wreath', as the foliage sits atop a swollen succulent stem (*Vitaceae*)

Cypripedium

sip-ri-PEED-ee-um

From Greek *Kypris* (=Aphrodite) and *pedilon* meaning 'slipper' (*Orchidaceae*)

cyprius

SIP-ree-us

cypria, cyprium

Connected with the island of Cyprus, as in *Cistus × cyprius*

Cyrilla

si-RIL-uh

Named after Domenico Maria Leone Cirillo (1739–99), Italian physician and botanist (*Cyrillaceae*)

Cyrtanthus

sir-TAN-thus

From Greek *kyrtos* meaning 'curved' and *anthos* meaning 'flower' (*Amaryllidaceae*)

Cyrtomium

sir-TOH-mee-um

From Greek *kyrtos* meaning 'curved', referring to the arching leaf veins or fronds (*Dryopteridaceae*)

Cyrtostachys

sir-toh-STA-kis

From Greek *kurtos* meaning 'curved' and *stachys* meaning 'ear of grain', a reference to the curved inflorescence stalks (*Arecaceae*)

Cystopteris

sis-TOP-ter-us

From Greek *kystos* meaning 'bladder' and *pteris* meaning 'fern' as the membrane protecting the sporangia is inflated when young (*Woodsiaceae*)

cytisoides

sit-iss-OY-deez

Resembling broom (*Cytisus*), as in *Lotus cytisoides*

Cytisus

sy-TIS-us

From Greek *kytisos*, the classical name for several leguminous shrubs (*Fabaceae*)

Daboecia
da-BEE-see-uh
Named after Saint Dabheog (dates unknown), Irish founder of a monastery in Lough Derg (*Ericaceae*)

Dacrydium
dah-CRID-ee-um
From Greek *dakrydion* meaning 'small tear', as the wood weeps resin (*Podocarpaceae*)

Dactylicapnos
dak-til-ee-KAP-nos
From Greek *daktylos* meaning 'finger' and *kapnos* meaning 'smoke'; the fruits are finger-like, while the soft, flimsy foliage appears smoky (*Papaveraceae*)

dactyliferus
dak-ty-LIH-fer-us
dactylifera, dactyliferum
With fingers; finger-like, as in *Phoenix dactylifera*

Dactylis
DAK-til-iss
From Greek *daktylos* meaning 'finger' or probably 'toe', the inflorescence resembling a bird foot (*Poaceae*)

dactyloides
dak-ty-LOY-deez
Resembling fingers, as in *Hakea dactyloides*

Dactylorhiza
dak-til-oh-RYE-zuh
From Greek *daktylos* meaning 'finger' and *rhiza* meaning 'root' (*Orchidaceae*)

Dahlia
DAH-lee-uh
Named after Anders Dahl (1751–89), Swedish botanist (*Asteraceae*)

dahuricus
da-HYUR-ih-kus
dahurica, dahuricum
Connected with Dahuria, a region incorporating parts of Siberia and Mongolia, as in *Codonopsis dahurica*

Dais
DYE-us
From Greek *dais* meaning 'torch' as the flower clusters sit atop long, straight stems (*Thymelaeaceae*)

Dalbergia
dal-BURG-ee-uh
Named after Nils Ericsson Dalberg (1736–1820), Swedish botanist (*Fabaceae*)

Dalea
DAY-lee-uh
Named after Samuel Dale (1659–1739), British apothecary and botanist (*Fabaceae*)

Dalechampia
dayle-CHAM-pee-uh
Named after Jacques Daléchamps (1513–88), French surgeon and botanist (*Euphorbiaceae*)

dalhousiae
dal-HOO-zee-ay
dalhousieae
Named after Susan Georgiana Ramsay, Marchioness of Dalhousie (1817–53), as in *Rhododendron dalhousiae*

dalmaticus
dal-MAT-ih-kus
dalmatica, dalmaticum
Connected with Dalmatia, Croatia, as in *Geranium dalmaticum*

damascenus
dam-ASK-ee-nus
damascena, damascenum
Connected with Damascus, Syria, as in *Nigella damascena*

dammeri
DAM-mer-ee
Named after Carl Lebrecht Udo Dammer (1860–1920), German botanist, as in *Cotoneaster dammeri*

Dampiera
dam-pee-AIR-uh
Named after William Dampier (1651–1715), British explorer and pirate (*Goodeniaceae*)

Danae
DAN-ay-ee
Named after Danaë, mother of Perseus in Greek mythology (*Asparagaceae*)

danfordiae
dan-FORD-ee-ay
Named after Mrs C.G. Danford, 19th-century traveller, as in *Iris danfordiae*

danicus
DAN-ih-kus
danica, danicum
From Denmark, as in *Erodium danicum*

Danthonia
dan-THO-nee-uh
Named after Étienne Danthoine (1739–94), French botanist (*Poaceae*)

Daphne
DAF-nee
The classical Greek name for laurel and a nymph of the same name (*Thymelaeaceae*)

Daphniphyllum
daf-ni-FIL-um
Leaves resembling *Daphne*, from Greek *phyllon* meaning 'leaf' (*Daphniphyllaceae*)

daphnoides
daf-NOY-deez
Resembling *Daphne*, as in *Salix daphnoides*

darleyensis
dar-lee-EN-sis
Of Darley Dale nursery (James Smith & Sons), Derbyshire, as in *Erica × darleyensis*

Darlingtonia
dar-ling-TOH-nee-uh
Named after William Darlington (1782–1863), American politician and botanist (*Sarraceniaceae*)

Darmera
DAR-muh-ruh
Named after Karl Darmer (1843–1918), German botanist and horticulturist (*Saxifragaceae*)

Darwinia
dar-WIN-ee-uh
Named after Erasmus Darwin (1731–1802), British physician and botanist, grandfather to Charles Darwin (*Myrtaceae*)

darwinii
dar-WIN-ee-eye
Named after Charles Darwin (1809–82), British naturalist, as in *Berberis darwinii*

Dasiphora
da-zee-FOR-uh
From Greek *dasys* meaning 'hairy' and *phoros* meaning 'bearing' and may refer to the hairy bark, seeds or hypanthium (*Rosaceae*)

dasyacanthus

day-see-uh-KAN-thus

dasyacantha, dasyacanthum

With thick spines, as in *Escobaria dasyacantha*

dasyanthus

day-see-AN-thus

dasyantha, dasyanthum

With shaggy flowers, as in *Spiraea dasyantha*

dasycarpus

day-see-KAR-pus

dasycarpa, dasycarpum

With hairy fruit, as in *Angraecum dasycarpum*

Dasylirion

da-zee-LI-ree-on

From Greek *dasy* meaning 'dense' and *lirion* meaning 'lily', as this lily relation has an inflorescence with densely packed flowers (*Asparagaceae*)

dasyphyllus

das-ee-FIL-us

dasyphylla, dasyphyllum

With shaggy leaves, as in *Sedum dasyphyllum*

dasystemon

day-see-STEE-mon

With hairy stamens, as in *Tulipa dasystemon*

Datisca

dah-TIS-kuh

From Greek *datiska*, the vernacular name for *Catananche caerulea* (*Asteraceae*), probably from *datessai* meaning 'to heal' as the latter plant has medicinal properties; Linnaeus applied the name to the unrelated *Datisca* (*Datiscaceae*)

Datura [1]

dah-TEW-ruh

From Hindi *dhatura*, the vernacular name (*Solanaceae*)

daucifolius

daw-ke-FOH-lee-us

daucifolia, daucifolium

With leaves like carrot (*Daucus*), as in *Asplenium daucifolium*

daucoides

do-KOY-deez

Resembling carrot (*Daucus*), as in *Erodium daucoides*

Daucus [2]

DOW-kus

The Greek vernacular name for carrot, *D. carota* (*Apiaceae*)

dauricus

DOR-ih-kus

daurica, dauricum

Connected with Siberia, as in *Lilium dauricum*

Davallia

duh-VAY-lee-uh

Named after Edmund Davall (1762–98), Swiss botanist (*Davalliaceae*)

Davidia [3]

duh-VID-ee-uh

Named after Père Armand David (1826–1900), French missionary, botanist and zoologist (*Nyssaceae*)

davidianus

duh-vid-ee-AH-nus

davidiana, davidianum

—

davidii

davidii duh-vid-ee-eye

Named after Père Armand David (1826–1900), French naturalist and missionary, as in *Buddleja davidii*

davuricus

dav-YUR-ih-kus

davurica, davuricum

Connected with Siberia, as in *Juniperus davurica*

dawsonianus

daw-son-ee-AH-nus

dawsoniana, dawsonianum

Named after Jackson T. Dawson (1841–1916), the first Superintendent of the Arnold Arboretum, Boston, USA, as in *Malus × dawsoniana*

Datura metel,
downy thorn apple

Daucus carota,
carrot

Davidia involucrata,
handkerchief tree

Decaisnea fargesii,
blue bean shrub

Rhododendron decorum,
great white rhododendron

Decumaria barbara,
climbing hydrangea

dealbatus
day-al-BAH-tus
dealbata, dealbatum
Covered with an opaque white powder, as in
Acacia dealbata

debilis
deb-IL-is
debilis, debile
Weak and frail, as in *Asarum debile*

Decaisnea [4]
duh-KAYZ-nee-uh
Named after Joseph Decaisne (1807–82),
French botanist (*Lardizabalaceae*)

decaisneanus
de-kane-ee-AY-us
decaisneana, decaisneanum
—
decaisnei
de-KANE-ee-eye
Named after Joseph Decaisne (1807–82),
French botanist, as in *Aralia decaisneana*

decandrus
dek-AN-drus
decandra, decandrum
With ten stamens, as in *Combretum
decandrum*

decapetalus
dek-uh-PET-uh-lus
decapetala, decapetalum
With ten petals, as in *Caesalpinia decapetala*

Decarya
deh-CAH-ree-uh
Named after Raymond Decary (1891–
1973), French botanist and anthropologist
(*Didiereaceae*)

deciduus
dee-SID-yu-us
decidua, deciduum
Deciduous, as in *Larix decidua*

decipiens
de-SIP-ee-enz
Deceptive; not obvious, as in *Sorbus
decipiens*

declinatus
dek-lin-AH-tus
declinata, declinatum
Bending downwards, as in *Cotoneaster
declinatus*

decompositus
de-kom-POZ-ee-tus
decomposita, decompostitum
Divided several times, as in *Paeonia
decomposita*

decoratus
dek-kor-RAH-tus
decorata, decoratum
—
decorus [5]
dek-kor-RUS
decora, decorum
Decorative, as in *Rhododendron decorum*

decumanus
dek-yoo-MAH-nus
decumana, decumanum
Very large, as in *Phlebodium decumanum*

Decumaria [6]
dek-ew-MAH-ree-uh
From Latin *decem* meaning 'ten' as the
flower parts are in tens (*Hydrangeaceae*)

decumbens
de-KUM-benz
Trailing with upright tips, as in *Correa
decumbens*

decurrens
de-KUR-enz
Running down the stem, as in *Calocedrus
decurrens*

decussatus
de-KUSS-ah-tus
decussata, decussatum
With leaves that are borne in pairs at right
angles to each other, as in *Microbiota decussata*

deflexus
de-FLEKS-us
deflexa, deflexum
Bending downwards, as in *Enkianthus deflexus*

deformis
de-FOR-mis
deformis, deforme
Deformed; misshapen, as in *Haemanthus
deformis*

degronianum

de-gron-ee-AH-num

Named after Henri Joseph Degron, director
of the French Post Office in Yokohama from
1865–1880, as in *Rhododendron
degronianum*

Deinanthe

dye-NAN-thee

From Greek *deinos* meaning 'wondrous' and
anthos meaning 'flower' (*Hydrangeaceae*)

dejectus

dee-JEK-tus

dejecta, dejectum

Debased, as in *Opuntia dejecta*

delavayi

del-uh-VAY-ee

Named after Père Jean Marie Delavay
(1834–1895), French missionary, explorer
and botanist, as in *Magnolia delavayi*

delicatus

del-ih-KAH-tus

delicata, delicatum

Delicate, as in *Dendrobium* × *delicatum*

deliciosus

de-lis-ee-OH-sus

deliciosa, deliciosum

Delicious, as in *Monstera deliciosa*

Delonix [1]

deh-LON-iks

From Greek *delos* meaning 'visible' and *onux*
meaning 'claw', as the petals have a narrow
limb or claw (*Fabaceae*)

Delosperma

del-oh-SPER-muh

From Greek *delos* meaning 'visible' and
sperma meaning 'seed', as the fruits open to
reveal the seeds (*Aizoaceae*)

delphiniifolius

del-fin-uh-FOH-lee-us

delphiniifolia, delphiniifolium

With leaves like *Delphinium*, as in *Aconitum
delphiniifolium*

Delphinium

del-FIN-ee-um

From Greek *delphin* meaning 'dolphin', as
the blue flowers are said to resemble these
aquatic mammals (*Ranunculaceae*)

deltoides

del-TOY-deez

—

deltoideus

el-TOY-dee-us

deltoidea, deltoideum

Triangular, as in *Dianthus deltoides*

demersus

DEM-er-sus

demersa, demersum

Living under water, as in *Ceratophyllum
demersum*

deminutus

dee-MIN-yoo-tus

deminuta, deminutum

Small, diminished, as in *Rebutia deminuta*

demissus

dee-MISS-us

demissa, demissum

Hanging downwards; weak, as in *Cytisus
demissus*

Dendrobium

den-DRO-bee-um

From Greek *dendron* meaning 'tree' and *bios*
meaning 'life', as most of these orchids are
epiphytic, living perched on tree branches
(*Orchidaceae*)

Dendrocalamus

den-dro-KAL-uh-mus

From Greek *dendron* meaning 'tree' and
kalamos meaning 'reed', as this is a genus of
large, woody bamboos (*Poaceae*)

Dendrochilum

den-dro-KY-lum

From Greek *dendron* meaning 'tree' and
cheilos meaning 'lip', as the floral lip is large,
or possibly *chilos* meaning 'green food', as
these orchids grow as epiphytes
(*Orchidaceae*)

dendroides

den-DROY-deez

—

dendroideus

den-DROY-dee-us

dendroidea, dendroideum

Resembling a tree, as in *Sedum dendroideum*

Dendromecon

den-dro-ME-kon

From Greek *dendron* meaning 'tree' and
mekon meaning 'poppy' (*Papaveraceae*)

dendrophilus

den-dro-FIL-us

dendrophila, dendrophilum

Tree-loving, as in *Tecomanthe dendrophila*

1

Delonix regia,
flamboyant tree

Fuchsia denticulata,
saw-leaved fuchsia

Denmoza
den-MOH-zuh
An anagram of Mendoza, a province in western Argentina (*Cactaceae*)

Dennstaedtia
den-STAY-tee-uh
Named after August Wilhelm Dennstädt (1776–1826), German physician and botanist (*Dennstaedtiaceae*)

dens-canis
denz-KAN-is
Term for dog's tooth, as in *Erythronium dens-canis*

densatus
den-SA-tus
densata, densatum
—

densus
den-SUS
densa, densum
Compact; dense, as in *Trichodiadema densum*

densiflorus
den-see-FLOR-us
densiflora, densiflorum
Densely flowered, as in *Verbascum densiflorum*

densifolius
den-see-FOH-lee-us
densifolia, densifolium
Densely leaved, as in *Gladiolus densifolius*

dentatus
den-TAH-tus
dentata, dentatum
With teeth, as in *Ligularia dentata*

denticulatus [2]
den-tik-yoo-LAH-tus
denticulata, denticulatum
Slightly toothed, as in *Primula denticulata*

denudatus
dee-noo-DAH-tus
denudata, denudatum
Bare; naked, as in *Magnolia denudata*

deodara
dee-oh-DAR-uh
From the Indian name for the deodar, as in *Cedrus deodara*

depauperatus
de-por-per-AH-tus
depauperata, depauperatum
Not properly developed; dwarfed, as in *Carex depauperata*

dependens
de-PEN-denz
Hanging down, as in *Celastrus dependens*

deppeanus
dep-ee-AH-nus
deppeana, deppeanum
Named after Ferdinand Deppe (1794–1861), German botanist, as in *Juniperus deppeana*

depressus
de-PRESS-us
depressa, depressum
Flattened or pressed down, as in *Gentiana depressa*

Deschampsia
deh-SHAMP-see-uh
Named after Louis Auguste Deschamps (1765–1842), French naturalist and surgeon (*Poaceae*)

deserti
DES-er-tee
Connected with the desert, as in *Agave deserti*

desertorum
de-zert-OR-um
Of deserts, as in *Alyssum desertorum*

Desfontainia
dez-fon-TAYN-ee-uh
Named after René Louiche Desfontaines (1750–1833), French botanist (*Columelliaceae*)

Desmodium
dez-MOH-dee-um
From Greek *desmos* meaning 'chain' as the seed pods break into segments (*Fabaceae*)

detonsus
de-TON-sus
detonsa, detonsum
Bare; shorn, as in *Gentianopsis detonsa*

Dianthus caryophyllus,
border carnation

Deuterocohnia

dew-ter-oh-COH-nee-uh

Named after Ferdinand Julius Cohn (1828–98), German biologist; the genus *Cohnia* (=*Cordyline*) already existed, so the Greek prefix *deuter* (meaning 'second') was added (*Bromeliaceae*)

deustus

dee-US-tus

deusta, deustum

Burned, as in *Tritonia deusta*

Deutzia

DOYT-zee-uh

Named after Johan van der Deutz (1743–88), Dutch lawyer and botanist (*Hydrangeaceae*)

diabolicus

dy-oh-BOL-ih-kus

diabolica, diabolicum

Devilish, as in *Acer diabolicum*

diacanthus

dy-ah-KAN-thus

diacantha, diacanthum

With two spines, as in *Ribes diacanthum*

diadema

dy-uh-DEE-ma

Crown; diadem, as in *Begonia diadema*

Dianella

dy-ah-NEL-uh

From Diana, Roman goddess of the hunt, plus Latin diminutive *ella*, perhaps alluding to a woodland habitat (*Asphodelaceae*)

diandrus

dy-AN-drus

diandra, diandrum

With two stamens, as in *Bromus diandrus*

dianthiflorus

die-AN-thuh-flor-us

dianthiflora, dianthiflorum

With flowers like pinks (*Dianthus*), as in *Episcia dianthiflora*

Dianthus

dy-AN-thus

From Greek *dios* meaning 'god' and *anthos* meaning 'flower', as pinks smell divine (*Caryophyllaceae*)

diaphanus

dy-AF-a-nus

diaphana, diaphanum

Transparent, as in *Berberis diaphana*

Diascia

dy-AS-ee-uh

From Greek *dis* meaning 'two' and *askos* meaning 'sack', as in the type species *D. bergiana*, each flower has two nectar-filled spurs (*Scrophulariaceae*)

Dicentra

dy-SEN-truh

From Greek *dis* meaning 'two' and *kentron* meaning 'sharp point', as each flower has twin spurs (*Papaveraceae*)

Dichelostemma

dy-kel-oh-STEM-uh

From Greek *dichelos* meaning 'cloven-hooved' and *stemma* meaning 'wreath', as flowers contain a ring of two-lobed appendages (*Asparagaceae*)

Dichondra

dy-KON-druh

From Greek *dis* meaning 'two' and *chondros* meaning 'grain', referring to the twin fruits (*Convolvulaceae*)

Dichorisandra

dy-kor-is-AN-druh

From Greek *dis* ('two'), *chorizo* ('to separate') and *andros* ('male'), as each flower has stamens with two different postures (*Commelinaceae*)

dichotomus

dy-KAW-toh-mus

dichotoma, dichotomum

In forked pairs, as in *Iris dichotoma*

Dichroa

dy-KROW-uh

From Greek *dis* meaning 'two' and *chroa* meaning 'coloured', as the blooms can change colour depending on soil pH, as in some hydrangeas (*Hydrangeaceae*)

dichroanthus

dy-kroh-AN-thus

dichroantha, dichroanthum

With flowers of two quite different colours, as in *Rhododendron dichroanthum*

dichromus

dy-KROH-mus

dichroma, dichromum

—

dichrous

dy-KRUS

dichroa, dichroum

With two distinct colours, as in *Gladiolus dichrous*

Dicksonia

dik-SOH-nee-uh

Named after James Dickson (1738–1822), Scottish horticulturist and botanist, founding member of the RHS (*Dicksoniaceae*)

Dicliptera

dy-KLIP-ter-uh

From Greek *diklis* meaning 'twice folded' and *pteron* meaning 'wing', as the fruiting capsule has two wing-like divisions (*Acanthaceae*)

Dictamnus (also dictamnus)

dik-TAM-nus

From the Greek name for *Origanum dictamnus* (*Lamiaceae*), itself derived from Mount Dikti in Crete (*Rutaceae*)

dictyophyllus

dik-tee-oh-FIL-us

dictyophylla, dictyophyllum

With leaves that have a net pattern, as in *Berberis dictyophylla*

Didierea

di-DEER-ee-uh

Named after Alfred Grandidier (1836–1921), French naturalist and explorer (*Didiereaceae*)

Didymochlaena

di-dee-mok-LAY-nuh

From Greek *didymos* meaning 'twin' and *chlaina* meaning 'cloak', as the membrane covering the sporangia opens on two sides (*Dryopteridaceae*)

didymus

DID-ih-mus

didyma, didymum

In pairs, twin, as in *Monarda didyma*

Dieffenbachia

dee-fen-BAH-kee-uh

Named after Joseph Dieffenbach (1796–1863), Austrian horticulturist (*Araceae*)

Dierama
dy-uh-RAH-muh
From Greek *dierama* meaning 'funnel', the shape of the flowers (*Iridaceae*)

Diervilla
dee-er-VIL-uh
Named after N. Dièreville (dates unknown), French surgeon (*Caprifoliaceae*)

Dietes
dy-EE-teez
From Greek *dis* meaning 'two' and *etes* meaning 'relation', an allusion to the evolutionary closeness of this genus to both *Iris* and *Moraea* (*Iridaceae*)

difformis
dif-FOR-mis
difformis, difforme
With an unusual form, unlike the rest of the genus, as in *Vinca difformis*

diffusus
dy-FEW-sus
diffusa, diffusum
With a spreading habit, as in *Cyperus diffusus*

Digitalis
di-ji-TAH-lis
From Latin *digitus* meaning 'finger', probably from the German *fingerhut* meaning thimble (= finger hat), which the flowers resemble (*Plantaginaceae*)

digitalis
dij-ee-TAH-lis
digitalis, digitale
Like a finger, as in *Penstemon digitalis*

Digitaria
di-ji-TAIR-ee-uh
From Latin *digitus* meaning 'finger', as the inflorescence resembles a hand with spreading fingers (*Poaceae*)

dilatatus
di-la-TAH-tus
dilatata, dilatatum
Spread out, as in *Dryopteris dilatata*

Dillenia
dy-LEE-nee-uh
Named after Johann Jacob Dillen (1684–1747), German botanist (*Dilleniaceae*)

dilutus
di-LOO-tus
diluta, dilutum
Diluted (i.e. pale) as in *Alstroemeria diluta*

dimidiatus
dim-id-ee-AH-tus
dimidiata, dimidiatum
Divided into two different or unequal parts, as in *Asarum dimidiatum*

Dimorphotheca
dy-morf-oh-THEE-kuh
From Greek *dis* ('two'), *morphe* ('shape') and *theka* ('fruit'), as the ray and disc florets each produce a different-shaped achene (*Asteraceae*)

dimorphus
dy-MOR-fus
dimorpha, dimorphum
With two different forms of leaf, flower or fruit, as in *Ceropegia dimorpha*

dioicus
dy-OY-kus
dioica, dioicum
With the male reproductive organs on one plant and the female on another, as in *Arunus dioicus*

Digitalis

Most gardeners are familiar with the hardy foxglove (*D. purpurea*), a biennial producing towers of pink or white flowers in its second year. In the Canary Islands and Madeira, however, grow woody, shrub-like foxgloves, which were once separated into their own genus *Isoplexis*. It's thought that non-woody species colonised the islands from Europe and in the absence of other shrubs, evolved a woody habit. Despite their charms, woody foxgloves are not hardy, but plant breeders have crossed them with common foxgloves, creating *Digitalis* x *valinii*. This hybrid is neither woody nor biennial, but reliably perennial, with flowers in a range of apricot shades.

Digitalis purpurea, **common foxglove**

Dionaea
dy-OH-nee-uh
Named after Dione, the mother of Aphrodite in Greek mythology; in Roman mythology, Aphrodite was known as Venus and Venus's flytrap gets its name from the pure white flowers and elegant leaves (*Droseraceae*)

Dionysia
dy-oh-NISS-ee-uh
Named after the Greek god Dionysus (*Primulaceae*)

Dioon
dy-OON
From Greek *dis* meaning 'two' and *oon* meaning 'egg', as the seeds are in pairs (*Zamiaceae*)

Dioscorea
dy-os-KOR-ee-uh
Named after Pedanius Dioscorides (c. AD 40–90), Greek physician and herbalist (*Dioscoreaceae*)

Diosma
dy-OZ-muh
From Greek *dios* meaning 'divine' and *osme* meaning 'fragrance', as the foliage is strongly scented (*Rutaceae*)

Diospyros
dy-os-PIE-rus
From Greek *dios* meaning 'divine' and *pyros* meaning 'wheat', referring to the delicious fruits (*Ebenaceae*)

Dipcadi
dip-CAH-dee
From the Turkish name for *Muscari*, a related genus (*Asparagaceae*)

Dipelta
dy-PEL-tuh
From Greek *dis* meaning 'two' and *pelte* meaning 'shield', as two large bracts surround each fruit (*Caprifoliaceae*)

dipetalus
dy-PET-uh-lus
dipetala, dipetalum
With two petals, as in *Begonia dipetala*

Diphylleia
dy-fil-AY-uh
From Greek *dis* meaning 'two' and *phyllon* meaning 'leaf', as each leaf is divided into two lobes (*Berberidaceae*)

diphyllus
dy-FIL-us
diphylla, diphyllum
With two leaves, as in *Bulbine diphylla*

Diplarrhena
dip-luh-REE-nuh
From Greek *dis* meaning 'two' and *arrhen* meaning 'male', as each flower has only two functional stamens (*Iridaceae*)

Diplazium
dy-PLAY-zee-um
From Greek *dis* meaning 'two' and *plasion* meaning 'oblong' as the membrane protecting the sporangia covers both sides of the leaf vein (*Athyriaceae*)

dipsaceus
dip-SAK-ee-us
dipsacea, dipsaceum
Like teasel (*Dipsacus*), as in *Carex dipsacea*

Dipsacus
DIP-sak-us
From Greek *dipsao* meaning 'thirst', as water gathers at the base of the paired leaves (*Caprifoliaceae*)

dipterocarpus
dip-ter-oh-KAR-pus
dipterocarpa, dipterocarpum
With two-winged fruit, as in *Thalictrum dipterocarpum*

Dipteronia
dip-tuh-ROH-nee-uh
From Greek *dis* meaning 'two' and *pteron* meaning 'wing'; a confusing name as *Dipteronia* fruits each have a circular wing that surrounds the seed, while related *Acer* fruits have two separate wings (*Sapindaceae*)

dipterus
DIP-ter-us
diptera, dipterum
With two wings, as in *Halesia diptera*

DOCTOR OF MEDICINE

Pedanius Dioscorides, after whom the yam genus *Dioscorea* is named, was a Greek physician who worked as a medic in the Roman army. He compiled a book (a pharmacopeia) listing medicines and the plants that they came from, now widely known as *De Materia Medica*. For centuries, its five volumes were the go-to reference for physicians, only being supplanted by Renaissance herbals. The father of plant taxonomy, Carl Linnaeus, adopted many of Dioscorides' plant names in his binomial classification system, though not always applying them to the plant that Dioscorides had perhaps intended.

---

dipyrenus
dy-pie-REE-nus
dipyrena, dipyrenum
With two seeds or kernels, as in *Ilex dipyrena*

Dirca
DUR-kuh
From Greek mythology, Dirce was the wife of Lyceus and she was transformed into a fountain by Dionysus; her connection with this shrub is uncertain (*Thymelaeaceae*)

dis-
Used in compound words to denote apart

Disa
DY-suh
Named after Disa, a heroine of Swedish mythology; challenged to appear before god-king Freyr neither dressed or undressed, she wrapped herself in a fishing net; some *Disa* species have net-like patterning on their petals (*Orchidaceae*)

Disanthus [1]

dy-SAN-thus

From Greek *dis* meaning 'two' and *anthos* meaning 'flower', as the blooms are paired (*Hamamelidaceae*)

Discaria

dis-KAIR-ee-uh

From Greek *diskos* meaning 'disc', referring to the prominent disc within each flower (*Rhamnaceae*)

Dischidia

di-SHI-dee-uh

From Greek *dis* meaning 'two' and either *askidion* meaning 'pouch', as the paired leaves can form chambers that contain ant nests, or *schizo* meaning 'to divide', as the corona lobes are bifid (*Apocynaceae*)

disciformis

disk-ee-FOR-mis

disciformis, disciforme

Shaped like a disc, as in *Medicago disciformis*

Discocactus

DIS-koh-kak-tus

From Greek *diskos* meaning 'disc', referring to the circular shape of these cacti (*Cactaceae*)

discoideus

dis-KOY-dee-us

discoidea, discoideum

Without rays, as in *Matricaria discoidea*

discolor

DIS-kol-or

Of two quite different colours, as in *Salvia discolor*

Diselma

dy-SEL-muh

From Greek *dis* meaning 'two' and *selma* meaning 'upper deck', as each cone has two fertile scales (*Cupressaceae*)

Disocactus

DY-soh-kak-tus

From Greek *dis* meaning 'two' and *isos* meaning 'equal', as the outer and inner whorls of tepals are of equal length (*Cactaceae*)

dispar

DIS-par

Unequal; unusual for a genus, as in *Restio dispar*

dispersus

dis-PER-sus

dispersa, dispersum

Scattered, as in *Paranomus dispersus*

Disporopsis

dy-spor-OP-sis

Resembling the genus *Disporum* (*Asparagaceae*)

Disporum [2]

dy-SPOR-um

From Greek *dis* meaning 'two' and *spora* meaning 'seed', as each chamber within the ovary has two ovules (*Colchicaceae*)

1

Disanthus cercidifolius,
long-stiped disanthus

2

Disporum cantoniense,
Canton fairy bells

Distylium racemosum,
isu tree

Dodecatheon meadia,
shooting star

dissectus
dy-SEK-tus
dissecta, dissectum
Deeply cut or divided, as in *Cirsium dissectum*

dissimilis
dis-SIM-il-is
dissimilis, dissimile
Differing from the norm for a particular genus, as in *Columnea dissimilis*

distachyus
dy-STAK-yus
distachya, distachyum
With two spikes, as in *Billbergia distachya*

distans
DIS-tanz
Widely apart, as in *Watsonia distans*

distichophyllus
dis-ti-koh-FIL-us
distichophylla, distichophyllum
With leaves appearing in two ranks or levels, as in *Buckleya distichophylla*

distichus
DIS-tih-kus
disticha, distichum
In two ranks or levels, as in *Taxodium distichum*

Distictis
dy-STIK-tis
From Greek *dis* meaning 'two' and *stiktos* meaning 'spotted' as the two rows of seeds within each capsule leave two rows of spots once shed (*Bignoniaceae*)

distortus
DIS-tor-tus
distorta, distortum
Misshapen, as in *Adonis distorta*

Distylium [3]
dy-STIL-ee-um
From Greek *dis* meaning 'two' and *stylos* meaning 'style', as the flowers each have two styles (*Hamamelidaceae*)

distylus
DIS-sty-lus
distyla, distylum
With two styles, as in *Acer distylum*

diurnus
dy-YUR-nus
diurna, diurnum
Flowering by day, as in *Cestrum diurnum*

divaricatus
dy-vair-ih-KAH-tus
divaricata, divaricatum
With a spreading and straggling habit, as in *Phlox divaricata*

divergens
div-VER-jenz
Spreading out a long way from the centre, as in *Ceanothus divergens*

diversifolius
dy-ver-sih-FOH-lee-us
diversifolia, diversifolium
With diverse leaves, as in *Hibiscus diversifolius*

diversiformis
dy-ver-sih-FOR-mis
diversiformis, diversiforme
With diverse forms, as in *Romulea diversiformis*

divisus
div-EE-sus
divisa, divisum
Divided, as in *Pennisetum divisum*

Docynia
doh-SY-nee-uh
An anagram of *Cydonia*, a related genus (*Rosaceae*)

dodecandrus
doh-DEK-an-drus
dodecandra, dodecandrum
With twelve stamens, as in *Cordia dodecandra*

Dodecatheon [4]
doh-duh-KATH-ee-on
From Greek *dodeca* meaning 'twelve' and *theos* meaning 'gods', a name used by Pliny to refer to a primrose protected by the gods (*Primulaceae*)

Dodonaea
doh-DOH-nee-uh
Named after Rembert Dodoens (1517–85), Flemish botanist (*Sapindaceae*)

Doellingeria
doh-lin-GEER-ee-uh
Named after Ignaz Döllinger (1770–1841), German doctor and natural philosopher (*Asteraceae*)

doerfleri
DOOR-fleur-eye
Named after Ignaz Dörfler (1866–1950), German botanist, as in *Colchicum doerfleri*

dolabratus
dol-uh-BRAH-tus
dolabrata, dolabratum
—

dolabriformis
doh-la-brih-FOR-mis
dolabriformis, dolabriforme
Shaped like a hatchet, as in *Thujopsis dolabrata*

Dolichos
DOH-li-kos
From Greek *dolikhos* meaning 'long', a reference to the climbing habit (*Fabaceae*)

dolosus

do-LOH-sus

dolosa, dolosum

Deceitful; looking like another plant, as in *Cattleya × dolosa*

Dombeya

dom-BAY-uh

Named after Joseph Dombey (1742–94), French botanist (*Malvaceae*)

domesticus [1]

doh-MESS-tih-kus

domestica, domesticum

Domesticated, as in *Malus domestica*

Doodia

DOO-dee-uh

Named after Samuel Doody (1656–1706), British botanist (*Blechnaceae*)

Doronicum

duh-RON-ik-um

From Arabic *doronigi* or *durugi*, the vernacular name (*Asteraceae*)

Dorstenia

dor-STEE-nee-uh

Named after Theodor Dorsten (1492–1552), German physician (*Moraceae*)

Doryanthes

dor-ee-AN-thees

From Greek *doratos* meaning 'spear' and *anthos* meaning 'flower', a reference to the shape of the inflorescence in *D. palmeri* (*Doryanthaceae*)

Dorycnium

dor-IK-nee-um

From Greek *doratos* meaning 'spear' and *knaein* meaning 'to smear', as this plant was used to poison spear tips (*Fabaceae*)

Doryopteris

dor-ee-OP-ter-is

From Greek *doratos* meaning 'spear' and *pteris* meaning 'fern', as some species have lance-like fronds (*Pteridaceae*)

Douglasia

duh-GLA-see-uh

Named after David Douglas (1799–1834), Scottish botanist (*Primulaceae*)

douglasianus

dug-lus-ee-AH-nus

douglasiana, douglasianum

—

1

Malus domestica,
apple

douglasii

dug-lus-ee-eye

Named after David Douglas (1799–1834), Scottish plant hunter, as in *Limnanthes douglasii*

drabifolius

dra-by-FOH-lee-us

drabifolia, drabifolium

With leaves like whitlow-grass (*Draba*), as in *Centaurea drabifolia*

Dracaena

druh-SEE-nuh

From Greek *drakaina* meaning 'female dragon'; sap harvested from the Canary Island native *D. draco* is initially milky, turning blood-red when dry (*Asparagaceae*)

draco

DRAY-koh

Dragon, as in *Dracaena draco*

Dracocephalum

dray-koh-KEF-ah-lum

From Greek *drakon* meaning 'dragon' and *kephale* meaning 'head', an allusion to the shape of the corolla (*Lamiaceae*)

Dracophyllum

dray-koh-FIL-um

From Greek *drakon* meaning 'dragon' and *phyllon* meaning 'leaf', as these plants resemble the unrelated genus *Dracaena* (*Ericaceae*)

Dracula
DRAK-ew-luh
Named after the literarary character Count Dracula, due to the somewhat gothic flowers (*Orchidaceae*)

Dracunculus (also dracunculus)
druh-KUN-koo-lus
The diminutive form of Greek *drakon* meaning 'dragon', due to the shape of the spathe (*Araceae*)

Dregea
DRAY-gee-uh
Named after Johann Franz Drège (1794–1881), German botanist and horticulturist (*Apocynaceae*)

Drimys
DRIM-is
From Greek *drimys* meaning 'acrid', referring to the taste of the bark (*Winteraceae*)

Drosanthemum
druh-SAN-thuh-mum
From Greek *drosos* meaning 'dew' and *anthos* meaning 'flower', as the leaves and some parts of the flowers are covered in glistening bladders (*Aizoaceae*)

Drosera
DRO-sur-uh
From Greek *drosos* meaning 'dew' as the leaves of these insect-catching herbs are covered in a sticky residue (*Droseraceae*)

drummondianus
drum-mond-ee-AH-nus
drummondiana, drummondianum
—

drummondii
drum-mond-EE-eye
Named after either James Drummond (1786–1863) or Thomas Drummond (1793–1835), brothers who collected plants in Australia and North America respectively, as in *Phlox drummondii*

drupaceus
droo-PAY-see-us
drupacea, drupaceum
—

drupiferus
droo-PIH-fer-us
drupifera, drupiferum
With fleshy, hard-stoned fruits that resemble a peach or cherry, as in *Hakea drupacea*

Dryas
DRY-as
Named after dryads, tree nymphs in Greek mythology, as the leaves of some species resemble those of oaks (*Rosaceae*)

Drynaria
dry-NAIR-ee-uh
From Greek *dryas* meaning 'oak-leaf-shaped' (*Polypodiaceae*)

drynarioides
dri-nar-ee-OY-deez
Resembling oak-leaf fern (*Drynaria*), as in *Aglaomorpha drynarioides*

Dryopteris (also dryopteris)
dry-OP-ter-is
From Greek *dryas* meaning 'oak' and *pteris* meaning 'fern', a reference to their preferred habitat in deciduous forests (*Dryopteridaceae*)

dubius
DOO-bee-us
dubia, dubium
Doubtful, unlike the rest of the genus, as in *Ornithogalum dubium*

Duchesnea
doo-KES-nee-uh
Named after Antoine Nicolas Duchesne, (1747–1827), French botanist (*Rosaceae*)

Dudleya
DUD-lay-uh
Named after William Russel Dudley (1849–1911), American botanist (*Crassulaceae*)

dulcis
DUL-sis
dulcis, dulce
Sweet, as in *Prunus dulcis*

dumetorum
doo-met-OR-um
From hedges or bushes, as in *Fallopia dumetorum*

dumosus
doo-MOH-sus
dumosa, dumosum
Bushy; shrubby, as in *Alluaudia dumosa*

duplicatus
doo-plih-KAH-tus
duplicata, duplicatum
Double; duplicate, as in *Brachystelma duplicatum*

Duranta
duh-RAN-tuh
Named after Castore Durante (1529–90), Italian physician and botanist (*Verbenaceae*)

Durio
DEW-ree-oh
From Malay *duri* meaning 'thorn', as durian fruits (*D. zibethinus*) have thorny skins (*Malvaceae*)

durus
DUR-us
dura, durum
Hard, as in *Blechnum durum*

Duvalia
doo-VAH-lee-uh
Named after Henri-Auguste Duval (1777–1814), French physician and botanist (*Apocynaceae*)

Dyckia
DIK-ee-uh
Named after Joseph zu Salm-Reifferscheidt-Dyck (1773–1861), German botanist (*Bromeliaceae*)

dyeri
DY-er-eye
—

dyerianus
dy-er-ee-AH-nus
dyeriana, dyerianum
Named after Sir William Turner Thiselton-Dyer (1843–1928), British botanist and Director of Kew Gardens, London, England, as in *Strobilanthes dyeriana*

Dysosma
dy-SOZ-muh
From Greek *dys* meaning 'bad' and *osme* meaning 'fragrance', as the flowers may have a putrid scent (*Berberidaceae*)

e-, ex-
Used in compound words to denote without, out of

ebeneus
eb-en-NAY-us
ebenea, ebeneum
—

ebenus
eb-en-US
ebena, ebenum
Ebony-black, as in *Carex ebenea*

ebracteatus
e-brak-tee-AH-tus
ebracteata, ebracteatum
Without bracts, as in *Eryngium ebracteatum*

eburneus
eb-URN-ee-us
eburnea, eburneum
Ivory-white, as in *Angraecum eburneum*

Ecballium
ek-BAL-ee-um
From Greek *ekballein* meaning 'to cast out', as the fruits of squirting cucumber (*E. elaterium*) expel their seeds in vigorous fashion (*Cucurbitaceae*)

Eccremocarpus
ek-ree-moh-KAR-pus
From Greek *ekkremes* meaning 'hanging' and *karpos* meaning 'fruit' (*Bignoniaceae*)

Echeveria
ek-uh-VEER-ee-uh
Named after Atanasio Echeverría y Godoy (c. 1771–1803), Mexican botanical artist (*Crassulaceae*)

Echidnopsis
ek-id-NOP-sis
From Greek *echidna* meaning 'snake' and *opsis* meaning 'like', as the succulent stems are serpentine (*Apocynaceae*)

Echinacea
ek-in-AY-see-uh
From Greek *echinos* meaning 'hedgehog', as the inflorescence is prickly (*Asteraceae*)

echinatus
ek-in-AH-tus
echinata, echinatum
With prickles like a hedgehog, as in *Pelargonium echinatum*

Echinocactus
ek-i-noh-KAK-tus
From Greek *echinos* meaning 'hedgehog', plus cactus (*Cactaceae*)

Echinocereus
ek-i-noh-SER-ee-us
From Greek *echinos* meaning 'hedgehog' and *Cereus*, a related genus (*Cactaceae*)

Echinops
EK-in-ops
From Greek *echinos* meaning 'hedgehog', due to the spiny inflorescences (*Asteraceae*)

Echinopsis
ek-in-OP-sis
From Greek *echinos* meaning 'hedgehog' and *opsis* meaning 'like' (*Cactaceae*)

echinosepalus
ek-in-oh-SEP-uh-lus
echinosepala, echinosepalum
With prickly sepals, as in *Begonia echinosepala*

echioides
ek-ee-OY-deez
Resembling viper's bugloss (*Echium*), as in *Picris echioides*

Echium
EK-ee-um
From Greek *echis* meaning 'viper', as the seeds resemble snake heads and the roots were used to treat snake bites (*Boraginaceae*)

ecornutus
ek-kor-NOO-tus
ecornuta, ecornutum
Without horns, as in *Stanhopea ecornuta*

Edgeworthia
ej-WURTH-ee-uh
Named after Michael Pakenham Edgeworth (1812–81), Irish botanist (*Thymelaeaceae*)
—

edgeworthianus
edj-wor-thee-AH-nus
edgeworthiana, edgeworthianum
—

edgeworthii
edj-WOR-thee-eye
Named after Michael Pakenham Edgeworth (1812–81) of the East India Company, as in *Rhododendron edgeworthii*

Edithcolea
ee-dith-KOH-lee-uh
Named after Edith Cole (1859–1940), British entomologist and botanist (*Apocynaceae*)

Edraianthus
ed-rai-ANTH-us
From Greek *hedraios* meaning 'sitting' and *anthos* meaning 'flower' as the blooms are sessile (*Campanulaceae*)

edulis
ED-yew-lis
edulis, edule
Edible, as in *Dioon edule*

effusus
eff-YOO-sus
effusa, effusum
Spreading loosely, as in *Juncus effusus*

Egeria
eh-JEER-ee-uh
From Latin *egeri* meaning 'nymph', an allusion to its aquatic habitat (*Hydrocharitaceae*)

Ehretia
eh-RET-ee-uh
Named after Georg Dionysius Ehret (1708–70), German botanist and entomologist (*Boraginaceae*)

Eichhornia
ay-KOR-nee-uh
Named after Johann Albrecht Friedrich Eichhorn (1779–1856), Prussian politician (*Pontederiaceae*)

elaeagnifolius
el-ee-ag-ne-FOH-lee-us
elaeagnifolia, elaeagnifolium
With leaves like *Elaeagnus*, as in *Brachyglottis elaeagnifolia*

Elaeagnus
ee-lee-AG-nus
From Greek *elaiagnos* meaning 'a type of willow' (*Elaeagnaceae*)

Elaeis
el-AY-is
From Greek *elaia* meaning 'olive', an allusion to the valuable oil extracted from oil palm, *E. guineensis* (*Arecaceae*)

Elaeocarpus

el-ay-oh-KAR-pus

From Greek *elaia* meaning 'olive' and *karpos* meaning 'fruit', as the fleshy fruits resemble olives (*Elaeocarpaceae*)

elasticus

ee-LASS-tih-kus

elastica, elasticum

Elastic, producing latex, as in *Ficus elastica*

Elatostema

el-ah-toh-STEM-uh

From Greek *elatos* meaning 'striking' and *stema* meaning 'stamen', referring to the explosive fashion in which the stamens eject pollen (*Urticaceae*)

elatus [1]

el-AH-tus

elata, elatum

Tall, as in *Aralia elata*

elegans [2]

el-ee-GANS

—

elegantulus

el-eh-GAN-tyoo-lus

elegantula, elegantulum

Elegant, as in *Desmodium elegans*

elegantissimus

el-ee-gan-TISS-ih-mus

elegantissima, elegantissimum

Very elegant, as in *Schefflera elegantissima*

Elegia

uh-LEE-jee-uh

From Greek *elegeia* meaning 'song of lamentation' or elegy, perhaps an allusion to the sound of wind passing through the reed-like stems (*Restionaceae*)

elephantipes

ell-uh-fan-TY-peez

Resembling an elephant's foot, as in *Yucca elephantipes*

Elettaria

el-uh-TARE-ee-uh

From Malayalam (India) *elatarri*, the vernacular name for cardamom, *E. cardamomum* (*Zingiberaceae*)

Eleutherococcus

el-ew-thu-roh-KOK-us

From Greek *eleuthero* meaning 'free' and *kokkos* meaning 'berry', suggesting that the fruits are not fused together (*Araliaceae*)

Elliottia

el-ee-OTT-ee-uh

Named after Stephen Elliott (1771–1830), American botanist, politician and banker (*Ericaceae*)

1

Delphinium elatum,
candle larkspur

2

Desmodium elegans,
elegant tick clover

elliottianus

el-ee-ot-ee-AH-nus

elliottiana, elliottianum

Named after Captain George Henry Elliott (1813–92), as in *Zantedeschia elliottiana*

elliottii

el-ee-ot-EE-eye

Named after Stephen Elliott (1771–1830), American botanist, as in *Eragrostis elliottii*

ellipsoidalis

e-lip-soy-DAH-lis

ellipsoidalis, ellipsoidale

Elliptic, as in *Quercus ellipsoidalis*

ellipticus

ee-LIP-tih-kus

elliptica, ellipticum

Shaped like an ellipse, as in *Garrya elliptica*

Elodea

el-OH-dee-uh

From Greek *helos* meaning 'marsh', a reference to the aquatic habit (*Hydrocharitaceae*)

elongatus

ee-long-GAH-tus

elongata, elongatum

Lengthened; elongated, as in *Mammillaria elongata*

Elsholtzia

el-SHOLT-zee-uh

Named after Johann Sigismund Elsholtz (1623–88), German physician and botanist (*Lamiaceae*)

elwesii

el-WEZ-ee-eye

Named after Henry John Elwes (1846–1922), British plant collector, one of the inaugural recipients of the Victoria Medal of the Royal Horticultural Society, as in *Galanthus elwesii*

Elymus

EL-i-mus

From Greek *elymos* meaning 'millet' (*Poaceae*)

emarginatus

e-mar-jin-NAH-tus

emarginata, emarginatum

Slightly notched at the margins, as in *Pinguicula emarginata*

Embothrium

em-BOTH-ree-um

From Greek *en* meaning 'in' and *bothrion* meaning 'small pit', as the anthers are borne in pits (*Proteaceae*)

Emilia

eh-MIL-ee-uh

Named after Emilia (now Emilia-Romagna), an Italian Region where the botanist who named this plant worked, or possibly after someone named Emile or Emilie, though he did not specify (*Asteraceae*)

eminens

EM-in-enz

Eminent; prominent, as in *Sorbus eminens*

Emmenopterys

em-en-OP-ter-is

From Greek *emmeno* meaning 'abiding' and *pteron* meaning 'wing' as the flowers are surrounded by persistent bracts (*Rubiaceae*)

empetrifolius

em-pet-rih-FOH-lee-us

empetrifolia, empetrifolium

With leaves like crowberry (*Empetrum*), as in *Berberis empetrifolia*

Empetrum

em-PET-rum

From Greek *en* meaning 'in' and *petros* meaning 'rock' alluding to the stony habitat (*Ericaceae*)

Encephalartos

en-kef-al-AR-tos

From Greek *en* ('in'), *kephale* ('head') and *artos* ('bread'), as the tips of the trunks can be harvested to make a sago-like starchy food (*Zamiaceae*)

encliandrus

en-klee-AN-drus

encliandra, encliandrum

With half the stamens inside the flower tube, as in *Fuchsia encliandra*

Encyclia

en-SY-klee-uh

From Greek *enkyklos* meaning 'to encircle', as the lip petal partially encloses the column (*Orchidaceae*)

endresii

en-DRESS-ee-eye

endressii

Named after Philip Anton Christoph Endress (1806–31), German plant collector, as in *Geranium endressii*

engelmannii

en-gel-MAH-nee-eye

Named after Georg Engelmann (1809–84), German-born physician and botanist, as in *Picea engelmannii*

Enkianthus

en-kee-AN-thus

From Greek *enkyos* meaning 'pregnant' and *anthos* meaning 'flower' as in some species, the swollen sepals give the appearance of one flower emerging from within another (*Ericaceae*)

enneacanthus

en-nee-uh-KAN-thus

enneacantha, enneacanthum

With nine spines, as in *Echinocereus enneacanthus*

enneaphyllus

en-nee-a-FIL-us

enneaphylla, ennephyllum

With nine leaves or leaflets, as in *Oxalis enneaphylla*

ensatus

en-SA-tus

ensata, ensatum

In the shape of a sword, as in *Iris ensata*

Ensete

en-SET-eh

From Amharic (Ethiopia) *anset*, the vernacular name (*Musaceae*)

ensifolius

en-see-FOH-lee-us

ensifolia, ensifolium

With leaves shaped like a sword, as in *Kniphofia ensifolia*

ensiformis

en-see-FOR-mis

ensiformis, ensiforme

In the shape of a sword, as in *Pteris ensiformis*

Eomecon

ee-oh-MEE-kon

From Greek *eos* meaning 'dawn' or 'the east' and *mecon* meaning 'poppy', as this genus originates in China (*Papaveraceae*)

Epacris

ep-AH-kris

From Greek *epi* meaning 'upon' and *acris* meaning 'summit', an allusion to the high altitude habitat of some species (*Ericaceae*)

Ephedra

uh-FED-ruh

From Greek *epi* meaning 'upon' and *hedraios* meaning 'sitting', as the stem segments appear to sit one atop another; the classical name for the similar-looking, but unrelated *Equisetum* (*Ephedraceae*)

Epidendrum

eh-pi-DEN-dron

From Greek *epi* meaning 'upon' and *dendron* meaning 'tree', as these orchids are epiphytic (*Orchidaceae*)

Epigaea

eh-pi-JEE-uh

From Greek *epi* meaning 'upon' and *gaia* meaning 'earth'; the plant has a creeping habit (*Ericaceae*)

Epilobium

eh-pi-LOH-bee-um

From Greek *epi* meaning 'upon' and *lobos* meaning 'pod', as the corolla is at the tip of the ovary (*Onagraceae*)

Epimedium [1]

eh-pi-MEE-dee-um

From Greek *epimedion*, a vernacular name for an unknown plant (*Berberidaceae*)

Epipactis

eh-pi-PAK-tis

From Greek *epipaktis*, a vernacular name for a plant that is said to have curdled milk, perhaps *E. helleborine* (*Orchidaceae*)

Epiphyllum

eh-pi-FIL-um

From Greek *epi* meaning 'upon' and *phyllon*, 'a leaf'; the flowers appear to develop on the leaves, but this plant is leafless and the stems are foliose (*Cactaceae*)

epiphyllus

ep-ih-FIL-us

epiphylla, epiphyllum

On the leaf (e.g. flowers), as in *Saxifraga epiphylla*

epiphyticus

ep-ih-FIT-ih-kus

epiphytica, epiphyticum

Growing on another plant, as in *Cyrtanthus epiphyticus*

Epipremnum

eh-pi-PREM-num

From Greek *epi* meaning 'upon' and *premnon* meaning 'trunk', as this climber clings to tree trunks (*Araceae*)

Episcia

eh-PIS-ee-uh

From Greek *epi* meaning 'upon' and *skia* meaning 'shadow', as plants prefer shade (*Gesneriaceae*)

Epithelantha

eh-pi-thu-LAN-thu

From Greek *epi* ('upon'), *thele* ('nipple') and *anthos* ('flower'), as the blooms develop atop the stem tubercles (*Cactaceae*)

equestris

e-KWES-tris

equestris, equestre

—

equinus

e-KWEE-nus

equina, equinum

Relating to horses, equestrian, as in *Phalaenopsis equestris*

1

Epimedium hybridum, *E. versicolor* and *E. sulphureum*, barrenworts

2

Equisetum sylvaticum, wood horsetail

3

Erica cerinthoides,
fire heath

equisetifolius
ek-wih-set-ih-FOH-lee-us
equisetifolia, equisetifolium
—

equisetiformis
eck-kwiss-ee-tih-FOR-mis
equisetiformis, equisetiforme
Resembling horsetail (*Equisetum*), as in
Russelia equisetiformis

Equisetum [2]
ek-wi-SEE-tum
From Latin *equis* meaning 'horse' and *seta*
meaning 'bristle', as the stems and/or roots
of some species resemble horses' tails
(*Equisetaceae*)

Eragrostis
eh-ruh-GROS-tis
From Greek *eros* meaning 'love' and *agrostis*
meaning 'grass', as the spikelets are heart-
shaped (*Poaceae*)

Eranthemum
eh-ran-thu-mum
From Greek *er* meaning 'spring' and
anthemon meaning 'flower', suggesting an
early-blooming plant (*Acanthaceae*)

Eranthis
eh-RAN-this
From Greek *er* meaning 'spring' and *anthos*
meaning 'flower'; winter aconite (*E.
hyemalis*) is one of the earliest spring-
flowering perennials (*Ranunculaceae*)

Ercilla
er-SIH-luh
Named after Alonso de Ercilla y Zúñiga
(1533–94), Spanish soldier and poet
(*Phytolaccaceae*)

erectus
ee-RECK-tus
erecta, erectum
Erect; upright, as in *Trillium erectum*

Eremophila
eh-ruh-MOF-il-uh
From Greek *erema* meaning 'desert' and
philos meaning 'loving', as many species live
in arid parts of Australia (*Scrophulariaceae*)

Eremurus
eh-ruh-MEW-rus
From Greek *erema* meaning 'desert' and
ouros meaning 'tail', referring to both the
long, narrow inflorescence and the preferred
habitat (*Asphodelaceae*)

eri-
Used in compound words to denote woolly

Eria
EAR-ee-uh
From Greek *erion* meaning 'wool', as some
species have woolly flowers (*Orchidaceae*)

eriantherus
er-ee-AN-ther-uz
erianthera, eriantherum
With woolly anthers, as in *Penstemon
eriantherus*

erianthus
er-ee-AN-thus
eriantha, erianthum
With woolly flowers, as in *Kohleria eriantha*

Erica [3]
Eh-ri-kuh
From Greek *ereiko* meaning 'to break', as the
stems are brittle; the classical Latin name for
E. arborea (*Ericaceae*)

ericifolius
er-ik-ih-FOH-lee-us
ericifolia, ericifolium
With leaves like heather (*Erica*), as in
Banksia ericifolia

ericoides
er-ik-OY-deez
Resembling heather (*Erica*), as in *Aster
ericoides*

Erigeron
uh-RIG-uh-ron
The classical Latin name for groundsel
(*Senecio vulgaris*); derived from Greek *er*
('spring'), *erion* ('wool') and *geron* ('old
man'), as some species are early-flowering
and once the blooms fade, the pappus is like
the hair of an old man (*Asteraceae*)

Erinacea
er-in-AY-see-uh
From Latin *erinaceus* meaning 'hedgehog', as
these plants are spiny (*Fabaceae*)

erinaceus
er-in-uh-SEE-us
erinacea, erinaceum
Like a hedgehog, as in *Dianthus erinaceus*

Erinus
EH-ri-nus
From Greek *erinos*, a vernacular name for
another plant (*Plantaginaceae*)

Eriobotrya
eh-ree-oh-BOT-ree-uh
From Greek *erion* meaning 'wool' and *botrys*
meaning 'a bunch of grapes', as the edible
fruits (loquats) are clustered and somewhat
woolly (*Rosaceae*)

eriocarpus
er-ee-oh-KAR-pus
eriocarpa, eriocarpum
With woolly fruit, as in *Pittosporum
eriocarpum*

Eryngium

Most members of the carrot family (*Apiaceae*) are known for their ethereal flower clusters (umbels), where numerous small flowers sit atop wiry stalks all radiating out from a central point. Often long-lasting, these umbrella-like blooms provide border interest all year round. In sea hollies (*Eryngium*) however, it's not just the flowers that cause a stir; they are often subtended by elaborate spiny bracts enamelled in silver or blue. Cut the flowering stems before they fade and hang them to dry; they'll last a long time indoors and make attractive decorations.

Eryngium campestre,
field eryngo

eriocephalus
er-ri-oh-SEF-uh-lus
eriocephala, eriocephalum
With a woolly head, as in *Lamium
eriocephalum*

Eriogonum
eh-ree-oh-GOH-num
From Greek *erion* meaning 'wool' and *gonia*
meaning 'knee', in reference to *E.
tomentosum*, which is a woolly plant with
jointed stems (*Polygonaceae*)

Eriophorum
eh-ree-OF-oh-room
From Greek *erion* meaning 'wool' and
phorus meaning 'bearing', as the seeds are in
cottony clusters, thus the common name
cotton grass (*Cyperaceae*)

Eriophyllum
eh-ree-oh-FIL-um
From Greek *erion* meaning 'wool' and
phyllon meaning 'leaf' (*Asteraceae*)

eriostemon
er-ree-oh-STEE-mon
With woolly stamens, as in *Geranium
eriostemon*

Erodium
eh-ROH-dee-um
From Greek *erodios* meaning 'heron', as the
fruits are beak-like (*Geraniaceae*)

erosus
e-ROH-sus
erosa, erosum
Jagged, as in *Cissus erosa*

erubescens
er-oo-BESS-enz
Becoming red; blushing, as in *Philodendron
erubescens*

Eruca
eh-ROO-kuh
This is the Latin name used by Pliny for this
or a similar plant; the derivation is obscure,
but perhaps based on Greek *uro* meaning
'burn', alluding to the peppery flavour of *E.
vesicaria* subsp. *sativa* (rocket/arugula), or
perhaps *eruco* meaning 'caterpillar'
(*Brassicaceae*)

Eryngium
eh-RING-gee-um
From Greek *eryggion*, a bristly plant, possibly
referring to *E. campestre* (*Apiaceae*)

Erysimum
eh-RIS-i-mum
From Greek *erysimon*, a kind of mustard
(*Brassicaceae*)

Erythrina
eh-rith-REE-nuh
From Greek *erythros* meaning 'red', the
colour of the flowers and seeds (*Fabaceae*)

erythro-
Used in compound words to denote red

erythrocarpus
er-ee-throw-KAR-pus
erythrocarpa, erythrocarpum
With red fruit, as in *Actinidia erythrocarpa*

Erythronium
eh-rith-ROH-nee-um
From Greek *erythros* meaning 'red', referring
to the flowers of *E. dens-canis*; the Greek
erythronion was a vernacular name for
another plant (*Liliaceae*)

erythropodus
er-ee-THROW-pod-us
erythropoda, erythropodum
With a red stem, as in *Alchemilla
erythropoda*

erythrosorus
er-rith-roh-SOR-us
erythrosora, erythrosorum
Having red spore cases, as in *Dryopteris
erythrosora*

Escallonia
es-kuh-LOH-nee-uh
Named after Antonio José Escallón y Flóres
(1739–1819), Spanish explorer in Colombia
(*Escalloniaceae*)

Eucalyptus

Perhaps best known for the fragrant oil extracted from the leaves, *Eucalyptus* is a large genus of trees and shrubs centred in Australia. The name is derived from Greek and refers to the cap that covers the flowers in bud. In most flowers, the sepals surround the flower buds to protect them, while the petals are showy and attractive. In eucalypts, the sepals and/or petals are fused together to form a cap; when ready to open, the cap pops off and a dense tuft of stamens is revealed. These pollen-producing structures have taken on the role of petals and so they are profuse and sometimes colourful.

Eucalyptus globulus,
Tasmanian blue gum

Eschscholzia
esh-OLT-zee-uh
Named after Johann Friedrich von Eschscholtz (1793–1831), Baltic German physician and entomologist (*Papaveraceae*)

Escobaria
es-koh-BAR-ee-uh
Named after brothers Rómulo (1882–1946) and Numa Escobar Zerman (1874–1949), Mexican agronomists (*Cactaceae*)

esculentus
es-kew-LEN-tus
esculenta, esculentum
Edible, as in *Colocasia esculenta*

Espostoa
es-pos-TOH-uh
Named after Nicolas Esposto (1877–?), Italian-born Peruvian pharmacist and botanist (*Cactaceae*)

Etlingera
et-LIN-ger-uh
Named after Andreas Ernst Etlinger (c. 1756–85), German botanist and artist (*Zingiberaceae*)

etruscus
ee-TRUSS-kus
estrusca, estruscum
Connected with Tuscany, Italy, as in *Crocus etruscus*

eucalyptifolius
yoo-kuh-lip-tih-FOH-lee-us
eucalyptifolia, eucalyptifolium
With leaves like *Eucalyptus*, as in *Leucadendron eucalyptifolium*

Eucalyptus
yoo-kuh-LIP-tus
From Greek *eu* meaning 'good/well' and *kalyptos* meaning 'covered', as in the flowers, the sepals (and sometimes petals) are fused together creating a lid (*Myrtaceae*)

Eucharis
YOO-kuh-ris
From Greek *eukharis* meaning 'gracious', as befits this fragrant and attractive perennial (*Amaryllidaceae*)

euchlorus
YOO-klor-us
euchlora, euchlorum
A healthy green, as in *Tilia* × *euchlora*

Eucomis
yoo-KOH-mis
From Greek *eu* meaning 'good' and *kome* meaning 'hair', a beautiful head of hair, referring to the tuft of leaves atop the inflorescence (*Asparagaceae*)

Eucommia
yoo-KOH-mee-uh
From Greek *eu* meaning 'good' and *kommi* meaning 'gum' as latex can be extracted from the tree (*Eucommiaceae*)

Eucryphia
yoo-KRI-fee-uh
From Greek *eu* meaning 'good' and *kryphios* meaning 'hidden'; the sepals are joined at the tips of the flower buds, initially concealing the petals (*Cunoniaceae*)

Eugenia
yoo-JEE-nee-uh
Named after Prince Eugene of Savoy (1663–1736), soldier and politician in the Holy Roman Empire (*Myrtaceae*)

eugenioides
yoo-jee-nee-OY-deez
Resembling the genus *Eugenia*, as in *Pittosporum eugenioides*

Eulophia
yoo-LOH-fee-uh
From Greek *eu* meaning 'good' and *lophus* meaning 'crest', as the flower lip is crested (*Orchidaceae*)

Euodia
yoo-OH-dee-uh
From Greek *euodia* meaning 'sweet fragrance', as the foliage is scented (*Rutaceae*)

Euonymus [1]
yoo-ON-ee-mus
From Greek *eu* meaning 'good' and *onoma* meaning 'name', though the reason for this positive appellation is uncertain (*Celastraceae*)

eupatorioides
yoo-puh-TOR-ee-oy-deez
Resembling *Eupatorium*, as in *Agrimonia eupatoria*

Eupatorium
ew-puh-TOR-ee-um
Named after Mithridates Eupator, King of Pontus, comprising much of modern-day Turkey and the Black Sea coast (132–63 BC) (*Asteraceae*)

Euphorbia [2]
yoo-FOR-bee-uh
Named after Euphorbus (dates unknown), physician to Juba II, King of Numidia and Mauretania (*Euphorbiaceae*)

euphorbioides
yoo-for-bee-OY-deez
Resembling spurge (*Euphorbia*), as in *Neobuxbaumia euphorbioides*

Euptelea
yoop-TEE-lee-uh
From Greek *eu* meaning 'good' and *ptelea* meaning 'elm', which they resemble (*Eupteleaceae*)

europaeus
yoo-ROH-pay-us
europaea, europaeum
Connected with Europe, as in *Euonymus europaeus*

Eurya
YUR-ee-uh
From Greek *eurys* meaning 'large/wide', but allusion unclear (*Pentaphylacaceae*)

Euryale
yur-ee-AH-lee
Named after the gorgon Euryale from Greek mythology, perhaps a reference to the writhing petioles and spiny-coated leaf surfaces (*Nymphaeaceae*)

Eurybia
yoo-RY-bee-uh
From Greek *eurys* meaning 'wide' and *baios* meaning 'few', as the capitulae have few, but broad ray florets (*Asteraceae*)

1

Euonymus alatus,
winged spindle

Euryops
YOO-ry-ops
From Greek *eurys* meaning 'wide' and *opsis* meaning 'eye', alluding to the large flower heads (*Asteraceae*)

Eustoma
yoo-STOH-muh
From Greek *eu* meaning 'good' and *stoma* meaning 'mouth', a reference to the attractive tubular flowers (*Gentianaceae*)

Euthamia
yoo-THAM-ee-uh
From Greek *eu* meaning 'good' and *thama* meaning 'crowded', an allusion to the crowded branches (*Asteracaeae*)

Eutrochium
yoo-TROH-kee-um
From Greek *eu* meaning 'good' and *trocho* meaning 'wheel', as the leaves are whorled (*Asteraceae*)

evansianus
eh-vanz-ee-AH-nus
evansiana, evansianum
—
evansii
eh-VANS-ee-eye
Named after various people called Evans, including Thomas Evans (1751–1814), as in *Begonia grandis* subsp. *evansiana*

2

Euphorbia characias,
Mediterranean spurge

3

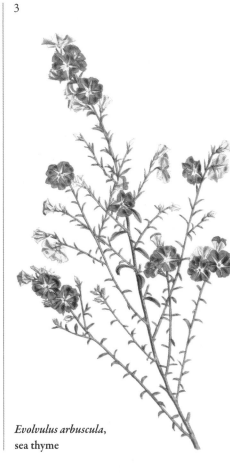

Evolvulus arbuscula,
sea thyme

Evolvulus [3]
ee-VOL-voo-lus
From Latin *evolvo* meaning 'to untwine', as
unlike climbing *Convolvulus*, these plants do
not twine (*Convolvulaceae*)

Exacum
eks-AH-kum
From Celtic Gaulish *exacon*, the vernacular
name for *Centaurium*, a plant in the same
family (*Gentianaceae*)

exaltatus
eks-all-TAH-tus
exaltata, exaltatum
Very tall, as in *Nephrolepis exaltata*

exaratus
ex-a-RAH-tus
exarata, exaratum
Engraved; furrowed, as in *Agrostis exarata*

excavatus
ek-ska-VAH-tus
excavata, excavatum
Hollowed out, as in *Calochortus excavatus*

excellens
ek-SEL-lenz
Excellent, as in *Sarracenia × excellens*

excelsior
eks-SEL-see-or
Taller, as in *Fraxinus excelsior*

excelsus
ek-SEL-sus
excelsa, excelsum
Tall, as in *Araucaria excelsa*

excisus
eks-SIZE-us
excisa, excisum
Cut away; cut out, as in *Adiantum excisum*

excorticatus
eks-kor-tih-KAH-tus
excorticata, excorticatum
Lacking or stripped of bark, as in *Fuchsia
excorticata*

exiguus
eks-IG-yoo-us
exigua, exiguum
Very little; poor, as in *Salix exigua*

eximius
eks-IM-mee-us
eximia, eximium
Distinguished, as in *Eucalyptus eximia*

Exochorda
eks-oh-KOR-duh
From Greek *exo* meaning 'outside' and
chorde meaning 'string', referring to fibres on
the ovary outer wall (*Rosaceae*)

exoniensis
eks-oh-nee-EN-sis
exoniensis, exoniense
From Exeter, England, as in *Passiflora ×
exoniensis*

expansus
ek-SPAN-sus
expansa, expansum
Expanded, as in *Catasetum expansum*

exsertus
ek-SER-tus
exserta, exsertum
Protruding, as in *Acianthus exsertus*

extensus
eks-TEN-sus
extensa, extensum
Extended, as in *Acacia extensa*

eyriesii
eye-REE-see-eye
Named after Alexander Eyries, French
19th-century cactus collector, as in
Echinopsis eyriesii

fabaceus

fab-AY-see-us

fabacea, fabaceum

Like a broad bean, as in *Marah fabacea*

Fabiana

fah-bee-AH-nuh

Named after Francisco Fabián y Fuero (1719–1801), Spanish cleric (*Solanaceae*)

facetus

fa-CEE-tus

faceta, facetum

Elegant, as *Rhododendron facetum*

fagifolius

fag-ih-FOH-lee-us

fagifolia, fagifolium

With leaves like beech (*Fagus*), as in *Clethra fagifolia*

Fagopyrum

fay-goh-PY-rum

From Latin *fagus* meaning 'beech' and Greek *pyros* meaning 'wheat', as the seeds resemble beech mast (*Polygonaceae*)

Fagus [1]

FAY-gus

The classical Latin name for beech, possibly derived from Greek *fagein* meaning 'to eat', as the seeds are edible (*Fagaceae*)

falcatus

fal-KAH-tus

falcata, falcatum

Shaped like a sickle, as in *Cyrtanthus falcatus*

falcifolius

fal-sih-FOH-lee-us

falcifolia, falcifolium

With leaves in the shape of a sickle, as in *Allium falcifolium*

falciformis

fal-sif-FOR-mis

falciformis, falciforme

Shaped like a sickle, as in *Falcatifolium falciforme*

falcinellus

fal-sin-NELL-us

falcinella, falcinellum

Like a small sickle, as in *Polystichum falcinellum*

fallax

FAL-laks

Deceptive; false, as in *Crassula fallax*

1

Fagus sylvatica, common beech

Fallopia

fuh-LOH-pee-uh

Named after Gabriele Falloppio (1523–62), Italian anatomist who described the Fallopian tube (*Polygonaceae*)

Fallugia

fuh-LOO-jee-uh

Named after Virgilio Fallugi (1627–1707), Italian cleric and botanist (*Rosaceae*)

Farfugium

far-FOO-jee-um

From Latin *farfaria*, vernacular name for related *Tussilago farfara* (*Asteraceae*)

Fargesia

far-JEE-see-uh

Named after Paul Guillaume Farges (1844–1912), French missionary (*Poaceae*)

farinaceus

far-ih-NAH-kee-us

farinacea, farinaceum

Producing starch; mealy, like flour, as in *Salvia farinacea*

farinosus

far-ih-NOH-sus

farinosa, farinosum

Mealy; powdery, as in *Rhododendron farinosum*

farnesianus

far-nee-zee-AH-nus

farnesiana, farnesianum

Connected with the Farnese Gardens, Rome, Italy, as in *Acacia farnesiana*

farreri

far-REY-ree

Named after Reginald Farrer (1880–1920), British plant hunter and botanist, as in *Viburnum farreri*

fasciatus

fash-ee-AH-tus

fasciata, fasciatum

Bound together, as in *Aechmea fasciata*

Fascicularia

fah-sik-ew-LAIR-ee-uh

From Latin *fasciculus*, meaning 'bundle' and *arius* meaning 'pertaining to', as the habit is clustered (*Bromeliaceae*)

fascicularis

fas-sik-yoo-LAH-ris

fascicularis, fasciculare

—

fasciculatus

fas-sik-yoo-LAH-tus

fasciculata, fasciculatum

Clustered or grouped together in bundles, as in *Ribes fasciculatum*

fastigiatus

fas-tij-ee-AH-tus

fastigiata, fastigiatum

With erect, upright branches, often creating the effect of a column, as in *Cotoneaster fastigiatus*

fastuosus

fast-yoo-OH-sus

fastuosa, fastuosum

Proud, as in *Cassia fastuosa*

Fatsia [1]

FAT-see-uh

From Japanese *yatsude* meaning 'eight fingers', as the leaves typically have eight finger-like lobes (*Araliaceae*)

fatuus

FAT-yoo-us

fatua, fatuum

Insipid; poor quality, as in *Avena fatua*

Faucaria

faw-KAH-ree-uh

From Latin *fauces* meaning 'animal mouth', as the toothed leaves look like jaws (*Aizoaceae*)

febrifugus [2]

feb-ri-FEW-gus

febrifuga, febrifugum

Can reduce fever, as in *Dichroa febrifuga*

fecundus

feh-KUN-dus

fecunda, fecundum

Fertile; fruitful, as in *Aeschynanthus fecundus*

fejeensis

fee-jee-EN-sis

fejeensis, fejeense

From the Fiji Islands, South Pacific, as in *Davallia fejeensis*

Felicia

fuh-LIS-ee-uh

Named after the mysterious Herr Felix, a German official who died in 1846 (*Asteraceae*)

Fendlera

FEND-lur-uh

Named after August Fendler (1813–83), Prussian-born American naturalist (*Hydrangeaceae*)

1

Fatsia japonica,
Japanese aralia

2

Dichroa febrifuga,
Chinese quinine

fenestralis

fen-ESS-tra-lis

fenestralis, fenestrale

With openings like a window, as in *Vriesea fenestralis*

Fenestraria

fen-us-TRAIR-ee-uh

From Latin *fenestra* meaning 'window', as each leaf has a transparent tip (*Aizoaceae*)

fennicus

FEN-nih-kus

fennica, fennicum

Connected with Finland, as in *Picea fennica*

ferax

FER-aks

Fruitful, as in *Fargesia ferax*

Ferocactus

fer-oh-KAK-tus

From Latin *ferus* meaning 'fierce', plus cactus (*Cactaceae*)

ferox

FER-oks

Ferocious; thorny, as in *Datura ferox*

Ferraria

fuh-RAIR-ee-uh

Named after Giovanni Baptista Ferrari (1584–1655), Italian cleric and botanist (*Iridaceae*)

ferreus

FER-ee-us

ferrea, ferreum

Connected with iron; hard as iron, as in *Caesalpinia ferrea*

ferrugineus [3]

fer-oo-GIN-ee-us

ferruginea, ferrugineum

Rust-coloured, as in *Digitalis ferruginea*

fertilis

fer-TIL-is

fertilis, fertile

With plenty of fruit; with many seeds, as in *Robinia fertilis*

Ferula [4]

FE-roo-luh

From Latiun *ferula* meaning 'rod', as the stem was used to make walking sticks and splints (*Apiaceae*)

festalis

FES-tuh-lis

festalis, festale

—

festivus

fes-TEE-vus

festiva, festivum

Festive; bright, as in *Hymenocallis* × *festalis*

Festuca

fes-TOO-kuh

From Latin *festuca* meaning 'straw' or 'stalk' (*Poaceae*)

fibrillosus

fy-BRIL-oh-sus

fibrillosa, fibrillosum

—

fibrosus

fy-BROH-sus

fibrosa, fibrosum

Fibrous, as in *Dicksonia fibrosa*

Ficaria

fy-KAIR-ee-uh

Resembling *Ficus*, as the tubers resemble figs (*Ranunculaceae*)

3

Digitalis ferruginea, rusty foxglove

4

Ferula assa-foetida, devil's dung

ficifolius
fik-ee-FOH-lee-us
ficifolia, ficifolium
With fig-like leaves, as in *Cucumis ficifolius*

ficoides
fy-KOY-deez
—

ficoideus
fy-KOY-dee-us
ficoidea, ficoideum
Resembling a fig (*Ficus*), as in *Senecio ficoides*

Ficus
FY-kus
From Latin *ficus*, the edible fig, *F. carica* (*Moraceae*)

filamentosus
fil-uh-men-TOH-sus
filamentosa, filamentosum
—

filarius
fil-AH-ree-us
filaria, filarium
With filaments or threads, as in *Yucca filamentosa*

fili-
Used in compound words to denote thread-like

filicaulis
fil-ee-KAW-lis
filicaulis, filicaule
With a thread-like stem, as in *Alchemilla filicaulis*

filicifolius
fil-ih-see-FOH-lee-us
filicifolia, filicifolium
With leaves like a fern, as in *Polyscias filicifolia*

filicinus
fil-ih-SEE-nus
filicina, filicinum
—

filiculoides
fil-ih-kyu-LOY-deez
Resembling a fern, as in *Asparagus filicinus*

Filipendula
fi-li-PEN-doo-luh
From Latin *filus* meaning 'thread' and *pendulus* meaning 'hanging', as the tubers of *F. vulgaris* are connected by thread-like roots (*Rosaceae*)

filipendulus
fil-ih-PEN-dyoo-lus
filipendula, filipendulum
Like meadowsweet (*Filipendula*), as in *Oenanthe filipendula*

filipes
fil-EE-pays
With thread-like stalks, as in *Rosa filipes*

fimbriatus
fim-bry-AH-tus
fimbriata, fimbriatum
Fringed, as in *Silene fimbriata*

firmatus
fir-MAH-tus
firmata, firmatum
—

firmus
fir-MUS
firma, firmum
Strong, as in *Abies firma*

Firmiana
fur-me-AH-nuh
Named after Karl Joseph von Firmian (1716–82), Austrian politician (*Malvaceae*)

fissilis
FISS-ill-is
fissilis, fissile
—

fissus
FISS-us
fissa, fissum
—

fissuratus
fis-zhur-RAH-tus
fissurata, fissuratum
With a split, as in *Alchemilla fissa*

fistulosus
fist-yoo-LOH-sus
fistulosa, fistulosum
Hollow, as in *Asphodelus fistulosus*

Fittonia
fih-TOH-nee-uh
Named after sisters Elizabeth (dates unknown) and Sarah Mary Fitton (c. 1796–1874), Irish botanists (*Acanthaceae*)

Fitzroya
fitz-ROY-uh
Named after Robert FitzRoy (1805–65), British sailor, politician and scientist; captained HMS *Beagle* while Charles Darwin was onboard naturalist (*Cupressaceae*)

flabellatus
fla-bel-AH-tus
flabellata, flabellatum
Like an open fan, as in *Aquilegia flabellata*

flabellifer
fla-BEL-lif-er
flabellifera, flabelliferum
Bearing a fan-like structure, as in *Borassus flabellifer*

flabelliformis
fla-bel-ih-FOR-mis
flabelliformis, flabelliforme
Shaped like a fan, as in *Erythrina flabelliformis*

flaccidus
FLA-sih-dus
flaccida, flaccidum
Weak: soft; feeble, as in *Yucca flaccida*

flagellaris
fla-gel-AH-ris
flagellaris, flagellare
—

flagelliformis
fla-gel-ih-FOR-mis
flagelliformis, flagelliforme
Like a whip; with long, thin shoots, as in *Celastrus flagellaris*

flammeus
FLAM-ee-us
flammea, flammeum
Flame-coloured; flame-like, as in *Tigridia flammea*

Ficus carica,
common fig

flavens

flav-ENZ

—

flaveolus

fla-VEE-oh-lus

flaveola, flaveolum

—

flavescens

flav-ES-enz

—

flavidus

FLA-vid-us

flavida, flavidum

Various kinds of yellow, as in *Anigozanthos flavidus*

flavicomus

flay-vih-KOH-mus

flavicoma, flavicomum

With yellow hair, as in *Euphorbia flavicoma*

flavissimus

flav-ISS-ih-mus

flavissima, flavissimum

Deep yellow, as in *Zephyranthes flavissima*

flavovirens

fla-voh-VY-renz

Greenish yellow, as in *Callistemon flavovirens*

flavus

FLA-vus

flava, flavum

Pure yellow, as in *Crocus flavus*

flexicaulis

fleks-ih-KAW-lis

flexicaulis, flexicaule

With a supple stem, as in *Strobilanthes flexicaulis*

flexilis

FLEKS-il-is

flexilis, flexile

Pliant, as in *Pinus flexilis*

flexuosus

fleks-yoo-OH-sus

flexuosa, flexuosum

Indirect; zigzagging, as in *Corydalis flexuosa*

floccigerus

flok-KEE-jer-us

floccigera, floccigerum

—

floccosus

flok-KOH-sus

floccosa, floccosum

With a woolly texture, as in *Rhipsalis floccosa*

florentinus

flor-en-TEE-nus

florentina, florentinum

Connected with Florence, Italy, as in *Malus florentina*

flore-pleno

FLOR-ee PLEE-no

With double flowers, as in *Aquilegia vulgaris* var. *flore-pleno*

floribundus

flor-ih-BUN-dus

floribunda, floribundium

—

floridus

flor-IH-dus

florida, floridum

Very free-flowering, as in *Wisteria floribunda*

GENUS SPOTLIGHT

Foeniculum

Fennel has an identity crisis! This English name is applied to several different plants, some related, others not. *Foeniculum* is the main fennel genus and it, like the English name, derives from the Latin word for hay. Both Florence fennel, with its edible bulb (actually a collection of leaf bases), and the herb fennel (cultivated for edible leaves and seeds) are varieties of *Foeniculum vulgare*. Giant fennel is *Ferula vulgare*, sea fennel is *Crithmum maritimum*, while hog fennel is *Peucedanum ostruthium*, all in the same family as *Foeniculum*. Dog's fennel (*Anthemis cotula*, *Symphyotrichum ericoides*) and fennel-flower (*Nigella sativa*) definitely are not.

Foeniculum vulgare,
common fennel

floridanus

flor-ih-DAH-nus

floridana, floridanum

Connected with Florida, USA, as in *Illicium floridanum*

floriferus

flor-IH-fer-us

florifera, floriferum

Very free-flowering, as in *Townsendia florifera*

flos

flos

Used in combination to denote flower, as in *Lychnis flos-cuculi* (meaning cuckooflower)

fluitans

FLOO-ih-tanz

Floating, as in *Glyceria fluitans*

fluminensis

floo-min-EN-sis

fluminensis, fluminense

From Rio de Janeiro, Brazil, as in *Tradescantia fluminensis*

fluvialis

floo-vee-AHL-is

fluvialis, fluviale

—

fluviatilis

floo-vee-uh-TIL-is

fluviatilis, fluviatile

Growing in a river or running water, as in *Isotoma fluviatilis*

Fockea

FOK-ee-uh

Named after Hendrik Charles Focke (1802–56), Dutch botanist (*Apocynaceae*)

foeniculaceus

fen-ee-kul-ah-KEE-us

foeniculacea, foeniculaceum

Like fennel (*Foeniculum*), as in *Argyranthemum foeniculaceum*

Foeniculum

fen-IK-ew-lum

From Greek *fenum* meaning 'hay', an allusion to the scent of the leaves of fennel (*F. vulgare*), which supposedly resemble hay (*Apiaceae*)

foetidissimus

fet-uh-DISS-ih-mus

foetidissima, foetidissimum

With a very bad smell, as in *Iris foetidissima*

1

Forsythia viridissima, Chinese golden bell tree

foetidus

FET-uh-dus

foetida, foetidum

With a bad smell, as in *Vestia foetida*

Fokienia

foh-kee-EN-ee-uh

Named after Fukien (now Fujian) Province in China (*Cupressaceae*)

foliaceus

foh-lee-uh-SEE-us

foliacea, foliaceum

Like a leaf, as in *Aster foliaceus*

foliatus

fol-ee-AH-tus

foliata, foliatum

With leaves, as in *Aletris foliata*

foliolotus

foh-lee-oh-LOH-tus

foliolota, foliolotum

—

foliolosus

foh-lee-oh-LOH-sus

foliolosa, foliolosum

With leaflets, as in *Thalictrum foliolosum*

foliosus

foh-lee-OH-sus

foliosa, foliosum

With many leaves; leafy, as in *Dactylorhiza foliosa*

follicularis

fol-lik-yoo-LAY-ris

follicularis, folliculare

With follicles, as in *Cephalotus follicularis*

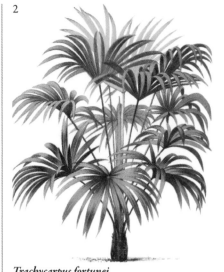

2

Trachycarpus fortunei, Chusan palm

fontanus

FON-tah-nus

fontana, fontanum

Growing in fast-running water, as in *Cerastium fontanum*

formosanus

for-MOH-sa-nus

formosana, formosanum

Connected with Taiwan (formerly Formosa), as in *Pleione formosana*

formosus

for-MOH-sus

formosa, formosum

Handsome; beautiful, as in *Pieris formosa*

forrestianus

for-rest-ee-AH-nus

forrestiana, forrestianum

—

forrestii

for-rest-EE-eye

Named after George Forrest (1873–1932), Scottish plant collector, as in *Hypericum forrestii*

Forsythia [1]

for-SYTH-ee-uh

Named after William Forsyth (1737–1804), Scottish botanist and founding member of the RHS (*Oleaceae*)

fortunei [2]

for-TOO-nee-eye

Named after Robert Fortune (1812–80), Scottish plant hunter and horticulturist, as in *Trachycarpus fortunei*

1

Fothergilla gardenii,
dwarf witchelder

2

Fragaria virginiana,
Virginia strawberry

3

Fuchsia magellanica,
lady's eardrops

Fothergilla [1]
foth-ur-GIL-uh
Named after John Fothergill (1712–80),
British physician and naturalist
(*Hamamelidaceae*)

Fouquieria
foo-kee-AIR-ee-uh
Named after Pierre Éloi Fouquier (1776–
1850), French physician (*Fouquieriaceae*)

foveolatus
toh-vee-oh-LAH-tus
foveolata, foveolatum
With slight pitting, as in *Chionanthus
foveolatus*

fragantissimus
fray-gran-TISS-ih-mus
fragrantissima, fragrantissimum
Very fragrant, as in *Lonicera fragrantissima*

Fragaria [2]
fruh-GAIR-ee-uh
From Latin *fraga* meaning 'fragrant', as are
the fruits of strawberry (*Rosaceae*)

fragarioides
fray-gare-ee-OY-deez
Resembling strawberry (*Fragaria*), as in
Waldsteinia fragarioides

fragilis
FRAJ-ih-lis
fragilis, fragile
Brittle; quick to wilt, as in *Salix fragilis*

fragrans
FRAY-granz
Fragrant, as in *Osmanthus fragrans*

Frailea
FRAY-lee-uh
Named after Manuel Fraile (1850–?),
Spanish horticulturist (*Cactaceae*)

Francoa
fran-KOH-uh
Named after Francisco Franco (16th
century), Spanish physician (*Francoaceae*)

Frangula
FRANG-ew-luh
From Latin *frango* meaning 'to break', as they
have brittle branches (*Rhamnaceae*)

Franklinia
frank-LIN-ee-uh
Named after Benjamin Franklin (1706–90),
American statesman (*Theaceae*)

fraseri
FRAY-zer-ee
Named after John Fraser (1750–1811),
Scottish plant collector and nurseryman, as
in *Magnolia fraseri*

fraxineus
FRAK-si-nus
fraxinea, fraxineum
Like ash (*Fraxinus*), as in *Blechnum
fraxineum*

fraxinifolius
fraks-in-ee-FOH-lee-us
fraxinifolia, fraxinifolium
With leaves like ash (*Fraxinus*), as in
Pterocarya fraxinifolia

Fraxinus
FRAKS-in-us
From the classical Latin name for ash tree
(*Oleaceae*)

Freesia
FREE-shuh
Named after Friedrich Heinrich Theodor
Freese (1797–1876), German physician
(*Iridaceae*)

Fremontodendron
fre-mont-oh-DEN-dron
Named after John Charles Frémont
(1813–90), American soldier and politician,
plus Greek *dendron* meaning 'tree'
(*Malvaceae*)

frigidus
FRIH-jih-dus
frigida, frigidum
Growing in cold regions, as in *Artemisia
frigida*

Fritillaria
fri-tuh-LAIR-ee-uh
From Latin *fritillus* meaning 'checkered', as
in the tepals of *F. meleagris* (*Liliaceae*)

frondosus
frond-OH-sus
frondosa, frondosum
Very leafy, as in *Primula frondosa*

frutescens
froo-TESS-enz
—

fruticans
FROO-tih-kanz
—

fruticosus
froo-tih-KOH-sus
fruticosa, fruticosum
Shrubby; bushy, as in *Argyranthemum frutescens*

fruticola
froo-TIH-koh-luh
Growing in bushy places, as in *Chirita fruticola*

fruticulosus
froo-tih-koh-LOH-sus
fruticulosa, fruticulosum
Dwarf and shrubby, as in *Matthiola fruticulosa*

fucatus
few-KAH-tus
fucata, fucatum
Painted; dyed, as in *Crocosmia fucata*

Fuchsia [3]
FEW-shuh or FOOK-see-uh
Named after Leonhart Fuchs (1501–66), German physician (*Onagraceae*)

fuchsioides
few-shee-OY-deez
Resembling *Fuchsia*, as in *Iochroma fuchsioides*

fugax
FOO-gaks
Withering quickly; fleeting, as in *Urginea fugax*

fulgens
FUL-jenz
—

fulgidus
FUL-jih-dus
fulgida, fulgidum
Shining; glistening, as in *Rudbeckia fulgida*

fuliginosus
few-lih-gin-OH-sus
fuliginosa, fuliginosum
A dirty brown or sooty colour, as in *Carex fuliginosa*

fulvescens
ful-VES-enz
Becoming tawny in colour, as in *Masdevallia fulvescens*

fulvidus
FUL-vee-dus
fulvida, fulvidum
Slightly tawny in colour, as in *Cortaderia fulvida*

fulvus
FUL-vus
fulva, fulvum
Tawny orange in colour, as in *Hemerocallis fulva*

Fumaria
foo-MAIR-ee-uh
From Latin *fumus* meaning 'smoke', which is what the roots smell of (*Papaveraceae*)

fumariifolius
foo-mar-ee-FOH-lee-us
fumariifolia, fumariifolium
With leaves like fumitory (*Fumaria*), as in *Scabiosa fumariifolia*

funebris
fun-EE-bris
funebris, funebre
Connected to graveyards, as in *Cupressus funebris*

fungosus
fun-GOH-sus
fungosa, fungosum
Like fungus; spongy, as in *Borinda fungosa*

furcans
fur-kanz
—

furcatus
fur-KA-tus
furcata, furcatum
Forked, as in *Pandanus furcatus*

Furcraea
fur-KREE-uh
Named after Antoine François de Fourcroy (1755–1809), French chemist (*Asparagaceae*)

fuscatus
fus-KA-tus
fuscata, fuscatum
Brownish in colour, as in *Sisyrinchium fuscatum*

fuscus
FUS-kus
fusca, fuscum
A dusky or swarthy brown, as in *Nothofagus fusca*

futilis
FOO-tih-lis
futilis, futile
Without use, as in *Salsola futilis*

gaditanus
gad-ee-TAH-nus
gaditana, gaditanum
Connected with Cadiz, Spain, as in
Narcissus gaditanus

Gagea
GAGE-ee-uh
Named after Thomas Gage (1781–1820),
British botanist (*Liliaceae*)

Gaillardia
gay-LAR-dee-uh
Named after M. Gaillard de Charentonneau
(18th century), French magistrate and
patron of botany (*Asteraceae*)

galacifolius
guh-lay-sih-FOH-lee-us
galacifolia, galacifolium
With leaves like wandflower (*Galax*), as in
Shortia galacifolia

Galanthus
gah-LAN-thus
From Greek *gala* meaning 'milk' and *anthos*
meaning 'flower', referring to the white
flowers of snowdrops (*Amaryllidaceae*)

Galax
GAY-lax
From Greek *gala* meaning 'milk' as the
flowers are white (*Diapensiaceae*)

galeatus
ga-le-AH-tus
galeata, galeatum
—

galericulatus
gal-er-ee-koo-LAH-tus
galericulata, galericulatum
Shaped like a helmet, as in *Sparaxis galeata*

Galega
GA-leh-guh
From Greek *gala* meaning 'milk' as this
fodder was said to improve milk yield from
goats (*Fabaceae*)

galegifolius
guh-lee-gih-FOH-lee-us
galegifolia, galegifolium
With leaves like goat's rue (*Galega*), as in
Swainsona galegifolia

1

Campanula garganica,
Adriatic bellflower

Galium
GA-lee-um
From Greek *galion*, the vernacular name for
a bedstraw, originating in *gala* meaning
'milk', as the flowers of *G. verum* were said to
curdle milk, while the stems of *G. aparine*
were used to strain milk (*Rubiaceae*)

gallicus
GAL-ih-kus
gallica, gallicum
Connected with France, as in *Rosa gallica*

Galtonia
gawl-TOH-nee-uh
Named after Francis Galton (1822–1911),
British statistician and psychologist
(*Amaryllidaceae*)

gangeticus
gan-GET-ih-kus
gangetica, gangeticum
Of the Ganges regions of India and
Bangladesh, as in *Asystasia gangetica*

Gardenia
gar-DEE-nee-uh
Named after Alexander Garden (1730–91),
Scottish physician and biologist (*Rubiaceae*)

garganicus [1]
gar-GAN-ih-kus
garganica, garganicum
Connected with Monte Gargano, Italy, as in
Campanula garganica

Garrya
GA-ree-uh
Named after Nicholas Garry (c. 1782–
1856), British-born deputy-governor of the
Hudson's Bay Company (*Garryaceae*)

Gasteria
gas-TEER-ee-uh
From Greek *gaster* meaning 'stomach', which
the flowers resemble (*Asphodelaceae*)

Gaultheria
gawl-THEER-ee-uh
Named after Jean-François Gaultier
(1708–56), Canadian botanist and
physician (*Ericaceae*)

Geranium

When is a geranium not a *Geranium*? When it's a *Pelargonium*! Cranesbills are members of the genus *Geranium*, but though many gardeners prefer common names over Latin, 'geranium' is now so widely known that it has become a common name. It's also the common name for *Pelargonium*, a close relation of *Geranium*. But this causes confusion because most true *Geranium* are hardy herbaceous perennials, while most *Pelargonium* are tender shrubs used as bedding. To avoid confusion, perhaps we should stick with the name 'cranesbill' for the former and 'storksbill' for the latter?

Geranium pratense,
meadow cranesbill

Gaura
GOW-ruh
From Greek *gauros* meaning 'superb'
(*Onagraceae*)

Gaylussacia
gay-loo-SAY-see-uh
Named after Louis Joseph Gay-Lussac
(1778–1850), French chemist (*Ericaceae*)

Gazania
guh-ZAY-nee-uh
From Greek *gaza* meaning 'riches', in
reference to the great show of flowers; or
named after Theodorus Gaza (1398–1478),
Greek scholar (*Asteraceae*)

Geissorhiza
guy-so-RY-zuh
From Greek *geissos* meaning 'tile' and *rhiza*
meaning 'root', due to the overlapping corm
tunics (*Iridaceae*)

gelidus
JEL-id-us
gelida, gelidum
Connected with ice-cold regions, as in
Rhodiola gelida

Gelsemium
jel-SEE-mee-um
From Italian *gelsomino*, meaning 'jasmine'
(*Gelsemiaceae*)

gemmatus
jem-AH-tus
gemmata, gemmatum
Bejewelled, as in *Wikstroemia gemmata*

gemmiferus
jem-MIH-fer-us
gemmifera, gemmiferum
With buds, as in *Primula gemmifera*

generalis
jen-er-RAH-lis
generalis, generale
Normal, as in *Canna × generalis*

genevensis
gen-EE-ven-sis
genevensis, genevense
From Geneva, Switzerland, as in *Ajuga
genevensis*

geniculatus
gen-ik-yoo-LAH-tus
geniculata, geniculatum
With a sharp bend like a knee, as in *Thalia
geniculata*

Genista
jen-IS-tuh
The classical Latin name for broom, from
which the royal House of Plantagenet gets
its name, *planta-genista* (*Fabaceae*)

genistifolius
jih-nis-tih-FOH-lee-us
genistifolia, genistifolium
With leaves like broom (*Genista*), as in
Linaria genistifolia

Gentiana
jen-shee-AH-nuh
Named after King Gentius of Illyria (2nd
century), who supposedly discovered the
medicinal properties of *G. lutea*
(*Gentianaceae*)

Gentianopsis
jen-shee-ah-NOP-sis
Resembling the related genus *Gentiana*
(*Gentianaceae*)

geoides
jee-OY-deez
Like avens (*Geum*), as in *Waldsteinia geoides*

geometrizans
jee-oh-MET-rih-zanz
With markings in a formal pattern, as in
Myrtillocactus geometrizans

georgianus
jorj-ee-AH-nus
georgiana, georgianum
Connected with Georgia, USA, as in
Quercus georgiana

georgicus

JORJ-ih-kus

georgica, georgicum

Connected with Georgia (Eurasia), as in *Pulsatilla georgica*

geranioides

jer-an-ee-OY-deez

Resembling *Geranium*, as in *Saxifraga geranioides*

Geranium

juh-RAY-nee-um

From Greek *geranos* meaning 'crane', as the fruits resemble this bird's beak, thus the common name cranesbill (*Geraniaceae*)

Gerbera

JER-bur-uh

Named after Traugott Gerber (1710–43), German physician and botanist (*Asteraceae*)

germanicus

jer-MAN-ih-kus

germanica, germanicum

Connected with Germany, as in *Iris germanica*

Gesneria

jez-NEER-ee-uh

Named after Konrad Gessner (1516–65), Swiss biologist (*Gesneriaceae*)

Geum [1]

JEE-oom

From Greek *geuo* meaning 'to give relish' as the roots of *G. urbanum* are said to taste good (*Rosaceae*)

Gevuina

geh-voo-AY-nuh

From Mapuche (Chile) *guevin*, the vernacular name (*Proteaceae*)

Gibbaeum

gib-AY-um

From Latin *gibbus* meaning 'hunched' as the succulent leaves are swollen and rounded (*Aizoaceae*)

gibberosus

gib-er-OH-sus

gibberosa, gibberosum

With a hump on one side, as in *Scaphosepalum gibberosum*

gibbiflorus

gib-bih-FLOR-us

gibbiflora, gibbiflorum

With flowers that have a hump on one side, as in *Echeveria gibbiflora*

gibbosus

gib-OH-sus

gibbosa, gibbosum

—

gibbus

gib-us

gibba, gibbum

With a swelling on one side, as in *Fritillaria gibbosa*

gibraltaricus

jib-ral-TAH-rih-kus

gibraltarica, gibraltaricum

Connected with Gibraltar, Europe, as in *Iberis gibraltarica*

giganteus

jy-GAN-tee-us

gigantea, giganteum

Unusually tall or large, as in *Stipa gigantea*

giganthus

jy-GAN-thus

gigantha, giganthum

With large flowers, as in *Hemsleya gigantha*

Gilia

GIL-ee-uh

Named after Filippo Luigi Gilii (1756–1821), Italian naturalist (*Polemoniaceae*)

Gillenia

gil-EN-ee-uh

Named after Arnold Gille (1586–1633), German alchemist (*Rosaceae*)

gilvus

GIL-vus

gilva, gilvum

Dull yellow, as in *Echeveria × gilva*

1

Geum urbanum, herb bennet

Ginkgo
GINK-goh
From Chinese *yinxing* meaning 'silver apricot', in reference to the edible seed; when translated into Japanese, it is *ginkyo*, but Linnaeus misread the name, switching the 'y' for a 'g', giving the current spelling (*Ginkgoaceae*)

glabellus
gla-BELL-us
glabella, glabellum
Smooth, as in *Epilobium glabellum*

glaber
gla-ber
glabra, glabrum
Smooth, hairless, as in *Bougainvillea glabra*

glabratus
GLAB-rah-tus
glabrata, glabratum
—

glabrescens
gla-BRES-senz
—

glabriusculus
gla-bree-US-kyoo-lus
glabriuscula, glabriusculum
Rather hairless, as in *Corylopsis glabrescens*

glacialis
glass-ee-AH-lis
glacialis, glaciale
Connected with ice-cold, glacial regions, as in *Dianthus glacialis*

gladiatus
glad-ee-AH-tus
gladiata, gladiatum
Like a sword, as in *Coreopsis gladiata*

Gladiolus
gla-dee-OH-lus
From Latin *gladiolus* meaning 'little sword', the shape of the leaves (*Iridaceae*)

Glandora
glan-DOR-uh
From Latin *glandulosus* meaning 'glandular' and *Lithodora*, a related genus; these plants differ from *Lithodora* in that they have glands inside the corolla (*Boraginaceae*)

Glandularia
glan-dew-LAIR-ee-uh
From Latin *glandula* meaning 'small acorn', a reference to the shape of the fruit, or *glandulosus* meaning 'glandular', as in the stigmas (*Verbenaceae*)

glanduliferus
glan-doo-LIH-fer-us
glandulifera, glanduliferum
With glands, as in *Impatiens glandulifera*

glanduliflorus
gland-yoo-LIH-flor-us
glanduliflora, glanduliflorum
With glandular flowers, as in *Stapelia glanduliflora*

glandulosus
glan-doo-LOH-sus
glandulosa, glandulosum
Glandular, as in *Erodium glandulosum*

glaucescens
glaw-KES-enz
With a bloom; blue-green in colour, as in *Ferocactus glaucescens*

Glaucidium
glaw-KID-ee-um
The Greek *glaucidium* means 'owl', but in this case, the name refers to the poppy genus *Glaucium*, which has similar foliage (*Ranunculaceae*)

glaucifolius
glau-see-FOH-lee-us
glaucifolia, glaucifolium
With grey-green leaves; with leaves with a bloom, as in *Diospyros glaucifolia*

Glaucium
GLAW-kee-um
From Greek *glaukon* meaning 'blue-grey', the colour of the leaves (*Papaveraceae*)

glaucophyllus
glaw-koh-FIL-us
glaucophylla, glaucophyllum
With grey-green leaves, or with a bloom, as in *Rhododendron glaucophyllum*

Ginkgo

The maidenhair is a lonely tree. Known scientifically as *Ginkgo biloba*, it's a genus of a single species, the only member of its family, order, class and division. This has not always been the case – the fossil record suggests that *Ginkgo* and its relatives were once common and widely distributed. The remaining species, which has earned the title 'living fossil', only occurs naturally in a handful of sites in China. Given its long history, it is not surprising that this tree is a survivor, and grows well as a city street tree, despite high levels of environmental pollution.

Ginkgo biloba,
maidenhair tree

1

Globba radicalis,
dancing girl ginger

glaucus
GLAW-kus
glauca, glaucum
With a bloom on the leaves, as in *Festuca glauca*

Glebionis
gle-bee-OH-nis
From Greek *gleba* meaning 'soil' and *ionis* meaning 'characteristic of', perhaps in reference to how these plants can appear in ploughed fields (*Asteraceae*)

Glechoma
gle-KOH-muh
From Greek *glechon* meaning 'mint' or 'thyme' (*Lamiaceae*)

Gleditsia
gleh-DIT-zee-uh
Named after Johann Gottlieb Gleditsch (1714–86), German physician and botanist (*Fabaceae*)

Globba [1]
GLOH-buh
From Ambonese (Indonesia) *galoba*, the vernacular name for a spice (*Zingiberaceae*)

globiferus
glo-BIH-fer-us
globifera, globiferum
With spherical clusters of small globes, as in *Pilularia globifera*

globosus
glo-BOH-sus
globosa, globosum
Round, as in *Buddleja globosa*

Globularia
gloh-bew-LAIR-ee-uh
From Latin *globosus* meaning 'like a small ball', from the shape of the flower heads (*Plantaginaceae*)

globularis
glob-YOO-lah-ris
globularis, globulare
Relating to a small sphere, as in *Carex globularis*

globuliferus
glob-yoo-LIH-fer-us
globulifera, globuliferum
With small spherical clusters, as in *Saxifraga globulifera*

globuligemma
glob-yoo-lih-JEM-uh
With round buds, as in *Aloe globuligemma*

globulosus
glob-yoo-LOH-sus
globulosa, globulosum
Small and spherical, as in *Hoya globulosa*

glomeratus
glom-er-AH-tus
glomerata, glomeratum
With clusters of rounded heads, as in *Campanula glomerata*

Gloriosa
glor-ee-oh-suh
From Latin *gloriosus* meaning 'glorious', like the flowers (*Colchicaceae*)

gloriosus
glo-ree-OH-sus
gloriosa, gloriosum
Superb; glorious, as in *Yucca gloriosa*

Glottiphyllum
glot-i-FIL-um
From Greek *glotta* meaning 'tongue' and *phyllon* meaning 'leaf' (*Aizoaceae*)

Gloxinia
gloks-IN-ee-uh
Named after Benjamin Peter Gloxin (1765–94), German physician and botanist (*Gesneriaceae*)

gloxinioides
gloks-in-ee-OY-deez
Resembling *Gloxinia*, as in *Penstemon gloxinioides*

glumaceus
gloo-MA-see-us
glumacea, glumaceum
With glumes (the bracts that enclose the flowers of grasses), as in *Dendrochilum glumaceum*

Glumicalyx
gloo-me-KAY-lix
From Latin *gluma* meaning 'husk', as the calyx resemble a grass husk (*Scrophulariaceae*)

Gossypium arboreum,
tree cotton

glutinosus
gloo-tin-OH-sus
glutinosa, glutinosum
Sticky; glutinous, as in *Eucryphia glutinosa*

Glyceria
gly-SEER-ee-uh
From Greek *glykeros* meaning 'sweet', in reference to the tasty seeds (*Poaceae*)

Glycine
gly-SEE-nee
From Greek *glykeros* meaning 'sweet', an allusion to the sweet-tasting tubers of *Apios americana*, which used to belong to this genus, as *G. apios* (*Fabaceae*)

glycinoides
gly-sin-OY-deez
Like soybean (*Glycine*), as in *Clematis glycinoides*

Glycyrrhiza (also glycyrrhiza)
gli-sur-RY-zuh
From Greek *glykeros* meaning 'sweet' and *rhiza* meaning 'root', as the roots of *G. glabra* are harvested to make liquorice (*Fabaceae*)

gnaphaloides
naf-fal-OY-deez
Like cudweed (*Gnaphalium*), as in *Senecio gnaphaloides*

Gomphocarpus
gom-foh-KAR-pus
From Greek *gomphos* meaning 'bolt' or 'club' and *karpos* meaning 'fruit', an allusion to the inflated fruits (*Apocynaceae*)

Gomphrena
gom-FREE-nuh
From Latin *gromphaena*, the name for this or a related plant (*Amaranthaceae*)

gongylodes
GON-jih-loh-deez
Swollen; roundish, as in *Cissus gongylodes*

goniocalyx
gon-ee-oh-KAL-iks
Calyx with corners or angles, as in *Eucalyptus goniocalyx*

Goniolimon
goh-nee-oh-LIM-on
From Latin *gonio* meaning 'angle' and *Limonium*, a related genus, as the inflorescence branches are angled (*Plumbaginaceae*)

Goodyera
good-ee-AIR-uh
Named after John Goodyer (1592–1664), British botanist (*Orchidaceae*)

Gordonia
gor-DOH-nee-uh
Named after James Gordon (1708–80), British nurseryman (*Theaceae*)

gossypinus
goss-ee-PEE-nus
gossypina, gossypinum
Like cotton (*Gossypium*), as in *Strobilanthes gossypina*

Gossypium
gos-IP-ee-um
From Greek *gossypion* meaning 'cotton', possibly derived from Arabic *goz* meaning a 'silky substance'; commercial cotton is harvested from *G. hirsutum* and other species (*Malvaceae*)

gracilentus
grass-il-EN-tus
gracilenta, gracilentum
Graceful; slender, as in *Rhododendron gracilentum*

graciliflorus
grass-il-ih-FLOR-us
graciliflora, graciliflorum
With slender or graceful flowers, as in *Pseuderanthemum graciliflorum*

gracilipes
gra-SIL-i-peez
With a slender stalk, as in *Mahonia gracilipes*

gracilis
GRASS-il-is
gracilis, gracile
Graceful; slender, as in *Geranium gracile*

graecus
GRAY-kus
graeca, graecum
Greek, as in *Fritillaria graeca*

gramineus
gram-IN-ee-us
graminea, gramineum
Like grass, as in *Iris graminea*

graminifolius
gram-in-ee-FOH-lee-us
graminifolia, graminifolium
With grass-like leaves, as in *Stylidium graminifolium*

granadensis
gran-uh-DEN-sis
granadensis, granadense
From Granada, Spain or Colombia, South America, as in *Drimys granadensis*

grandiceps
GRAN-dee-keps
With large head, as in *Leucogenes grandiceps*

grandicuspis
gran-dih-KUS-pis
grandicuspis, grandicuspe
With big points, as in *Sansevieria grandicuspis*

grandidentatus
gran-dee-den-TAH-tus
grandidentata, grandidentatum
With big teeth, as in *Thalictrum grandidentatum*

grandiflorus
gran-dih-FLOR-us
grandiflora, grandiflorum
With large flowers, as in *Platycodon grandiflorus*

grandifolius
gran-dih-FOH-lee-us
grandifolia, grandifolium
With large leaves, as in *Haemanthus grandifolius*

grandis
gran-DIS
grandis, grande
Big; showy, as in *Licuala grandis*

graniticus
gran-NY-tih-kus
granitica, graniticum
Growing on granite and rocks, as in *Dianthus graniticus*

granulatus
gran-yoo-LAH-tus
granulata, granulatum
Bearing grain-like structures, as in *Saxifraga granulata*

granulosus

gran-yool-OH-sus

granulosa, granulosum

Made of small grains, as in *Centropogon granulosus*

Graptopetalum

grap-toh-PET-uh-lum

From Greek *graptos* meaning 'inscribed' and *petalon* meaning 'petal', as the flowers of some species are curiously marked (*Crassulaceae*)

Graptophyllum

grap-toh-FIL-um

From Greek *graptos* meaning 'inscribed' and *phyllon* meaning 'leaf', for the often variegated foliage (*Acanthaceae*)

gratianopolitanus

grat-ee-an-oh-pol-it-AH-nus

gratianopolitana, gratianopolitanum

Connected with Grenoble, France, as in *Dianthus gratianopolitanus*

gratissimus

gra-TIS-ih-mus

gratissima, gratissimum

Very pleasing, as in *Luculia gratissima*

gratus

GRAH-tus

grata, gratum

Giving pleasure, as in *Conophytum gratum*

graveolens [1]

grav-ee-OH-lenz

With a heavy scent, as in *Ruta graveolens*

Grevillea

gre-VILL-ee-uh

Named after Charles Francis Greville (1749–1809), British politician, art collector and scientist, founding member of the RHS (*Proteaceae*)

Grewia

GROO-ee-uh

Named after Nehemiah Grew (1641–1712), British plant anatomist (*Malvaceae*)

Greyia

GREY-ee-uh

Named after George Grey (1812–98), British soldier, explorer and colonial administrator (*Francoaceae*)

Grindelia

grin-DEEL-ee-uh

Named after David Hieronymus Grindel (1776–1836), Latvian botanist (*Asteraceae*)

Griselinia

griz-uh-LIN-ee-uh

Named after Francesco Griselini (1717–87), Italian botanist (*Griseliniaceae*)

1

Ruta graveolens,
common rue

2

Guzmania monostachya,
one-spiked guzmania

griseus
GREE-see-us
grisea, griseum
Grey, as in *Acer griseum*

grosseserratus
groseser-AH-tus
grosseserrata, grosseserratum
With large saw teeth, as in *Clematis occidentalis* subsp. *grosseserrata*

grossus
GROSS-us
grossa, grossum
Very large, as in *Betula grossa*

Grusonia
groo-SOH-nee-uh
Named after Hermann Gruson (1821–95), German engineer (*Cactaceae*)

guianensis
gee-uh-NEN-sis
guianensis, guianense
From Guiana, South America, as in *Couroupita guianensis*

guineensis
gin-ee-EN-sis
guineensis, guineense
From the Guinea coast, West Africa, as in *Elaeis guineensis*

gummifer
GUM-mif-er
gummifera, gummiferum
Producing gum, as in *Seseli gummiferum*

gummosus
gum-MOH-sus
gummosa, gummosum
Gummy, as in *Ferula gummosa*

Gunnera
GUH-ner-uh
Named after Johan Ernst Gunner (1718–73), Norwegian cleric and botanist (*Gunneraceae*)

guttatus
goo-TAH-tus
guttata, guttatum
With spots, as in *Mimulus guttatus*

Guzmania [2]
gooz-MAN-ee-uh
Named after Anastasio Guzmán (unknown–1807), Spanish pharmacist and naturalist (*Bromeliaceae*)

3

Gypsophila elegans,
annual baby's breath

Gymnocalycium
jim-noh-kay-LIS-ee-um
From Greek *gymnos* meaning 'naked' and calyx, the ring of sepals that protect the flower bud; these cacti have no spines on the calyx (*Cactaceae*)

Gymnocarpium
jim-noh-KAR-pee-um
From Greek *gymnos* meaning 'naked' and *karpos* meaning 'fruit', as the sporangia are not covered with a membrane (*Woodsiaceae*)

gymnocarpus
jim-noh-KAR-pus
gymnocarpa, gymnocarpum
With naked, uncovered fruit, as in *Rosa gymnocarpa*

Gymnocladus
jim-noh-KLAY-dus
From Greek *gymnos* meaning 'naked' and *klados* meaning 'branch'; the type species (*G. dioica*) is deciduous and slow to produce new leaves in spring and shed old leaves in autumn (*Fabaceae*)

Gynura
jy-NOOR-uh
From Greek *gyne* meaning 'female' and *oura* meaning 'tail', perhaps an allusion to the female floral part, which has a branched style (*Asteraceae*)

Gypsophila [3]
jip-SOF-i-luh
From Greek *gypsos* meaning 'gypsum/chalk' and *philos* meaning 'loving', as some species prefer to grow on lime-rich soils (*Caryophyllaceae*)

Haageocereus
hah-jee-oh-SER-ee-us
Named after the Haage family of Germany, famous cactus growers, plus *Cereus*, a related genus (*Cactaceae*)

Haastia
HAHS-tee-uh
Named after Sir Johann Franz Julius von Haast (1822–87), German-born New Zealand geologist and explorer (*Asteraceae*)

haastii
HAAS-tee-eye
Named after Sir Johann Franz Julius von Haast (1822–87), German explorer and geologist, as in *Olearia* × *haastii*

Habenaria
ha-ben-AIR-ee-uh
From Latin *habena* meaning 'reins', an allusion to the flower spur (*Orchidaceae*)

Haberlea
hah-bur-LEE-uh
Named after Karl Konstantin Christian Haberle (1764–1832), Austrian scientist (*Gesneriaceae*)

Habranthus
ha-BRAN-thus
From Greek *habros* meaning 'delicate' and *anthos* meaning 'flower' (*Amaryllidaceae*)

Hacquetia
ha-KET-ee-uh
Named after Balthazar Hacquet (1739–1815), French-born Austrian scientist (*Apiaceae*)

hadriaticus
had-ree-AT-ih-kus
hadriatica, hadriaticum
Connected with the shores of the Adriatic Sea, Europe, as in *Crocus hadriaticus*

Haemanthus
HE-man-thus
From Greek *haimatos* meaning 'blood' and *anthos* meaning 'flower', as many species have scarlet blooms (*Amaryllidaceae*)

haematocalyx
hem-at-oh-KAL-icks
With a blood-red calyx, as in *Dianthus haematocalyx*

haematochilus
hem-mat-oh-KY-lus
haematochila, haematochilum
With a blood-red lip, as in *Oncidium haematochilum*

haematodes
hem-uh-TOH-deez
Blood-red, as in *Rhododendron haematodes*

Hakea
HAH-kee-uh
Named after Christian Ludwig von Hake (1745–1818), German administrator (*Proteaceae*)

hakeoides
hak-ee-OY-deez
Resembles *Hakea*, as in *Berberis hakeoides*

Hakonechloa
ha-kon-uh-KLOH-uh
Named for the town of Hakone in Japan, plus Greek *chloa*, 'a blade of grass' (*Poaceae*)

Halesia
ha-LEE-see-uh, HAIL-see-uh
Named after Stephen Hales (1677–1761), British cleric and botanist (*Styracaceae*)

Halimium
ha-LIM-ee-um
From Greek *halimos*, the name for *Atriplex halimus*, which has similar leaves (*Cistaceae*)

Halimodendron
ha-lim-oh-DEN-dron
From Greek *halos* meaning 'the sea' and *dendron* meaning 'tree', as this genus thrives on saline soils (*Fabaceae*)

halophilus
hal-oh-FIL-ee-us
halophila, halophilum
Salt-loving, as in *Iris spuria* subsp. *halophila*

Hamamelis
ha-muh-MEL-is
From Greek *hama* meaning 'with' and *melon* meaning 'apple', as plants have both flowers and fruits at the same time; the medlar (*Mespilus germanica*) was known as *hamamelis* for this reason (*Hamamelidaceae*)

hamatus
ham-AH-tus
hamata, hamatum
—

hamosus
ham-UH-sus
hamosa, hamosum
Hooked, as in *Euphorbia hamata*

Haplopappus
hap-loh-PAP-us
From Greek *haplo* meaning 'simple' and *pappos* meaning 'fluff', as each fruit has a single ring of bristles (*Asteraceae*)

Hardenbergia
har-den-BURG-ee-uh
Named after Franziska von Hardenberg (unknown–1853), Austrian patron of botany (*Fabaceae*)

harpophyllus
harp-oh-FIL-us
harpophylla, harpophyllum
With leaves shaped like sickles, as in *Laelia harpophylla*

Harrisia
ha-RIS-ee-uh
Named after William Harris (1860–1920), Irish botanist (*Cactaceae*)

hastatus
hass-TAH-tus
hastata, hastatum
Shaped like a spear, as in *Verbena hastata*

hastilabius
hass-tih-LAH-bee-us
hastilabia, hastilabium
With a spear-shaped lip, as in *Oncidium hastilabium*

hastulatus
hass-TOO-lat-tus
hastulata, hastulatum
Shaped somewhat like a spear, as in *Acacia hastulata*

Hatiora
hat-ee-OR-uh
An anagram of the genus *Hariota*, named after Thomas Harriot (1560–1621), British mathematician and astronomer (*Cactaceae*)

Haworthia

huh-WORTH-ee-uh

Named after Adrian Hardy Haworth (1768–1833), British botanist and entomologist (*Asphodelaceae*)

Hebe

HE-bee

Named after Hebe, the Greek goddess of youth, though the allusion is unclear (*Plantaginaceae*)

hebecarpus

hee-be-KAR-pus

hebecarpa, hebecarpum

With down-covered fruit, as in *Senna hebecarpa*

hebephyllus

hee-bee-FIL-us

hebephylla, hebephyllum

With down-covered leaves, as in *Cotoneaster hebephyllus*

Hechtia

HECH-tee-uh

Named after Julius Gottfried Conrad Hecht (1771–1837), Prussian botanist and politician (*Bromeliaceae*)

Hedera

HED-uh-ruh

From Latin *hedera*, the vernacular name, possibly originating in Celtic *hedra* meaning 'cord' (*Araliaceae*)

hederaceus

hed-er-AYE-see-us

hederacea, hederaceum

Like ivy (*Hedera*), as in *Glechoma hederacea*

hederifolius

hed-er-ih-FOH-lee-us

hederifolia, hederifolium

With leaves like ivy (*Hedera*), as in *Veronica hederifolia*

Hedychium

he-dik-ee-um

From Greek *hedys* meaning 'sweet' and *chios* meaning 'snow', referring to the white, fragrant flowers of *H. coronarium* (*Zingiberaceae*)

Helenium (also helenium)

huh-LEE-nee-um

Named after Helen of Troy in Greek mythology, as the flowers were said to spring up from her tear drops (*Asteraceae*)

Heliamphora

he-lee-am-FOR-uh

From Greek *helos* meaning 'marsh' and *amphora* meaning 'vessel/container', as these pitcher plants live in bogs (*Sarraceniaceae*)

Helianthemum

he-lee-ANTH-uh-mum

From Greek *helios* meaning 'sun' and *anthemis* meaning 'flower', as the blooms only open in sunny weather (*Cistaceae*)

helianthoides

hel-ih-anth-OH-deez

Resembling sunflower (*Helianthus*), as in *Heliopsis helianthoides*

Helianthus

he-lee-ANTH-us

From Greek *helios* meaning 'sun' and *anthos* meaning 'flower' as the flower heads resemble the sun, and the flower buds follow it (*Asteraceae*)

Helichrysum

he-li-KRY-sum

From Greek *helios* meaning 'sun' and *khrysos* meaning 'gold', as some species have yellow flowers (*Asteraceae*)

GENUS SPOTLIGHT

Helianthus

The sunflower (*Helianthus annuus*) is a firm favourite with children due to its ease of cultivation and vigorous growth – the tallest recorded was over 9 metres (30 ft) tall. Both its English and Latin names refer to the flower head, which looks like the sun, an inflorescence composed of small brown disc florets surrounded by yellow ray florets. Contrary to popular belief, mature sunflowers don't follow the sun (a process known as heliotropism) and generally face eastwards. However, the developing flower buds can track the sun, returning to an easterly position each night.

Helianthus annuus, common sunflower

Hedera helix,
common ivy

Helleborus orientalis,
Lenten rose

Helonias bullata,
swamp pink

Hemerocallis dumortieri,
copper lily

Heliconia
he-li-KOH-nee-uh
Named after Mount Helicon in Greece,
home of the Muses (*Heliconiaceae*)

Helictotrichon
he-lik-to-TRY-kon
From Greek *helictos* meaning 'twisted' and
trichon meaning 'hair', as the seeds have
twisted awns (*Poaceae*)

Heliopsis
he-lee-OP-sis
From Greek *helios* meaning 'sun' and *opsis*
meaning 'like', as the flower heads resemble
the sun (*Asteraceae*)

Heliotropium
he-lee-oh-TROH-pee-um
From Greek *helios* meaning 'sun' and *tropos*
meaning 'to turn', from the mistaken idea
that these flowers follow the sun
(*Boraginaceae*)

helix
HEE-licks
Spiral-shaped; applied to twining plants, as
in *Hedera helix*

Helleborus [1]
he-lee-BORE-us
From Greek *helein* meaning 'to injure' and
bora meaning 'food', an allusion to the
hellebore's poisonous properties
(*Ranunculaceae*)

hellenicus
hel-LEN-ih-kus
hellenica, hellenicum
Connected with Greece, as in *Linaria
hellenica*

helodes
hel-OH-deez
From boggy land, as in *Drosera helodes*

Helonias [2]
huh-LOW-nee-as
From Greek *helos* meaning 'marsh', a
common habitat (*Melanthiaceae*)

Heloniopsis
huh-low-nee-OP-sis
Resembling the related genus *Helonias*
(*Melanthiaceae*)

helveticus
hel-VET-ih-kus
helvetica, helveticum
Connected with Switzerland, as in
Erysimum helveticum

helvolus
HEL-vol-us
helvola, helvolum
Reddish yellow, as in *Vanda helvola*

Helwingia
hel-WING-ee-uh
Named after Georg Andreas Helwing
(1666–1748), Prussian cleric and botanist
(*Helwingiaceae*)

Hemerocallis [3]
hem-er-oh-KAH-lis, hem-uh-ROK-uh-lis
From Greek *hemeros* meaning 'day' and
kallos meaning 'beauty', as day-lily flowers
only last one day (*Asphodelaceae*)

Hemigraphis
he-mee-GRAF-is
From Greek *hemi* meaning 'half' and *graphis*
meaning 'brush', as the outer stamens are
coated in hairs, but the inner ones are not
(*Acanthaceae*)

Hemionitis
hem-ee-oh-NY-tis
From Greek *hemionos* meaning 'mule', as a
similar plant was said to ward off pregnancy,
and mules are sterile (*Pteridaceae*)

Hemiptelea

hem-ip-TEE-lee-uh

From Greek *hemi* meaning 'half' and *ptelea* meaning 'elm', as this genus is related to true elms, *Ulmus* (*Ulmaceae*)

hemisphaericus

hem-is-FEER-ih-kus

hemisphaerica, hemisphaericum

In the shape of half a sphere, as in *Quercus hemisphaerica*

henryi

HEN-ree-eye

Named after Augustine Henry (1857–1930), Irish plant collector, as in *Lilium henryi*

Hepatica

he-PAT-i-kuh

From Greek *hepatos* meaning 'liver', which the leaves resemble (*Ranunculaceae*)

hepaticifolius

hep-at-ih-sih-FOH-lee-us

hepaticifolia, hepaticifolium

With leaves like liverwort (*Hepatica*), as in *Cymbalaria hepaticifolia*

hepaticus

hep-AT-ih-kus

hepatica, hepaticum

Dull brown; the colour of liver, as in *Anemone hepatica*

hepta-

Used in compound words to denote seven

Heptacodium

hep-tuh-KOH-dee-um

From Greek *hepta* meaning 'seven' and *codeia* meaning 'poppy', as the flowers were said to occur in clusters of seven, though the central bloom is actually the bud of a developing flower cluster (*Caprifoliaceae*)

heptaphyllus

hep-tah-FIL-us

heptaphylla, heptaphyllum

With seven leaves, as in *Parthenocissus heptaphylla*

heracleifolius

hair-uh-klee-ih-FOH-lee-us

heracleifolia, heracleifolium

With leaves like hogweed (*Heracleum*), as in *Begonia heracleifolia*

Heracleum

huh-RAK-lee-um

Named after Hercules/Heracles, hero of Greek mythology, a reference to the great size of some hogweeds (*Apiaceae*)

herbaceus

her-buh-KEE-us

herbacea, herbaceum

Herbaceous, i.e. not woody, as in *Salix herbacea*

Herbertia

her-BUR-tee-uh

Named after William Herbert (1778–1847), British botanist, cleric and politician (*Iridaceae*)

Herpolirion

her-poh-LIR-ee-on

From Greek *herp* meaning 'to creep' and *lirion* meaning 'lily', in reference to the creeping habit (*Asphodelaceae*)

Hesperaloe

hes-per-AL-oh

From Greek *hesperos* meaning 'western' plus the genus *Aloe*; distant relatives of *Aloe* from western North America (*Asparagaceae*)

Hesperantha

hes-puh-RANTH-uh

From Greek *hesperos* meaning 'evening' and *anthos* meaning 'flower', as some species bloom in the evening (*Iridaceae*)

Hesperis

HES-puh-ris

From Greek *hesperos* meaning 'evening', when the flowers are most strongly scented (*Brassicaceae*)

Hesperocallis

hes-per-oh-KAL-is

From Greek *hesperos* meaning 'western' and *kallos* meaning 'beauty' (*Asparagaceae*)

heter-, hetero-

Used in compound words to denote various or diverse

OFFICER AND GENTLEMAN

The discovery of new plant species has long stimulated the imagination. While professional botanists are responsible for many such discoveries, people from other walks of life have also contributed to our understanding of the world's flora. Soldiers posted to far-flung stations were well positioned. John C. Frémont collected *Fremontodendron* while exploring the western United States, while *Colquhounia* was found by Sir Robert Colquhoun, stationed in Nepal. *Briggsia* was named in commemoration of a soldier, Munro Briggs Scott. A promising young botanist at Kew, he joined the army during the First World War and was killed in France at the age of 28.

Heuchera

Plant breeders continue to develop new *Heuchera* cultivars with leaves in a range of vivid shades. They expanded the colour palette by crossing plants of different colours and selecting the best-looking offspring. *Heuchera* will also cross-breed with the related genus *Tiarella*, and the offspring are known as intergeneric hybrids. These hybrids are given a unique genus name that combines both parental names: *Heuchera* plus *Tiarella* equals x *Heucherella*. Several hybrid genera are widely grown including x *Fatshedera* (*Fatsia* x *Hedera)* and x *Cuprocyparis* (*Cupressus* x *Xanthocyparis*). Intergeneric hybrids may be vigorous, as in Leyland cypress (x *Cuprocyparis leylandii*), and can combine the best characteristics of each parent.

Heuchera sanguinea
coral bells

heteracanthus
het-er-a-KAN-thus
heteracantha, heteracanthum
With various or diverse spines, as in *Agave heteracantha*

heteranthus
het-er-AN-thus
heterantha, heteranthum
With various or diverse flowers, as in *Indigofera heterantha*

heterocarpus
het-er-oh-KAR-pus
heterocarpa, heterocarpum
With various or diverse fruit, as in *Ceratocapnos heterocarpa*

heterodoxus
het-er-oh-DOKS-us
heterodoxa, heterodoxum
Differing from the type of the genus, as in *Heliamphora heterodoxa*

Heteromeles
het-uh-roh-ME-leez
From Greek *heteros* meaning 'different' and *melon* meaning 'apple'; either a comparison with apple (*Malus*) fruits or an allusion to the flowers, which only have ten stamens each, while those of an apple have 15+ each (*Rosaceae*)

heteropetalus
het-er-oh-PET-uh-lus
heteropetala, heteropetalum
With various or diverse petals, as in *Erepsia heteropetala*

heterophyllus
het-er-oh-FIL-us
heterophylla, heterophyllum
With various or diverse leaves, as in *Osmanthus heterophyllus*

heteropodus
het-er-oh-PO-dus
heteropoda, heteropodum
With various or diverse stalks, as in *Berberis heteropoda*

Heterotheca
het-uh-roh-THEE-kuh
From Greek *heteros* meaning 'different' and *theke* meaning 'container', an allusion to the different types of fruit produced by ray and disc florets (*Asteraceae*)

Heuchera
HOOK-uh-ruh
Named after Johann Heinrich von Heucher (1677–1747), Austrian physician and botanist (*Saxifragaceae*)

hexa-
Used in compound words to denote six

hexagonopterus
heks-uh-gon-OP-ter-us
hexagonoptera, hexagonopterum
With six-angled wings, as in *Phegopteris hexagonoptera*

hexagonus
hek-sa-GON-us
hexagona, hexagonum
With six angles, as in *Cereus hexagonus*

hexandrus
heks-AN-drus
hexandra, hexandrum
With six stamens, as in *Sinopodophyllum hexandrum*

hexapetalus
heks-uh-PET-uh-lus
hexapetala, hexapetalum
With six petals, as in *Ludwigia grandiflora* subsp. *hexapetala*

hexaphyllus
heks-uh-FIL-us
hexaphylla, hexaphyllum
With six leaves or leaflets, as in *Stauntonia hexaphylla*

hians
HY-anz
Gaping, as in *Aeschynanthus hians*

Hibbertia

hi-BER-tee-uh

Named after George Hibbert (1757–1837),
British merchant, politician and botanist
(*Dilleniaceae*)

hibernicus

hy-BER-nih-kus

hibernica, hibernicum

Connected with Ireland, as in *Hedera
hibernica*

Hibiscus [1]

hi-BIS-kus

From Greek *hibiskos*, the vernacular name
for related marshmallow (*Althaea
officinalis*); perhaps deriving from *ibiskum*,
suggesting these plants live with ibis,
marshland birds (*Malvaceae*)

hiemalis

hy-EH-mah-lis

hiemalis, hiemale

Of the winter; winter-flowering, as in
Leucojum hiemale

Hieracium

hy-er-AY-see-um

From Greek *hierax* meaning 'hawk', though
etymology obscure (*Asteraceae*)

Hierochloe

hy-er-oh-KLO-ee

From Greek *hieros* meaning 'sacred' and
chloa, 'a blade of grass'; used in religious
ceremonies (*Poaceae*)

hierochunticus

hi-er-oh-CHUN-tih-kus

hierochuntica, hierochunticum

Connected with Jericho, as in *Anastatica
hierochuntica*

himalaicus

him-al-LAY-ih-kus

himalaica, himalaicum

Connected with the Himalayas, as in
Stachyurus himalaicus

Himalayacalamus

him-uh-lay-oh-KAL-uh-mus

From the Himalayas, plus Greek *kalamos*
meaning 'reed', a bamboo (*Poaceae*)

himalayensis

him-uh-lay-EN-is

himalayensis, himalayense

From the Himalayas, as in *Geranium
himalayense*

Hippeastrum

hip-ee-AS-trum

From Greek *hippeus* meaning 'horseman'
and *astros* meaning 'star', perhaps because the
flowers resemble a weapon or ornament
worn by a knight, though etymology
obscure (*Amaryllidaceae*)

Hippocrepis

hip-oh-KREP-is

From Greek *hippos* meaning 'horse' and
krepis meaning 'slipper', as the seed pods
resemble horseshoes (*Fabaceae*)

Hippophae

HIP-oh-fee

From Greek *hippos* meaning 'horse' and
phaos meaning 'shining', as the foliage was
fed to horses to improve their health and
appearance (*Elaeagnaceae*)

Hippuris

hip-ew-ris

From Greek *hippos* meaning 'horse' and *oura*
meaning 'tail', which the plant resembles
(*Plantaginaceae*)

hircinus

her-SEE-nus

hircina, hircinum

Goat-like, or with a goat-like odour, as in
Hypericum hircinum

hirsutissimus

her-soot-TEE-sih-mus

hirsutissima, hirsutissimum

Very hairy, as in *Clematis hirsutissima*

hirsutus

her-SOO-tus

hirsuta, hirsutum

Hairy, as in *Lotus hirsutus*

hirsutulus

her-SOOT-oo-lus

hirsutula, hirsutulum

Somewhat hairy, as in *Viola hirsutula*

hirtellus

her-TELL-us

hirtella, hirtellum

Rather hairy, as in *Plectranthus hirtellus*

hirtiflorus

her-tih-FLOR-us

hirtiflora, hirtiflorum

With hairy flowers, as in *Passiflora hirtiflora*

hirtipes

her-TYE-pees

With hairy stems, as in *Viola hirtipes*

hirtus

HER-tus

hirta, hirtum

Hairy, as in *Columnea hirta*

1

**Hibiscus syriacus,
rose of Sharon**

hispanicus

his-PAN-ih-kus

hispanica, hispanicum

Connected with Spain, as in *Narcissus hispanicus*

hispidus

HISS-pih-dus

hispida, hispidum

With bristles, as in *Leontodon hispidus*

Hohenbergia

hoh-un-BUR-ge-uh

Named after the Prince of Württemberg, called Hohenberg, a German or Austrian noble, though his exact identity is uncertain (*Bromeliaceae*)

Hoheria

ho-HEER-ee-uh

From Maori (New Zealand) *houhere*, the vernacular name (*Malvaceae*)

Holboellia [1]

hol-BOWL-ee-uh

Named after Frederik Ludvig Holbøll (1765–1829), Danish botanist (*Lardizabalaceae*)

Holcus

HOL-kus

From Greek *holkos* meaning 'a kind of grain', or possibly meaning 'strap', a reference to the strap-like leaves of this grass (*Poaceae*)

hollandicus

hol-LAN-dih-kus

hollandica, hollandicum

Connected with Holland, as in *Allium hollandicum*

Holmskioldia

holm-ski-OLD-ee-uh

Named after Johan Theodor Holmskjold (1731–93), Danish botanist and courtier (*Lamiaceae*)

holo-

Used in compound words to denote completely

holocarpus

ho-loh-KAR-pus

holocarpa, holocarpum

With complete fruit, as in *Staphylea holocarpa*

1

Holboellia latifolia, sausage vine

holochrysus

ho-loh-KRIS-us

holochrysa, holochrysum

Completely golden, as in *Aeonium holochrysum*

Holodiscus

ho-loh-DIS-kus

From Greek *holos* meaning 'whole' and *diskus* meaning 'disc', as each flower has a circular, unlobed nectar-producing structure (*Rosaceae*)

holosericeus

ho-loh-ser-ee-KEE-us

holosericea, holosericeum

With silky hairs all over, as in *Convolvulus holosericeus*

Homalocladium

hom-uh-loh-KLAY-dee-um

From Greek *homalos* meaning 'flat/smooth' and *klados* meaning 'branch', in reference to the flat stems that give the plant the name 'tapeworm plant' (*Polygonaceae*)

Hoodia

HOOD-ee-uh

Named after Van Hood (19th century), British horticulturist (*Apocynaceae*)

Hordeum

HOR-dee-um

From the classical Latin name for barley, *H. vulgare* (*Poaceae*)

horizontalis

hor-ih-ZON-tah-lis

horizontalis, horizontale

Close to the ground; horizontal, as in *Cotoneaster horizontalis*

Horminum (also horminum)

hor-MINE-um

From the classical Latin name for sage, possibly *Salvia horminum* (*Lamiaceae*)

horridus

HOR-id-us

horrida, horridum

With many prickles, as in *Euphorbia horrida*

hortensis

hor-TEN-sis

hortensis, hortense

—

hortorum

hort-OR-rum

—

hortulanus

hor-tew-LAH-nus

hortulana, hortulanum

Relating to gardens, *Lysichiton × hortensis*

Hydrangea macrophylla,
big-leaf hydrangea or mophead hydrangea

Hosta
HOS-tuh
Named after Nicolaus Thomas Host
(1761–1834), Croatian botanist and
physician (*Asparagaceae*)

Hottonia
huh-TOH-nee-uh
Named after Petrus Houttuyn
(1648–1709), Dutch physician and botanist
(*Primulaceae*)

Houstonia
hoo-STOW-nee-uh
Named after William Houstoun
(c. 1695–1733), Scottish botanist
(*Rubiaceae*)

Houttuynia
how-TEE-nee-uh
Named after Maarten Houttuyn (1720–98),
Dutch physician and naturalist
(*Saururaceae*)

Hovenia
hoh-VEE-nee-uh
Named after David ten Hove (1724–87),
Dutch politician (*Rhamnaceae*)

Howea
HOW-ee-uh
Named after Lord Howe Island, Australia,
where both species reside; the island is
named after Richard Howe (1726–99),
British naval officer (*Arecaceae*)

Hoya
HOY-uh
Named after Thomas Hoy (c. 1750–1822),
British horticulturist and botanist
(*Apocynaceae*)

Huernia
HER-nee-uh
Named after Justin Heurnius (1587–1652),
Dutch missionary (*Apocynaceae*)

hugonis
hew-GO-nis
Named after Father Hugh Scallon,
missionary in China in the late 19th and
early 20th centuries, as in *Rosa hugonis*

humifusus
hew-mih-FEW-sus
humifusa, humifusum
Of a sprawling habit, as in *Opuntia humifusa*

humilis
HEW-mil-is
humilis, humile
Low-growing, dwarfish, as in *Chamaerops
humilis*

Humulus
HUM-ew-lus
From German *humela*, an old name for
hops, *H. lupulus* (*Cannabaceae*)

hungaricus
hun-GAR-ih-kus
hungarica, hungaricum
Connected with Hungary, as in *Colchicum
hungaricum*

Hunnemannia
hoon-MAN-ee-uh
Named after John Hunnemann (1760–
1839), British botanist (*Papaveraceae*)

hunnewellianus
hun-ee-we-el-AH-nus
hunnewelliana, hunnewellianum
Named after the Hunnewell family of the
Hunnewell Arboretum, Wellesley, USA, as
in *Rhododendron hunnewellianum*

hupehensis
hew-pay-EN-sis
hupehensis, hupehense
From Hupeh (Hubei), China, as in *Sorbus
hupehensis*

Hyacinthella
hy-uh-sinth-ELL-uh
From *Hyacinthus*, a related genus, plus
diminutive *ella* (*Asparagaceae*)

hyacinthinus
hy-uh-sin-THEE-nus
hyacinthina, hyacinthinum
—

Hyacinthoides
hy-uh-sinth-OY-deez
Resembling the related genus *Hyacinthus*
(*Asparagaceae*)

Hyacinthus (also hyacinthus)
hy-uh-SIN-thus
hyacintha, hyacinthum
Dark purple-blue, or like a hyacinth, as in
Triteleia hyacinthina

hyalinus
hy-yuh-LEE-nus
hyalina, hyalinum
Transparent; almost transparent, as in
Allium hyalinum

hybridus
hy-BRID-us
hybrida, hybridum
Mixed; hybrid, as in *Helleborus* × *hybridus*

Hydrangea [2]
hy-DRANE-juh
From Greek *hydor* meaning 'water' and
angeion meaning 'small vessel', a reference to
the cup-like fruits (*Hydrangeaceae*)

hydrangeoides
hy-drain-jee-OY-deez
Resembling *Hydrangea*, as in *Schizophragma
hydrangeoides*

Hydrocharis
hy-DRO-kar-is
From Greek *hydor* meaning 'water' and *chari*
meaning 'grace', as these are delicate floating
aquatic plants (*Hydrocharitaceae*)

Hydrocleys
hy-DROK-lee-is
From Greek *hydor* meaning 'water' and *clavis* meaning 'club', a reference to the club-shaped female floral parts (*Alismataceae*)

Hydrocotyle
hr-droh-KOT-il-ee
From Greek *hydor* meaning 'water' and *kotyle* meaning 'cup', as this aquatic herb may have cup-shaped leaves (*Araliaceae*)

Hydrophyllum
hy-droh-FIL-um
From Greek *hydor* meaning 'water' and *phyllon* meaning 'leaf', as the leaf spots look like water drops (*Boraginaceae*)

hyemalis [1]
hy-EH-mah-lis
hyemalis, hyemale
Relating to winter; winter-flowering, as in *Eranthis hyemalis*

Hygrophila
hy-GRO-fil-uh
From Greek *hygro* meaning 'damp' and *phila* meaning 'loving' (*Acanthaceae*)

hylaeus
hy-la-ee-us
hylaea, hylaeum
From the woods, as in *Rhododendron hylaeum*

Hylocereus
hy-loh-SER-ee-us
From Greek *hyle* meaning 'wood' and *Cereus*, a related genus, as these cacti climb trees (*Cactaceae*)

Hylomecon
hy-loh-ME-kon
From Greek *hyle* meaning 'wood' and *mekon* meaning 'poppy', a plant of woodlands (*Papaveraceae*)

Hylotelephium
hy-loh-tel-EFF-ee-um
From Greek *hyle* meaning 'wood' and *Telephium*, another genus; wild plants can be found on woodland margins (*Crassulaceae*)

hymen-
Used in compound words to denote membranous

hymenanthus
hy-men-AN-thus
hymenantha, hymenanthum
With flowers with a membrane, as in *Trichopilia hymenantha*

Hymenocallis [2]
hy-men-OK-uh-lis
From Greek *hymen* meaning 'membrane' and *kallis* meaning 'beauty', for the membranous corona in the centre of the flower (*Amaryllidaceae*)

hymenorrhizus
hy-men-oh-RY-zus
hymenorrhiza, hymenorrhizum
With membranous roots, as in *Allium hymenorrhizum*

hymenosepalus
hy-men-no-SEP-uh-lus
hymenosepala, hymenosepalum
With membranous sepals, as in *Rumex hymenosepalus*

Hymenosporum
hy-men-oh-SPORE-um
From Greek *hymen* meaning 'membrane' and *spora* meaning 'seed', as the seeds have membranous wings (*Pittosporaceae*)

Hymenoxys
hy-men-OX-is
From Greek *hymen* meaning 'membrane' and *oxys* meaning 'sharp', as the scales surrounding each flower are sharp-tipped (*Asteraceae*)

Hyophorbe
hy-oh-FOR-bee
From Greek *hyos* meaning 'swine' and *phorba* meaning 'food', as the fruits were fed to pigs (*Arecaceae*)

1

Eranthis hyemalis,
winter aconite

2

Hymenocallis littoralis,
beach spider lily

3

Hypericum perforatum,
perforate St. John's wort

Hyoscyamus

hy-oh-SY-ah-mus

From Greek *hyos* meaning 'swine' and *kyamos* meaning 'bean'; this is henbane (*H. niger*), which is poisonous to humans, but supposedly not to pigs (*Solanaceae*)

hyperboreus

hy-puh-BOR-ee-us

hyperborea, hyperboreum

Connected with the far north, as in *Sparganium hyperboreum*

hypericifolius

hy-PER-ee-see-FOH-lee-us

hypericifolia, hypericifolium

With leaves like St John's wort (*Hypericum*), as in *Melalaeuca hypericifolia*

hypericoides

hy-per-ih-KOY-deez

Resembling *Hypericum*, as in *Ascyrum hypericoides*

Hypericum [3]

hy-PER-ik-um

From Greek *hyper* meaning 'above' and *eikon* meaning 'icon', as the plant was often hung above religious figures (*Hypericaceae*)

hypnoides

hip-NO-deez

Resembling moss, as in *Saxifraga hypnoides*

hypo-

Used in compound words to denote under

Hypocalymma

hy-poh-ka-LIM-uh

From Greek *hypo* meaning 'under' and *kalymma* meaning 'veil', as the calyx forms a cap over the flower bud (*Myrtaceae*)

Hypochaeris

hy-poh-KEER-is

From Greek *hypo* meaning 'under' and *choiras* meaning 'pig', suggesting that swine consume the roots, though the name may also derive from *kharieis* meaning 'beauty' (*Asteraceae*)

hypochondriacus

hy-po-kon-dree-AH-kus

hypochondriaca, hypochondriacum

With a melancholy appearance; with dull-coloured flowers, as in *Amaranthus hypochondriacus*

Hypoestes

hy-poh-ES-teez

From Greek *hypo* meaning 'below' and *estia* meaning 'house', an allusion to the flowers, which emerge from within several bracts (*Acanthaceae*)

hypogaeus

hy-poh-JEE-us

hypogaea, hypogaeum

Underground; developing in the earth, as in *Copiapoa hypogaea*

hypoglaucus

hy-poh-GLAW-kus

hypoglauca, hypoglaucum

Glaucous underneath, as in *Cissus hypoglauca*

hypoglottis

hh-poh-GLOT-tis

Underside of the tongue, from the shape of the pods, as in *Astragalus hypoglottis*

hypoleucus

hy-poh-LOO-kus

hypoleuca, hypoleucum

White underneath, as in *Centaurea hypoleuca*

hypophyllus

hy-poh-FIL-us

hypophylla, hypophyllum

Underneath the leaf, as in *Ruscus hypophyllum*

hypopitys

hi-po-PY-tees

Growing under pines, as in *Monotropa hypopitys*

Hypoxis

hy-POKS-iss

From Greek *hypo* meaning 'below' and *oxys* meaning 'sharp', a reference to the fruiting capsules, which have a pointed base (*Hypoxidaceae*)

hyrcanus

hyr-KAH-nus

hyrcana, hyrcanum

Connected with the region of the Caspian Sea (Hyrcania in antiquity), as in *Hedysarum hyrcanum*

hyssopifolius

hiss-sop-ih-FOH-lee-us

hyssopifolia, hyssopifolium

With leaves like hyssop (*Hyssopus*), as in *Cuphea hyssopifolia*

Hyssopus

his-OP-us

Classical Greek name for an aromatic herb (*Lamiaceae*)

hystrix

HIS-triks

Bristly; like a porcupine, as in *Colletia hystrix*

TAXONOMIC SHORTCUTS

Pity the poor taxonomist who's obliged to create Latin names for every new plant discovered. One useful shortcut is to incorporate the name of an existing genus, an approach especially common in cacti. By adding a descriptor to *Opuntia*, *Cereus* and *Cactus*, new genera are easily created, including *Cylindropuntia*, *Brasiliopuntia*, *Pachycereus*, *Stenocereus*, *Echinocactus* and *Ferocactus*. It's an approach not restricted to cacti. In palms, *Phoenix* and *Thrinax* are popular (*Archontophoenix*, *Coccothrinax*), while in myrtles, it's *Myrtus* (*Amomyrtus*, *Lophomyrtus*). These portmanteau names suggest some similarity between the plants, though not always close relationships.

ibericus

eye-BEER-ih-kus

iberica, ibericum

Connected with Iberia (Spain and Portugal), as in *Geranium ibericum*

iberidifolius

eye-beer-id-ih-FOH-lee-us

iberidifolia, iberidifolium

With leaves that resemble *Iberis*, as in *Brachyscome iberidifolia*

Iberis

AY-ber-is

From Greek *Iberes* meaning 'of Iberia', as several species come from Spain (*Brassicaceae*)

Ibervillea

ay-ber-VILL-ee-uh

Possibly named after Iberville Parish, Louisiana, USA, as the type species was collected in that state (*Cucurbitaceae*)

Ichtyoselmis

ik-tee-oh-SEL-mis

From Greek *ichthys* meaning 'fish' and *selmis* meaning 'fishing line', as the flowers look like fish hooked on a line (*Papaveraceae*)

icos-

Used in compound words to denote twenty

icosandrus

eye-koh-SAN-drus

icosandra, icosandrum

With twenty stamens, as in *Phytolacca icosandra*

idaeus

eye-DAY-ee-us

idaea, idaeum

Connected with Mount Ida, Crete, as in *Rubus idaeus*

Idesia

ay-DEE-see-uh

Named after Eberhard Ysbrants Ides (1657–1708), Dutch diplomat and explorer (*Salicaceae*)

ignescens

ig-NES-enz

—

igneus

ig-NE-us

ignea, igneum

Fiery red, as in *Cuphea ignea*

ikariae

eye-KAY-ree-ay

Of the island of Ikaria, in the Aegean Sea, as in *Galanthus ikariae*

Ilex (also ilex)

AY-leks

From the classical Latin name *ilex* for holm oak (*Quercus ilex*), as both are evergreen trees with spiny leaves (*Aquifoliaceae*)

ilicifolius

il-liss-ee-FOH-lee-us

ilicifolia, ilicifolium

With leaves like holly (*Ilex*), as in *Itea ilicifolia*

illecebrosus

il-lee-see-BROH-sus

illecebrosa, illecebrosum

Enticing; charming, as in *Tigridia illecebrosa*

Illicium

i-LISS-ee-um

From Latin *illicere* meaning 'to allure', an allusion to the scented flowers and foliage (*Schisandraceae*)

GENUS SPOTLIGHT

Ilex

The holly genus *Ilex* is often incorporated into other Latin names to indicate that a plant has spiny, holly-like leaves, as in *Itea ilicifolia* and *Olearia ilicifolia*. Somewhat ironic as hollies were named *Ilex* due to their similarity to the spiny leaves of holm oak (*Quercus ilex*). Furthermore, most hollies don't have the traditional spiny leaves you find in English (*I. aquifolium*) or American (*I. opaca*) holly. And even in these species, not all of the leaves are spiny. As hollies mature, leaves near the top of the tree are often spine-free – why waste energy forming spines when no herbivore can reach them?

Ilex aquifolium,
common holly

Gladiolus imbricatus,
Turkish marsh gladiolus

Impatiens balsamina,
rose balsam

Imperata cylindrica,
cogon grass

illinitus
il-lin-EYE-tus
illinita, illinitum
Smeared; smirched, as in *Escallonia illinita*

illinoinensis
il-ih-no-in-EN-sis
illinoinensis, illinoinense
From Illinois, USA, as in *Carya illinoinensis*

illustris
il-LUS-tris
illustris, illustre
Brilliant; lustrous, as in *Amsonia illustris*

illyricus
il-LEER-ih-kus
illyrica, illyricum
Connected with Illyria, the name for an area of the western Balkan
Peninsula in antiquity, as in *Gladiolus illyricus*

ilvensis
il-VEN-sis
ilvensis, ilvense
Of Elba, Italy, or the River Elbe, as in *Woodsia ilvensis*

imberbis
IM-ber-bis
imberbis, imberbe
Without spines or beard, as in *Rhododendron imberbe*

imbricans
IM-brih-KANS
—

imbricatus [1]
IM-brih-KA-tus
imbricata, imbricatum
With elements that overlap in a regular pattern, as in *Gladiolus
imbricatus*

immaculatus
im-mak-yoo-LAH-tus
immaculata, immaculatum
Spotless, as in *Aloe immaculata*

immersus
im-MER-sus
immersa, immersum
Growing under water, as in *Pleurothallis immersa*

Impatiens [2]
im-PAT-ee-enz, im-PAY-shunz
From Latin *impatiens* meaning 'impatient', as the ripe fruits suddenly
burst open (*Balsaminaceae*)

Imperata [3]
im-puh-RAH-tuh
Named after Ferrante Imperato (1550–1625), Italian apothecary
(*Poaceae*)

imperialis
im-peer-ee-AH-lis
imperialis, imperiale
Very fine; showy, as in *Fritillaria imperialis*

Dactylorhiza incarnata,
early marsh-orchid

Narcissus incomparabilis,
nonesuch daffodil

implexus
im-PLECK-sus
implexa, implexum
Tangled, as in *Kleinia implexa*

impressus
im-PRESS-us
impressa, impressum
With impressed or sunken surfaces, as in *Ceanothus impressus*

inaequalis
in-ee-KWA-lis
inaequalis, inaequale
Unequal, as in *Geissorhiza inaequalis*

incanus
in-KAN-nus
incana, incanum
Grey, as in *Geranium incanum*

incarnatus [4]
in-kar-NAH-tus
incarnata, incarnatum
The colour of flesh, as in *Dactylorhiza incarnata*

Incarvillea
in-kar-VILL-ee-uh
Named after Pierre Nicolas Le Chéron d'Incarville (1706–57),
French missionary and botanist (*Bignoniaceae*)

incertus
in-KER-tus
incerta, incertum
Doubtful; uncertain, as in *Draba incerta*

incisus
in-KYE-sus
incisa, incisum
With deeply cut and irregular incisions, as in *Prunus incisa*

inclaudens
in-KLAW-denz
Not closing, as in *Erepsia inclaudens*

inclinatus
in-klin-AH-tus
inclinata, inclinatum
Bent downwards, as in *Moraea inclinata*

incomparabilis [5]
in-kom-par-RAH-bih-lis
incomparabilis, incomparabile
Incomparable, as in *Narcissus* × *incomparabilis*

incomptus
in-KOMP-tus
incompta, incomptum
Without adornment, as in *Verbena incompta*

inconspicuus
in-kon-SPIK-yoo-us
inconspicua, inconspicuum
Inconspicuous, as in *Hoya inconspicua*

Masdevallia infracta,
crooked masdevallia

incrassatus
in-kras-SAH-tus
incrassata, incrassatum
Thickened, as in *Leucocoryne incrassata*

incurvatus
in-ker-VAH-tus
incurvata, incurvatum
—

incurvus
in-ker-VUS
incurva, incurvum
Bent inwards, as in *Carex incurva*

indicus
IN-dih-kus
indica, indicum
Connected with India; may also apply to plants originating from the East Indies or China, as in *Lagerstroemia indica*

Indigofera
in-di-GOF-er-uh
From Latin *indigo*, a blue dye, and *fera* meaning 'to bear', as this important commercial dye was extracted from *I. tinctoria* and a few other species (*Fabaceae*)

indivisus
in-dee-VEE-sus
indivisa, indivisum
Without divisions, as in *Cordyline indivisa*

Indocalamus
in-doh-KAL-uh-mus
From Latin *Indos* meaning 'the Indies' and Greek *kalamos*, a reed; this bamboo genus occurs primarily in China, reaching into Indochina (*Poaceae*)

induratus
in-doo-RAH-tus
indurata, induratum
Hard, as in *Cotoneaster induratus*

inebrians
in-ee-BRI-enz
Intoxicating, as in *Ribes inebrians*

inermis
IN-er-mis
inermis, inerme
Without arms, e.g. without prickles, as in *Acaena inermis*

infaustus
in-FUS-tus
infausta, infaustum
Unfortunate (sometimes therefore used of poisonous plants), unlucky, as in *Colletia infausta*

infectorius
in-fek-TOR-ee-us
infectoria, infectorium
Dyed; coloured, as in *Quercus infectoria*

infestus
in-FES-tus
infesta, infestum
Dangerous; troublesome, as in *Melilotus infestus*

inflatus
in-FLAH-tus
inflata, inflatum
Swollen up, as in *Codonopsis inflata*

infortunatus
in-for-tu-NAH-tus
infortunata, infortunatum
Unfortunate (of poisonous plants), as in *Clerodendrum infortunatum*

infractus
in-FRAC-tus
infracta, infractum
Curving inwards, as in *Masdevallia infracta*

infundibuliformis
in-fun-dih-bew-LEE-for-mis
infundibuliformis, infundibuliforme
In the shape of a funnel or trumpet, as in *Crossandra infundibuliformis*

infundibulus
in-fun-DIB-yoo-lus
infundibula, infundibulum
A funnel, as in *Dendrobium infundibulum*

ingens
IN-genz
Enormous, as in *Tulipa ingens*

inodorus
in-oh-DOR-us
inodora, inodorum
Without scent, as in *Hypericum × inodorum*

inornatus
in-or-NAH-tus
inornata, inornatum
Without ornament, as in *Boronia inornata*

inquinans
in-KWIN-anz
Polluted; stained; defiled, as in *Pelargonium inquinans*

insignis
in-SIG-nis
insignis, insigne
Distinguished; remarkable, as in *Rhododendron insigne*

insititius
in-si-tih-TEE-us
insititia, insititium
Grafted, as in *Prunus insititia*

insulanus
in-su-LAH-nus
insulana, insulanum
—

insularis
in-soo-LAH-ris
insularis, insulare
Relating to an island, as in *Tilia insularis*

integer
IN-teg-er
integra, integrum
Entire, as in *Cyananthus integer*

integrifolius
in-teg-ree-FOH-lee-us
integrifolia, integrifolium
With leaves that are complete, uncut, as in *Meconopsis integrifolia*

intermedius
in-ter-MEE-dee-us
intermedia, intermedium
Intermediate in colour, form or habit, as in *Forsythia × intermedia*

interruptus
in-ter-UP-tus
interrupta, interruptum
Interrupted; not continuous, as in *Bromus interruptus*

intertextus
in-ter-TEKS-tus
intertexta, intertextum
Intertwined, as in *Matucana intertexta*

intortus
in-TOR-tus
intorta, intortum
Twisted, as in *Melocactus intortus*

intricatus

in-tree-KAH-tus

intricata, intricatum

Tangled, as in *Asparagus intricatus*

intumescens

in-tu-MES-enz

Swollen, as in *Carex intumescens*

intybaceus

in-tee-BAK-ee-us

intybacea, intybaceum

Like chicory (*Cichorium intybus*), as in *Hieracium intybaceum*

Inula

IN-ew-luh

From Greek *inaein* meaning 'to clean', an allusion to medicinal properties (*Asteraceae*)

inversus

in-VERS-us

inversa, inversum

Turned over, as in *Quaqua inversa*

involucratus

in-vol-yoo-KRAH-tus

involucrata, involucratum

With a ring of bracts surrounding several flowers, as in *Cyperus involucratus*

involutus

in-vol-YOO-tus

involuta, involutum

Rolled inwards, as in *Gladiolus involutus*

Iochroma

eye-oh-KRO-muh

From Greek *ios* meaning 'violet' and *chroma* meaning 'colour', as some species have violet-coloured flowers (*Solanaceae*)

ioensis

eye-oh-EN-sis

ioensis, ioense

From Iowa, USA, as in *Malus ioensis*

ionanthus

eye-oh-NAN-thus

ionantha, ionanthum

With violet-coloured flowers, as in *Saintpaulia ionantha*

ionopterus

eye-on-OP-ter-us

ionoptera, ionopterum

With violet wings, as in *Koellensteinia ionoptera*

Ipomoea

eye-poh-MEE-uh

From Greek *ipos* meaning 'worm' and *homoios* meaning 'resembling', alluding to the twining stems (*Convolvulaceae*)

Ipomopsis

eye-poh-MOP-sis

Resembling the genus *Ipomoea* (*Polemoniaceae*)

Iresine

eye-ri-SEE-nee

From Greek *eiresione* meaning 'a staff wrapped in wool', as in some species there are woolly hairs on the sepals surrounding the flowers (*Amaranthaceae*)

iridescens

ir-id-ES-enz

Iridescent, as in *Phyllostachys iridescens*

iridiflorus

ir-id-uh-FLOR-us

iridiflora, iridiflorum

With flowers like *Iris*, as in *Canna iridiflora*

iridifolius

ir-id-ih-FOH-lee-us

iridifolia, iridifolium

With leaves like *Iris*, as in *Billbergia iridifolia*

iridioides

ir-id-ee-OY-deez

Resembling *Iris*, as in *Dietes iridioides*

Iris [1]

EYE-ris

Named after the Greek goddess of the rainbow, as the flowers are colourful (*Iridaceae*)

irregularis

ir-reg-yoo-LAH-ris

irregularis, irregulare

With parts of different sizes, as in *Primula irregularis*

irriguus

ir-EE-gyoo-us

irrigua, irriguum

Watered, as in *Pratia irrigua*

Isatis

eye-SAH-tis

From Greek *isatis*, a dye plant, as *I. tinctoria* (woad) gives a blue dye (*Brassicaceae*)

1

Iris japonica, **fringed iris**

Arum italicum,
Italian arum

Ixora coccinea,
flame of the woods

Isolepis
eye-so-LEP-is
From Greek *isos* meaning 'equal' and *lepis* meaning 'scale', as the glumes in the inflorescence are all of similar size (*Cyperaceae*)

isophyllus
eye-so-FIL-us
isophylla, isophyllum
With leaves of the same size, as in *Penstemon isophyllus*

Isopogon
eye-soh-POH-gon
From Greek *isos* meaning 'equal' and *pogon* meaning 'beard', in reference to the fringed flowers or because some species have hairy fruits (*Proteaceae*)

Isopyrum
eye-soh-PY-rum
From Greek *isos* meaning 'equal' and *pyros* meaning 'wheat', an allusion to the grain-like fruits (*Ranunculaceae*)

Isotoma
eye-soh-TOH-muh
From Greek *isos* meaning 'equal' and *tome* meaning 'division', as the petal tubes are divided into sections of similar size (*Campanulaceae*)

italicus [2]
ee-TAL-ih-kus
italica, italicum
Connected with Italy, as in *Arum italicum*

Itea
eye-TEE-uh
From Greek *itea* meaning 'willow', as some species have willowy leaves (*Iteaceae*)

Ixia
IKS-ee-uh
From Greek *ixos* meaning 'mistletoe', a plant with sticky berries and a reference to the viscid sap of some *Ixia*; an alternative etymology is Greek *ixias* meaning 'chameleon', as this genus produces so many different flower colours (*Iridaceae*)

ixioides
iks-ee-OY-deez
Resembling corn lily (*Ixia*), as in *Libertia ixioides*

Ixiolirion
iks-ee-oh-LIR-ee-on
From *Ixia*, another genus, and Greek *lirion* meaning 'lily' (*Ixioliriaceae*)

ixocarpus
iks-so-KAR-pus
ixocarpa, ixocarpum
With sticky fruit, as in *Physalis ixocarpa*

Ixora [3]
iks-OR-uh
From Sanskrit *isvara* meaning 'ruler' or 'lord', perhaps from the use of the flowers in Hindu ceremonies (*Rubiaceae*)

Jaborosa

jab-uh-ROH-suh

From Arabic *jaborose*, vernacular name for mandrake (*Mandragora*), a plant in the same family (*Solanaceae*)

Jacaranda [1]

jah-kur-AN-duh

From a Guarani (Brazil) meaning 'fragrant', converted to Latin via Portuguese (*Bignoniaceae*)

jackii

JAK-ee-eye

Named after John George Jack (1861–1949), a Canadian dendrologist at the Arnold Arboretum, Boston, USA, as in *Populus × jackii*

Jacobaea

jak-oh-BEE-uh

Named after Saint James, as *J. vulgaris* flowers on or around his feast day (*Asteraceae*)

jacobaeus

jak-oh-BAY-ee-us

jacobaea, jacobaeum

Named for St James, or for Santiago (Cape Verde), as in *Senecio jacobaea*

Jacquemontia

jak-uh-MON-tee-uh

Named after Victor Jacquemont (1801–32), French botanist and geologist (*Convolvulaceae*)

jalapa [2]

juh-LAP-a

Connected with Xalapa, Mexico, as in *Mirabilis jalapa*

jamaicensis

ja-may-KEN-sis

jamaicensis, jamaicense

From Jamaica, as in *Brunfelsia jamaicensis*

Jamesbrittenia

james-bri-TEEN-ee-uh

Named after James Britten (1846–1924), British botanist (*Scrophulariaceae*)

Jamesia

JAME-zee-uh

Named after Edwin P. James (1797–1861), American physician, geologist and naturalist (*Hydrangeaceae*)

japonicus

juh-PON-ih-kus

japonica, japonicum

Connected with Japan, as in *Cryptomeria japonica*

Jasione

jaz-ee-OH-nee

From Greek *jasione*, the meaning of which is unclear, though it may refer to a *Campanula* or *Convolvulus* (*Campanulaceae*)

jasmineus

jaz-MIN-ee-us

jasminea, jasmineum

Like jasmine (*Jasminum*), as in *Daphne jasminea*

1

Jacaranda puberula,
caroba

2

Mirabilis jalapa,
four o'clock flower

Jasminum

The word 'jasmine' evokes two images, a vigorous flowering vine and a sweetly scented flower, which is why the name is so common in both Latin and English plant names. True jasmines belong to the genus *Jasminum* and while many are vines with fragrant blooms, both shrubby (e.g. *J. parkeri*) and unscented (e.g. *J. nudiflorum*) species occur. Outside *Jasminum*, other climbing jasmines can be found in *Trachelospermum* (Star jasmine), *Stephanotis* (Madagascar jasmine) and *Gelsemium* (Carolina jessamine), while *Gardenia jasminoides* and *Rhododendron jasminiflorum* are both non-climbing shrubs with scented flowers.

1

Jasminum didymum,
coastal jasmine

jasminiflorus
jaz-min-IH-flor-us
jasminiflora, jasminiflorum
With flowers like jasmine (*Jasminum*), as in *Rhododendron jasminiflorum*

jasminoides
jaz-min-OY-deez
Resembling jasmine (*Jasminum*), as in *Trachelospermum jasminoides*

Jasminum [1]
JAZ-min-um
From Persian-Farsi *yasamin*, meaning 'gift from God', and now the name of the plant (*Oleaceae*)

Jatropha
juh-TRO-fuh
From Greek *iatros* meaning 'doctor' and *trophe* meaning 'food', as the seeds of *J. curcas* (physic-nut) were a popular purgative (*Euphorbiaceae*)

javanicus
juh-VAHN-ih-kus
javanica, javanicum
Connected with Java, as in *Rhododendron javanicum*

Jeffersonia
jef-ur-SOH-nee-uh
Named after Thomas Jefferson (1743–1826), third president of the United States (*Berberidaceae*)

jejunus
jeh-JOO-nus
jejuna, jejunum
Small, as in *Eria jejuna*

Jovellana
joh-vuh-LAH-nuh
Named after Gaspar Melchor de Jovellanos (1744–1811), Spanish politician and author (*Calceolariaceae*)

Jovibarba
joh-vee-BAR-buh
From Latin *Jovis* meaning 'Jupiter' and *barba* meaning 'beard', an allusion to the fringed petals (*Crassulaceae*)

Juanulloa
wan-oo-LOH-uh
Named after Jorge Juan y Santacilia (1713–73) and Antonio Ulloa y de la Torre-Giral (1716–95), Spanish scientists and explorers (*Solanaceae*)

Jubaea
joo-BEE-uh
Named after Juba II, King of Numidia and Mauretania (c. 52 BC–AD 23), patron of the arts and sciences (*Arecaceae*)

Juniperus communis,
common juniper

3

Juglans cinerea,
butternut

jubatus

joo-BAH-tus

jubata, jubatum

With awns, as in *Cortaderia jubata*

jucundus

joo-KUN-dus

jucunda, jucundum

Agreeable; pleasing, as in *Osteospermum jucundum*

jugalis

joo-GAH-lis

jugalis, jugale

—

jugosus

joo-GOH-sus

jugosa, jugosum

Yoked, as in *Pabstia jugosa*

Juglans [3]

JUG-lunz

From classical Latin name for walnut, *J. regia*, meaning 'Jupiter's nut' (*Juglandaceae*)

julaceus

joo-LA-see-us

julacea, julaceum

With catkins, as in *Leucodon julaceus*

junceus

JUN-kee-us

juncea, junceum

Like a rush, as in *Spartium junceum*

Juncus

JUN-kus

From classical Latin name for rush, deriving from a word meaning 'to bind', as the leaves were used to make rope, etc. (*Juncaceae*)

juniperifolius

joo-nip-er-ih-FOH-lee-us

juniperifolia, juniperifolium

With leaves like a juniper (*Juniperus*), as in *Armeria juniperifolia*

juniperinus

joo-nip-er-EE-nus

juniperina, juniperinum

Like a juniper (*Juniperus*); blue-black, as in *Grevillea juniperina*

Juniperus [2]

joo-NIP-er-us

From classical Latin name for juniper, originating in Latin *junis* meaning 'youth' and *pario* meaning 'to birth'; etymologies include the evergreen foliage, the production of new berries while old ones remain on the tree, or Jupiter the father (Jovis-pater), as the plant was used in religious ceremonies (*Cupressaceae*)

Justicia

just-ISH-ee-uh

Named after James Justice (1698–1763), Scottish horticulturist (*Acanthaceae*)

juvenilis

joo-VEE-nil-is

juvenilis, juvenile

Young, as in *Draba juvenilis*

Kalanchoe flammea,
flaming Katy

Kalmia latifolia,
mountain laurel

Kadsura
kad-SOOR-uh
From Japanese vernacular name for *K. japonica* (*Schisandraceae*)

Kalanchoe [1]
kal-an-KOH-ee
From Chinese *kalanchauhuy*, the vernacular name reported by
missionary Georg Joseph Kamel (*Crassulaceae*)

Kalimeris
kal-i-MER-is
From Greek *kallos* meaning 'beautiful' and *meris* meaning 'parts'
(*Asteraceae*)

Kalmia [2]
KAL-me-uh
Named after Pehr Kalm (1716–79), Swedish botanist (*Ericaceae*)

Kalmiopsis
kal-me-OP-sis
Resembling the related genus *Kalmia* (*Ericaceae*)

Kalopanax
kal-oh-PAN-aks
From Greek *kallos* meaning 'beautiful' and *Panax*, a related genus
(*Araliaceae*)

kamtschaticus
kam-SHAY-tih-kus
kamtschatica, kamtschaticum
Connected with Kamchatka, Russia, as in *Sedum kamtschaticum*

kansuensis
kan-soo-EN-sis
kansuensis, kansuense
From Kansu (Gansu), China, as in *Malus kansuensis*

karataviensis
kar-uh-taw-vee-EN-sis
karataviensis, karataviense
From the Karatau mountains, Kazakhstan, as in *Allium karataviense*

kashmirianus
kash-meer-ee-AH-nus
kashmiriana, kashmirianum
Connected with Kashmir, as in *Actaea kashmiriana*

Keckiella
kek-ee-EL-uh
Named after David Daniels Keck (1903–95), American botanist,
plus the diminutive *ella* (*Plantaginaceae*)

Kelseya
KEL-see-uh
Named after Francis Duncan Kelsey (1849–1905), American botanist (*Rosaceae*)

Kennedia [1]
KEN-uh-dee-uh
Named after John Kennedy (1759–1842), Scottish horticulturist (*Fabaceae*)

kermesinus
ker-mes-SEE-nus
kermesina, kermesinum
Crimson, as in *Passiflora kermesina*

Kerria
KER-ee-uh
Named after William Kerr (?–1814), Scottish horticulturist (*Rosaceae*)

Keteleeria
ket-uh-LEER-ee-uh
Named after Jean Baptiste Keteleer (1813–1903), French horticulturist (*Pinaceae*)

kewensis
kew-EN-sis
kewensis, kewense
From Kew Gardens, London, England, as in *Primula kewensis*

Kigelia
ki-JEE-lee-uh
From Mozambican indigenous name *kigeli-keia* (*Bignoniaceae*)

Kirengeshoma [2]
ki-reng-i-SHOH-muh
From Japanese vernacular name, based on *ki* ('yellow'), *renge* ('lotus blossom') and *shoma* ('hat') (*Hydrangeaceae*)

kirkii
KIR-kee-eye
Named after Thomas Kirk (1828–98), renowned botanist of New Zealand flora; or after his son Harry Bower Kirk (1903–44), professor of biology at the University of New Zealand; or after Sir John Kirk (1832–1922), botanist and British Consul to Zanzibar, as in *Coprosma* × *kirkii* (after Thomas Kirk)

Kitaibela
kit-AY-bel-uh
Named after Pál Kitaibel (1757–1817), Hungarian botanist and chemist (*Malvaceae*)

kiusianus
key-oo-see-AH-nus
kiusiana, kiusianum
Connected with Kyushu, Japan, as in *Rhododendron kiusianum*

Kleinia
KLY-nee-uh
Named after Jacob Theodor Klein (1685–1759), German diplomat, historian and scientist (*Asteraceae*)

1

Kennedia carinata,
prostrate clover carpet

2

Kirengeshoma palmata,
yellow wax-bells

Knautia

NAWT-ee-uh
Named after brothers Christian (1659–1716) and Christoph Knaut (1638–94), German physicians and botanists (*Caprifoliaceae*)

Knightia

NITE-ee-uh
Named after Thomas Andrew Knight (1759–1838), British botanist and horticulturist, second president of the RHS (*Proteaceae*)

Kniphofia [3]

ny-FOH-fee-uh
Named after Johann Hieronymus Kniphof (1704–63), German physician and botanist (*Asphodelaceae*)

Koeleria

koh-LEER-ee-uh
Named after Georg Ludwig Koeler (1764–1807), German botanist (*Poaceae*)

Koelreuteria

kol-roy-TEER-ee-uh
Named after Joseph Gottlieb Kölreuter (1733–1806), German botanist (*Sapindaceae*)

Kohleria

koh-LEER-ee-uh
Named after Michael Kohler (dates unknown), Swiss educator (*Gesneriaceae*)

Kolkwitzia

kol-KWITZ-ee-uh
Named after Richard Kolkwitz (1873–1956), German botanist (*Caprifoliaceae*)

koreanus

kor-ee-AH-nus
koreana, koreanum
Connected with Korea, as in *Abies koreana*

Kunzea

KUN-zee-uh
Named after Gustave Kunze (1793–1851), German zoologist and botanist (*Myrtaceae*)

kurdicus

KUR-dih-kus
kurdica, kurdicum
Referring to the Kurdish homeland in western Asia, as in *Astragalus kurdicus*

3

Kniphofia triangularis,
dwarf red-hot poker

labiatus

la-bee-AH-tus

labiata, labiatum

Lipped, as in *Cattleya labiata*

labilis

LA-bih-lis

labilis, labile

Slippery; unstable, as in *Celtis labilis*

labiosus

la-bee-OH-sus

labiosa, labiosum

Lipped, as in *Besleria labiosa*

Lablab

LAB-lab

From Arabic *lablab*, vernacular name for morning glory (*Fabaceae*)

Laburnum [1]

lah-BUR-num

The classical Latin name for this plant (*Fabaceae*)

laburnifolius

lah-bur-nih-FOH-lee-us

laburnifolia, laburnifolium

With leaves like *Laburnum*, as in *Crotalaria laburnifolia*

lacerus

LASS-er-us

lacera, lacerum

Cut into fringe-like sections, as in *Costus lacerus*

Lachenalia

lak-uh-NAY-lee-uh

Named after Werner de Lachenal (1736–1800), Swiss botanist (*Asparagaceae*)

laciniatus

la-sin-ee-AH-tus

laciniata, laciniatum

Divided into narrow sections, as in *Rudbeckia laciniata*

lacrimans

LAK-ri-manz

Weeping, as in *Eucalyptus lacrimans*

lacteus

lak-TEE-us

Milk-white, as in *Cotoneaster lacteus*

lacticolor

lak-tee-KOL-or

Milk-white, as in *Protea lacticolor*

lactiferus

lak-TEE-fer-us

lactifera, lactiferum

Producing a milky sap, as in *Gymnema lactiferum*

lactiflorus

lak-tee-FLOR-us

lactiflora, lactiflorum

With milk-white flowers, as in *Campanula lactiflora*

Lactuca

lak-TOO-kuh

From Latin *lac* meaning 'milk', due to the milky sap (*Asteraceae*)

lacunosus

lah-koo-NOH-sus

lacunosa, lacunosum

With deep holes or pits, as in *Allium lacunosum*

lacustris

lah-KUS-tris

lacustris, lacustre

Relating to lakes, as in *Iris lacustris*

ladaniferus

lad-an-IH-fer-us

ladanifera, ladaniferum

—

ladanifer

lad-an-EE-fer

Producing ladanum, a fragrant gum resin, as in *Cistus ladanifer*

Laelia

LAY-lee-uh

Named after Laelia, one of the Vestal Virgins in ancient Rome, priestesses of the goddess of the hearth (*Orchidaceae*)

laetevirens

lay-tee-VY-renz

Vivid green, as in *Parthenocissus laetevirens*

laetiflorus

lay-tee-FLOR-us

laetiflora, laetiflorum

With bright flowers, as in *Helianthus* × *laetiflorus*

laetus

LEE-tus

laeta, laetum

Bright; vivid, as in *Pseudopanax laetum*

1

Laburnum anagyroides,
common laburnum

laevigatus

lee-vih-GAH-tus

laevigata, laevigatum

—

laevis

LEE-vis

laevis, laeve

Smooth, as in *Crocus laevigatus*

Lagarosiphon

lah-gur-oh-SY-fon

From Greek *lagaros* meaning 'lax' and *siphon* meaning 'tube', probably referring to the long, tubular hypanthium that carries female flowers to the water surface (*Hydrocharitaceae*)

Lagarostrobos

lah-gur-oh-STROH-bus

From Greek *lagaros* meaning 'lax' and *strobilus* meaning 'cone' (*Podocarpaceae*)

Lagerstroemia

lah-guh-STROH-mee-uh

Named after Magnus von Lagerström (c. 1696–1759), Swedish merchant and naturalist (*Lythraceae*)

lagodechianus

lah-go-chee-AH-nus

lagodechiana, lagodechianum

Connected with Lagodekhi, Georgia, as in *Galanthus lagodechianus*

Lagunaria

lah-goo-NAIR-ee-uh

Named after Andrés de Laguna (1499–1559), Spanish botanist and physician (*Malvaceae*)

Lagurus

lag-GOOR-us

From Greek *lagus* meaning 'hare' and *ourus* meaning 'tail', a reference to the shape of the inflorescence (*Poaceae*)

lamellatus

la-mel-LAH-tus

lamellata, lamellatum

Layered, as in *Vanda lamellata*

Lamium

LAY-mee-um

From the classical Latin name for the plant, probably derived from Greek *laimos* meaning 'throat', a reference to the flower shape (*Lamiaceae*)

Lampranthus

lam-PRAN-thus

From Greek *lampros* meaning 'lamp' and *anthos* meaning 'flower', as the blooms are said to shine (*Aizoaceae*)

Lamprocapnos [1]

lam-pro-KAP-nos

From Greek *lampros* meaning 'bright' and *kapnos* meaning 'smoke'; the first part refers to the vivid flowers, while the second is common in members of the family *Fumariaceae* (now subsumed in *Papaveraceae*), which are said to have a smoky smell (*Papaveraceae*)

lanatus

la-NA-tus

lanata, lanatum

Woolly, as in *Lavandula lanata*

lanceolatus

lan-see-oh-LAH-tus

lanceolata, lanceolatum

—

lanceus

lan-SEE-us

lancea, lanceum

In the shape of a spear, as in *Tasmannia lanceolata*

lanigerus

lan-EE-ger-rus

lanigera, lanigerum

—

lanosus

LAN-oh-sus

lanosa, lanosum

lanuginosus

lan-oo-gih-NOH-sus

lanuginosa, lanuginosum

Woolly, as in *Leptospermum lanigerum*

Lantana (also lantana)

lan-TAH-nuh

From Latin name for a viburnum (possibly *V. lantana*), as both genera have similar inflorescences (*Verbenaceae*)

1

Lamprocapnos spectabilis,
bleeding heart

Lapageria
la-puh-JEER-ee-uh
Named after Marie Josèphe Rose Tascher de
La Pagerie (1763–1814), first wife of
Napoléon Bonaparte (*Philesiaceae*)

Lapeirousia
la-pay-ROO-see-uh
Named after Philippe-Isidore Picot de
Lapeyrouse (1744–1818), French naturalist
(*Iridaceae*)

lappa
LAP-ah
A burr (prickly seed case or flower head), as
in *Arctium lappa*

lapponicus
Lap-PON-ih-kus
lapponica, lapponicum
—

lapponum
Lap-PON-num
Connected with Lapland, as in *Salix
lapponum*

Laportea
la-POR-tee-uh
Named after François Louis Nompar de
Caumont La Force, comte de Castelnau
[also known as François Laporte]
(1810–1880), French naturalist (*Urticaceae*)

Lapsana
lap-SAH-nuh
From Greek *lapsanae* meaning 'vegetable',
possibly radish, which has similar leaves
(*Asteraceae*)

Lardizabala
lar-di-ZAB-uh-luh
Named after Miguel de Lardizábal y Uribe
(1744–1824), Spanish-born Mexican
politician (*Lardizabalaceae*)

laricifolius
lah-ris-ih-FOH-lee-us
laricifolia, laricifolium
With leaves like a larch, as in *Penstemon
laricifolius*

laricinus
lar-ih-SEE-nus
laricina, laricinum
Like a larch (*Larix*), as in *Banksia laricina*

2

Lathyrus odoratus,
sweet pea

Larix
LA-riks
The classical Latin name for larch (*Pinaceae*)

lasi-
Used in compound words to denote woolly

lasiandrus
las-ee-AN-drus
lasiandra, lasiandrum
With woolly stamens, as in *Clematis
lasiandra*

lasioglossus
las-ee-oh-GLOSS-us
lasioglossa, lasioglossum
With a rough tongue, as in *Lycaste lasioglossa*

Latania
luh-TAY-nee-uh
From French vernacular name *latanier*, used
in Mauritius (*Arecaceae*)

lateralis
lat-uh-RAH-lis
lateralis, laterale
On the side, as in *Epidendrum laterale*

lateritius
la-ter-ee-TEE-us
lateritia, lateritium
Brick-red, as in *Kalanchoe lateritia*

Lathraea
LATH-ree-uh
From Greek *lathraios* meaning 'hidden', as
this parasitic plant is largely concealed
underground, only emerging to flower
(*Orobanchaceae*)

Lathyrus [2]
LATH-uh-rus
From Greek *lathyros* meaning 'pea'; true peas
belong to the genus *Pisum* (*Fabaceae*)

lati-
Used in compound words to denote broad

latiflorus
lat-ee-FLOR-us
latiflora, latiflorum
With broad flowers, as in *Dendrocalamus
latiflorus*

latifolius
lat-ee-FOH-lee-us
latifolia, latifolium
With broad leaves, as in *Lathyrus latifolius*

latifrons
lat-ee-FRONS
With broad fronds, as in *Encephalartos
latifrons*

latilobus

la-tih-LOH-bus

latiloba, latilobum

With wide lobes, as in *Campanula latiloba*

latispinus

la-tih-SPEE-nus

latispina, latispinum

With wide thorns, as in *Ferocactus latispinus*

laudatus

law-DAH-tus

laudata, laudatum

Worthy of praise, as in *Rubus laudatus*

Laurelia

law-REE-lee-uh

Named for it resemblance to the unrelated genus *Laurus* (*Atherospermataceae*)

Laureliopsis

law-ree-lee-OP-sis

Resembling the related genus *Laurelia* (*Atherospermataceae*)

laurifolius

law-ree-FOH-lee-us

laurifolia, laurifolium

With leaves like bay (*Laurus*), as in *Cistus laurifolius*

laurinus

law-REE-nus

laurina, laurinum

Like a laurel or bay tree (*Laurus*), as in *Hakea laurina*

laurocerasus

law-roh-KER-uh-sus

From the Latin for cherry and laurel, as in *Prunus laurocerasus*

Laurus

LAW-rus

The classical Latin name for laurel, *L. nobilis* (*Lauraceae*)

Lavandula

la-VAN-dew-luh

From Latin *lavare* meaning 'to wash', as often used in soaps (*Lamiaceae*)

lavandulaceus

la-van-dew-LAY-see-us

lavandulacea, lavandulaceum

Like lavender (*Lavandula*), as in *Chirita lavandulacea*

lavandulifolius

la-van-dew-lih-FOH-lee-us

lavandulifolia, lavandulifolium

With leaves like lavender (*Lavandula*), as in *Salvia lavandulifolia*

Lavatera

la-vuh-TEAR-uh

Named after brothers Johann Heinrich (c. 1611–91) and Johann Jacob Lavater (1594–1636), Swiss physicians and naturalists (*Malvaceae*)

Lawsonia

law-SOH-nee-uh

Named after Isaac Lawson (?–1747), Scottish physician (*Lythraceae*)

laxiflorus

laks-ih-FLO-rus

laxiflora, laxiflorum

With loose, open flowers, as in *Lobelia laxiflora*

laxifolius

laks-ih-FOH-lee-us

laxifolia, laxifolium

With loose, open leaves, as in *Athrotaxis laxifolia*

laxus

LAKS-us

laxa, laxum

Loose; open, as in *Freesia laxa*

Ledebouria

le-duh-BORE-ee-uh

Named after Carl Friedrich von Ledebour (1785–1851), German-Estonian botanist (*Asparagaceae*)

ledifolius

lee-di-FOH-lee-us

ledifolia, ledifolium

With leaves like *Ledum*, as in *Ozothamnus ledifolius*

Leea

LEE-uh

Named after James Lee (1715–95), Scottish horticulturist (*Vitaceae*)

Legousia

luh-GOO-see-uh

Named after Bénigne Le Gouz de Gerland (1695–1774), French academic (*Campanulaceae*)

leianthus

lee-AN-thus

leiantha, leianthum

With smooth flowers, as in *Bouvardia leiantha*

leichtlinii

leekt-LIN-ee-eye

Named after Max Leichtlin (1831–1910), German plant collector from Baden-Baden, Germany, as in *Camassia leichtlinii*

leiocarpus

lee-oh-KAR-pus

leiocarpa, leiocarpum

With smooth fruit, as in *Cytisus leiocarpus*

leiophyllus

lay-oh-FIL-us

leiophylla, leiophyllum

With smooth leaves, as in *Pinus leiophylla*

Lemna

LEM-nuh

From Greek name for a water plant, possibly *Callitriche verna*, which can resemble duckweed (*Araceae*)

Lens

LENZ

From Latin *lenticula* meaning 'lens', to which lentils (*L. culinaris*) resemble (*Fabaceae*)

lentiginosus

len-tig-ih-NOH-sus

lentiginosa, lentiginosum

With freckles, as in *Coelogyne lentiginosa*

lentus

LEN-tus

lenta, lentum

Tough but flexible, as in *Betula lenta*

leonis

le-ON-is

With the colour of, or teeth like, a lion, as in *Angraecum leonis*

Leonotis

lee-oh-NOH-tis

From Greek *leon* meaning 'lion' and *otis* meaning 'ear', which the petals are said to resemble (*Lamiaceae*)

Lavatera phoenicea,
Canary shrub mallow

Leontodon saxatilis,
lesser hawkbit

Leontopodium alpinum,
edelweiss

Leontice
lee-on-TY-kee
From Greek *leontike*, a vernacular name for an unknown plant, often translated as 'lion's foot' (*Berberidaceae*)

Leontodon [1]
lee-ON-toh-don
From Greek *leon* meaning 'lion' and *odons* meaning 'tooth'; the leaf margins are deeply toothed (*Asteraceae*)

leontoglossus
lee-on-toh-GLOSS-us
leontoglossa, leontoglossum
With a throat or tongue of a lion, as in *Masdevallia leontoglossa*

Leontopodium [2]
lee-on-toh-POH-dee-um
From Greek *leon* meaning 'lion' and *podion* meaning 'foot', as the inflorescence with its woolly bracts supposedly resembles a paw (*Asteraceae*)

leonurus
lee-ON-or-us
leonura, leonurum
Like a lion's tail, as in *Leonotis leonurus*

leopardinus
leh-par-DEE-nus
leopardina, leopardinum
With spots like a leopard, as in *Calathea leopardina*

Lepidium
le-PID-ee-um
From Greek *lepidion* meaning 'little scale', as the fruits are small and circular (*Brassicaceae*)

Lepidozamia
le-pid-oh-ZAY-mee-uh
From Greek *lepis* meaning 'scale' and *Zamia*, a related genus, as the trunk is covered in scale-like leaf bases (*Zamiaceae*)

lepidus
le-PID-us
lepida, lepidum
Graceful; elegant, as in *Lupinus lepidus*

lept-
Used in compound words to denote thin or slender

leptanthus
lep-TAN-thus
leptantha, leptanthum
With slender flowers, as in *Colchicum leptanthum*

Leptinella
lep-tin-EL-uh
From Greek *leptos* meaning 'slender', referring to the narrow ovary (*Asteraceae*)

leptocaulis
lep-toh-KAW-lis
leptocaulis, leptocaule
With thin stems, as in *Cylindropuntia leptocaulis*

leptocladus
lep-toh-KLAD-us
leptoclada, leptocladum
With thin branches, as in *Acacia leptoclada*

Leptospermum scoparium,
manuka

4

Leucanthemum vulgare,
ox-eye daisy

leptophyllus
lep-toh-FIL-us
leptophylla, leptophyllum
With thin leaves, as in *Cassinia leptophylla*

leptopus
LEP-toh-pus
With thin stalks, as in *Antigonon leptopus*

leptosepalus
lep-toh-SEP-a-lus
leptosepala, leptosepalum
With thin sepals, as in *Caltha leptosepala*

Leptospermum [3]
lep-toh-SPER-mum
From Greek *leptos* meaning 'slender' and *sperma* meaning 'seed', alluding to the filamentous seed (*Myrtaceae*)

leptostachys
lep-toh-STAH-kus
With slender spikes, as in *Aponogeton leptostachys*

Leschenaultia
lesh-uh-NAWL-tee-uh
Named after Jean-Baptiste Louis Claude Théodore Leschenault de La Tour (1773–1826), French botanist and ornithologist (*Goodeniaceae*)

Lespedeza
les-puh-DEE-zuh
Named after Vicente Manuel de Céspedes y Velasco (c. 1721–94), Spanish governor of East Florida (*Fabaceae*)

leuc-
Used in compound words to denote white

Leucadendron
lew-kuh-DEN-dron
From Greek *leukos* meaning 'white' and *dendron* meaning 'tree', due to the foliage that is covered in silvery silky hairs (*Proteaceae*)

Leucanthemum [4]
lew-KANTH-uh-mum
From Greek *leukos* meaning 'white' and *anthemon* meaning 'flower', as the inflorescences have white rays (*Asteraceae*)

leucanthus
loo-KAN-thus
leucantha, leucanthum
With white flowers, as in *Tulbaghia leucantha*

Leuchtenbergia
looch-ten-BURG-ee-uh
Named after Maximilian Joseph Eugene Auguste Napoleon de Beauharnais, 3rd Duke of Leuchtenberg (1817–52), Bavarian nobleman (*Cactaceae*)

leucocephalus
loo-koh-SEF-uh-lus
leucocephala, leucocephalum
With a white head, as in *Leucaena leucocephala*

leucochilus
loo-KOH-ky-lus
leucochila, leucochilum
With white lips, as in *Oncidium leucochila*

Leucocoryne
loo-koh-kor-AY-nee
From Greek *leukos* meaning 'white' and *koryne* meaning 'club', an allusion to the three sterile anthers (*Amaryllidaceae*)

leucodermis
loo-koh-DER-mis
leucodermis, leucoderme
With white skin, as in *Pinus leucodermis*

Leucogenes
loo-KOJ-en-eez
From Greek *leukos* meaning 'white'; variously interpreted as 'white genus' or 'generating white' or 'white noble', the latter an allusion to the similar-looking edelweiss (*Leontopodium*), a German name meaning 'noble white' (*Asteraceae*)

Leucojum [1]
loo-KOH-jum
From Greek *leucoion* meaning 'white violet', a name applied perhaps to *Matthiola incana* or *Galanthus*; the flowers are white and smell of violets (*Amaryllidaceae*)

leuconeurus
loo-koh-NOOR-us
leuconeura, leuconeurum
With white nerves, as in *Maranta leuconeura*

leucophaeus
loo-koh-FAY-us
leucophaea, leucophaeum
Dusky white, as in *Dianthus leucophaeus*

leucophyllus
loo-koh-FIL-us
leucophylla, leucophyllum
With white leaves, as in *Sarracenia leucophylla*

Leucopogon
loo-koh-POH-gon
From Greek *leukos* meaning 'white' and *pogon* meaning 'beard', named for the typically white, bearded petals (*Ericaceae*)

leucorhizus
loo-koh-RYE-zus
leucorhiza, leucorhizum
With white roots, as in *Curcuma leucorhiza*

Leucosceptrum
loo-koh-SEP-trum
From Greek *leukos* meaning 'white' and *skeptron* meaning 'rod/staff', referring to the white, sceptre-like inflorescence (*Lamiaceae*)

Leucospermum
loo-koh-SPER-mum
From Greek *leukos* meaning 'white' and *sperma* meaning 'seed', alluding to the white covering of the seed, an elaiosome (*Proteaceae*)

Leucothoe
loo-KOTH-oh-ee
Named for Leucothoe of Greek mythology, who was buried alive by her father, the King of Babylon, then transformed into a shrub by the sun god Helios (*Ericaceae*)

leucoxanthus
loo-koh-ZAN-thus
leucoxantha, leucoxanthum
Whitish yellow, as in *Sobralia leucoxantha*

leucoxylon
loo-koh-ZY-lon
With white wood, as in *Eucalyptus leucoxylon*

Levisticum
le-VISS-tik-um
From Latin *levo*, meaning 'to relieve', alluding to medicinal properties; alternatively from Latin *ligusticum apium*, or 'celery from Liguria' in northwest Italy (*Apiaceae*)

Lewisia
lew-IZ-ee-uh
Named after Meriwether Lewis (1774–1809), American soldier, politician and explorer (*Montiaceae*)

Leycesteria
lay-ses-TEER-ee-uh, les-ter-EE-uh
Named after William Leycester (1775–1831), British judge and horticulturist (*Caprifoliaceae*)

Leymus
LAY-mus
An anagram of the related genus *Elymus* (*Poaceae*)

Liatris
lee-AH-tris
Derivation unknown (*Asteraceae*)

1

***Leucojum vernum*,**
spring snowflake

2

Lilium maculatum,
Thunberg's lily

3

Lilium grayi,
Gray's lily

libani
LIB-an-ee
—

libanoticus
lib-an-OT-ih-kus
libanotica, libanoticum
Connected with Mount Lebanon, Lebanon,
as in *Cedrus libani*

libericus
li-BEER-ih-kus
liberica, libericum
From Liberia, as in *Coffea liberica*

Libertia
li-BERT-ee-uh
Named after Marie-Anne Libert
(1782–1865), Belgian botanist (*Iridaceae*)

Libocedrus
ly-boh-SEE-drus
From Greek *libos* meaning 'tears' and
Cedrus, another conifer genus, in reference
to resin droplets formed on the trunk
(*Cupressaceae*)

liburnicus
li-BER-nih-kus
liburnica, liburnicum
Connected with Liburnia (now in Croatia),
as in *Asphodeline liburnica*

Licuala
li-KWAH-luh
From Makassar (Indonesia) *leko wala*, the
vernacular name for *L. spinosa* (*Arecaceae*)

lignosus
lig-NOH-sus
lignosa, lignosum
Woody, as in *Tuberaria lignosa*

Ligularia
lig-ew-LAIR-ee-uh
From Latin *ligula* meaning 'little tongue', a
reference to the strap-like ray florets
(*Asteraceae*)

ligularis
lig-yoo-LAH-ris
ligularis, ligulare
—

ligulatus
lig-yoo-LAIR-tus
ligulata, ligulatum
Shaped like a strap, as in *Acacia ligulata*

ligusticifolius
lig-us-tih-kih-FOH-lee-us
ligusticifolia, ligusticifolium
With leaves like lovage, as in *Clematis
ligusticifolia*

Ligusticum
li-GUST-ik-um
From Latin *ligusticum apium*, or 'celery from
Liguria' in northwest Italy (*Apiaceae*)

ligusticus
lig-US-tih-kus
ligustica, ligusticum
Connected with Liguria, Italy, as in *Crocus
ligusticus*

ligustrifolius
lig-us-trih-FOH-lee-us
ligustrifolia, ligustrifolium
With leaves like privet (*Ligustrum*), as in
Hebe ligustrifolia

ligustrinus
lig-us-TREE-nus
ligustrina, ligustrinum
Like privet (*Ligustrum*), as in *Ageratina
ligustrina*

Ligustrum
lig-US-trum
From classical Latin name for privet,
L. vulgare (*Oleaceae*)

lilacinus
ly-luc-SEE-nus
lilacina, lilacinum
Lilac, as in *Primula lilacina*

lili-
Used in compound words to denote lily

liliaceus
lil-lee-AY-see-us
liliacea, liliaceum
Like lily (*Lilium*), as in *Fritillaria liliacea*

liliiflorus
lil-lee-ih-FLOR-us
liliiflora, liliiflorum
With flowers like lily (*Lilium*), as in
Magnolia liliiflora

liliifolius
lil-ee-eye-FOH-lee-us
liliifolia, liliifolium
With leaves like lily (*Lilium*), as in
Adenophora liliifolia

Lilium [2, 3]
LIL-ee-um
From Greek *lirion* meaning 'lily' (*Liliaceae*)

1

Linaria vulgaris,
common toadflax

2

Hakea linearis,
pincushion bush

limbatus
lim-BAH-tus
limbata, limbatum
Bordered, as in *Primula limbata*

limensis
lee-MEN-sis
limensis, limense
From Lima, Peru, as in *Haageocereus limensis*

limoniifolius
lim-on-ih-FOH-lee-us
limoniifolia, limoniifolium
With leaves like sea lavender (*Limonium*), as in *Asyneuma limoniifolium*

Limonium
li-MOW-nee-um
From Greek *leimon* meaning 'meadow' (*Plumbaginaceae*)

limosus
lim-OH-sus
limosa, limosum
Growing in marshy or muddy habitats, as in *Carex limosa*

Linanthus
ly-NAN-thus
From *Linum*, the flax genus, and Greek *anthos* meaning 'flower', suggesting resemblance (*Polemoniaceae*)

Linaria [1]
li-NAIR-ee-uh
Resembling the genus *Linum* (*Plantaginaceae*)

linariifolius
lin-ar-ee-FOH-lee-us
linariifolia, linariifolium
With leaves like toadflax (*Linaria*), as in *Melaleuca linariifolia*

Lindera
LIN-der-uh
Named after Johann Linder (1676–1724), Swedish physician and botanist (*Lauraceae*)

lindleyanus
lind-lee-AH-nus
lindleyana, lindleyanum
—
lindleyi
lind-lee-EYE
Named after John Lindley (1799–1865), British botanist associated with the Royal Horticultural Society, as in *Buddleja lindleyana*

linearis [2]
lin-AH-ris
linearis, lineare
With narrow, almost parallel sides, as in *Ceropegia linearis*

lineatus
lin-ee-AH-tus
lineata, lineatum
With lines or stripes, as in *Rubus lineatus*

lingua
LIN-gwa
A tongue or like a tongue, as in *Pyrrosia lingua*

linguiformis
lin-gwih-FORM-is
linguiformis, linguiforme
—
lingulatus
lin-gyoo-LAH-tus
lingulata, lingulatum
Shaped like a tongue, as in *Guzmania lingulata*

liniflorus
lin-ih-FLOR-us
liniflora, liniflorum
With flowers like flax (*Linum*), as in *Byblis liniflora*

linifolius
lin-ih-FOH-lee-us
linifolia, linifolium
With leaves like flax (*Linum*), as in *Tulipa linifolia*

Linnaea
lin-AY-uh
Named after Carl Linnaeus (1707–78), Swedish botanist, zoologist and father of taxonomy; this was his favourite flower (*Caprifoliaceae*)

linnaeanus
lin-ee-AH-nus
linnaeana, linnaeanum
—
linnaei
lin-ee-eye
Named after Carl Linnaeus (1707–78), Swedish botanist, as in *Solanum linnaeanum*

linoides
li-NOY-deez
Resembling flax (*Linum*), as in *Monardella linoides*

Linum
LY-num
From Latin *lin* meaning 'flax'; *Linum usitatissimum* is the source of linseed oil and linen (*Linaceae*)

Liquidambar

lik-wid-AM-bur

From Latin *liquidus* meaning 'liquid' and *ambar* meaning 'amber', as the trunk produces resin (*Altingiaceae*)

Liriodendron [3]

li-ree-oh-DEN-dron

From Greek *lirion* meaning 'lily' and *dendron* meaning 'tree', for the ornamental flowers (*Magnoliaceae*)

Liriope

li-ree-OH-pee

Named after Liriope, a nymph in Greek mythology and mother of Narcissus (*Asparagaceae*)

litangensis

lit-ang-EN-sis

litangensis, litangense

From Litang, China, as in *Lonicera litangensis*

Litchi

LY-chee

From Cantonese (China) *lai-zi* or Mandarin *lizhi*, the vernacular name for the fruit of *L. chinensis* (*Sapindaceae*)

Lithocarpus

lIth-oh-KAR-pus

From Greek *lithos* meaning 'stone' and *karpos* meaning 'fruit', as the acorns have a hard shell (*Fagaceae*)

Lithodora

lith-oh-DOR-uh

From Greek *lithos* meaning 'stone' and *dorea* meaning 'gift', suggesting this pretty alpine is a welcome contribution from a rocky habitat (*Boraginaceae*)

lithophilus

lith-oh-FIL-us

lithophila, lithophilum

Growing in rocky habitats, as in *Anemone lithophila*

Lithophragma

lith-oh-FRAG-muh

From Greek *lithos* meaning 'stone' and *phragma* 'fence/hedge', a reference to a rocky habitat; alternatively, an inaccurate Greek translation of *Saxifraga* (*Saxifragaceae*)

Lithops

LITH-ops

Resembling stones, from Greek *lithos* meaning 'stone' (*Aizoaceae*)

Litsea

LIT-see-uh

From Mandarin *litse* meaning 'small plum'; the fruits are small and fleshy (*Lauraceae*)

littoralis

lit-tor-AH-lis

littoralis, littorale

—

littoreus

lit-TOR-ee-us

littorea, littoreum

Growing by the sea, as in *Griselinia littoralis*

lividus

LI-vid-us

livida, lividum

Blue-grey; the colour of lead, as in *Helleborus lividus*

Livistona

liv-i-STOW-nuh

Named after Patrick Murray, second Lord Elibank, who lived in Livingston Peel, west of Edinburgh (1632–71), Scottish horticulturist (*Arecaceae*)

Lloydia

LOY-dee-uh

Named after Edward Lhuyd (1660–1709), Welsh botanist and linguist (*Liliaceae*)

lobatus

low-BAH-tus

lobata, lobatum

With lobes, as in *Cyananthus lobatus*

Lobelia

loh-BEE-lee-uh

Named after Mathias de l'Obel (1538–1616), Flemish physician and botanist (*Campanulaceae*)

lobelioides

lo-bell-ee-OH-id-ees

Resembling *Lobelia*, as in *Wahlenbergia lobelioides*

lobophyllus

lo-bo-FIL-us

lobophylla, lobophyllum

With lobed leaves, as in *Viburnum lobophyllum*

Lobularia

lob-yoo-LAIR-ee-uh

From Latin *lobulus* meaning 'small lobe/pod', referring to the small, round fruits (*Brassicaceae*)

3

Liriodendron tulipifera,
tulip tree

lobularis

lob-yoo-LAH-ris

lobularis, lobulare

With lobes, as in *Narcissus lobularis*

lobulatus

lob-yoo-LAH-tus

lobulata, lobulatum

With small lobes, as in *Crataegus lobulata*

Lodoicea

loh-doh-ISS-ee-uh

Named after Louis XV (1710–74), King of France (*Arecaceae*)

loliaceus

loh-lee-uh-SEE-us

loliacea, loliaceum

Like rye grass (*Lolium*), as in × *Festulolium loliaceum*

Lolium [1]

LOH-lee-um

From classical Latin name for a rye grass, probably *L. temulentum* (*Poaceae*)

Lomandra

loh-MAN-druh

From Greek *loma* meaning 'fringe' and *aner* meaning 'male', as in some species, the anthers have noticeable borders (*Asparagaceae*)

Lomatia

loh-MAH-tee-uh

From Greek *loma* meaning 'fringe', as the seeds have a papery wing (*Proteaceae*)

Lomatium

loh-MAH-tee-um

From Greek *loma* meaning 'fringe', as the seeds have a papery wing (*Apiaceae*)

longibracteatus

lon-jee-brak-tee-AH-tus

longibracteata, longibracteatum

With long bracts, as in *Pachystachys longibracteata*

longicaulis

lon-jee-KAW-lis

longicaulis, longicaule

With long stalks, as in *Aeschynanthus longicaulis*

longicuspis

lon-jee-KUS-pis

longicuspis, longicuspe

With long points, as in *Rosa longicuspis*

longiflorus

lon-jee-FLO-rus

longiflora, longiflorum

With long flowers, as in *Crocus longiflorus*

longifolius

lon-jee-FOH-lee-us

longifolia, longifolium

With long leaves, as in *Pulmonaria longifolia*

longilobus

lon-JEE-loh-bus

longiloba, longilobum

With long lobes, as in *Alocasia longiloba*

longipedunculatus

lon-jee-ped-un-kew-LAH-tus

longipedunculata, longipedunculatum

With a long peduncle, as in *Magnolia longipedunculata*

longipes

LON-juh-peez

With a long stalk, as in *Acer longipes*

longipetalus

lon-jee-PET-uh-lus

longipetala, longipetalum

With long petals, as in *Matthiola longipetala*

1

Lolium perenne,
perennial rye grass

2

Lonicera hildebrandiana,
giant Burmese honeysuckle

longiracemosus

lon-jee-ray-see-MOH-sus

longiracemosa, longiracemosum

With long racemes, as in *Incarvillea longiracemosa*

longiscapus

lon-jee-SKAY-pus

longiscapa, longiscapum

With a long scape, as in *Vriesea longiscapa*

longisepalus

lon-jee-SEE-pal-us

longisepala, longisepalum

With long sepals, as in *Allium longisepalum*

longispathus

lon-jis-PAY-thus

longispatha, longispathum

With long spathes, as in *Narcissus longispathus*

longissimus

lon-JIS-ih-mus

longissima, longissimum

Very long, as in *Aquilegia longissima*

longistylus

lon-jee-STY-lus

longistyla, longistylum

With a long style, as in *Arenaria longistyla*

3

Lotus corniculatus,
bird's foot trefoil

longus

LONG-us

longa, longum

Long, as in *Cyperus longus*

Lonicera [2]

lo-NIS-er-uh

Named after Adam Lonitzer (1528–86), German physician and botanist; the family takes its name from genus *Caprifolium*, now a synonym of *Lonicera*, derived from Latin *capri* meaning 'goat' and *folium* meaning 'leaves', either because goats like to feed on the foliage, or because this vine's ability to climb trees matches that of goats (*Caprifoliaceae*)

lophanthus

low-FAN-thus

lophantha, lophanthum

With crested flowers, as in *Paraserianthes lophantha*

Lophomyrtus

lof-oh-MER-tus

From Greek *lophos* meaning 'crest' and *Myrtus*, a related genus, as within the flower's ovary are ribbon-like placenta lobes (*Myrtaceae*)

Lophophora

luh-FOF-er-uh

From Greek *lophos* meaning 'crest' and *phoreus* meaning 'bearer', as the areoles on the stem bear prominent tufts of hair (*Cactaceae*)

Lophospermum

lof-oh-SPER-mum

From Greek *lophos* meaning 'crest' and *sperma* meaning 'seed', alluding to the membranous wing around each seed (*Plantaginaceae*)

Loropetalum

lor-oh-PET-ah-lum

From Greek *loron* meaning 'strap' and *petalon* meaning 'petal', as this witch hazel relation has similar strap-like petals (*Hamamelidaceae*)

lotifolius

lo-tif-FOH-lee-us

lotifolia, lotifolium

With leaves like *Lotus*, as in *Goodia lotifolia*

Lotus [3] (also lotus)

LOH-tus

From Greek *lotos*, a vernacular name for several different plants (*Fabaceae*)

louisianus

loo-ee-see-AH-nus

louisiana, louisianum

Connected with Louisiana, USA, as in *Proboscidea louisiana*

lucens

LOO-senz

—

lucidus

LOO-sid-us

lucida, lucidum

Bright; shining; clear, as in *Ligustrum lucidum*

Luculia

luh-KOO-lee-uh

From Nepalese *luculi-swa*, the vernacular name for *L. gratissima* (*Rubiaceae*)

1

Luffa cylindrica,
loofah, dish-cloth gourd

2

Lunaria annua,
honesty

Ludisia
loo-DIZ-ee-uh
Said to derive from Ludis, whose widower composed a mournful elegy after her death, a nod perhaps to the dark foliage, though evidence for this etymology is scant (*Orchidaceae*)

ludovicianus
loo-doh-vik-ee-AH-nus
ludoviciana, ludovicianum
Connected with Louisiana, USA, as in *Artemisia ludoviciana*

Ludwigia
lood-VIG-ee-uh
Named after Christian Gottlieb Ludwig (1709–73), German physician and botanist (*Onagraceae*)

Luffa [1]
LOO-fuh
From Arabic *lufah*, the vernacular name for *L. aegyptiaca* (*Cucurbitaceae*)

Luma (also luma)
LOO-muh
From Mapuche (Chile) vernacular name for this genus and/or *Amomyrtus luma* (*Myrtaceae*)

Lunaria [2]
loo-NAIR-ee-uh
From Latin *luna* meaning 'moon', as the fruits are circular (*Brassicaceae*)

lunatus
loo-NAH-tus
lunata, lunatum
—

lunulatus
loo-nu-LAH-tus
lunulata, lunulatum
Shaped like the crescent moon, as in *Cyathea lunulata*

Lupinus
loo-PIE-nus
From Latin *lupus* meaning 'wolf', as some weedy species are said to overrun fields and reduce fertility; the opposite is true as this plant is a nitrogen-fixer (*Fabaceae*)

lupulinus
lup-oo-LEE-nus
lupulina, lupulinum
Like hop (*Humulus lupulus*), as in *Medicago lupulina*

luridus
LEW-rid-us
lurida, luridum
Pale yellow, wan, as in *Moraea lurida*

lusitanicus
loo-si-TAN-ih-kus
lusitanica, lusitanicum
Connected with Lusitania (Portugal and some parts of Spain), as in *Prunus lusitanica*

luteolus
loo-tee-OH-lus
luteola, luteolum
Yellowish, as in *Primula luteola*

lutetianus
loo-tee-shee-AH-nus
lutetiana, lutetianum
Connected with Lutetia (Paris), France, as in *Circaea lutetiana*

luteus
LOO-tee-us
lutea, luteum
Yellow, as in *Calochortus luteus*

luxurians
luks-YOO-ee-anz
Luxuriant, as in *Begonia luxurians*

Luzula
luz-ew-luh
From Latin *luzulae* meaning 'little light', as the leaf hairs glisten with dew (*Juncaceae*)

Lycianthes
ly-see-AN-theez
From Greek *lykion* meaning 'thorny shrub' and *anthos* meaning 'flower' (*Solanaceae*)

Lycium
LY-see-um
From Greek *lykion* meaning 'thorny shrub from Lycia', now in southwest Turkey; possibly meant to refer to a species of *Rhamnus* (*Solanaceae*)

lycius
LY-cee-us
lycia, lycium
Connected with Lycia, now part of Turkey, as in *Phlomis lycia*

lycopersicum
ly-koh-PER-si-kum
'Wolf-peach', as in *Solanum lycopersicum*

lycopodioides
ly-kop-oh-dee-OY-deez
Resembling clubmoss (*Lycopodium*), as in *Cassiope lycopodioides*

Lycopodium
ly-koh-POH-dee-um
From Greek *lykos* meaning 'wolf' and *podion* meaning 'foot', which the stem tips are said to resemble (*Lycopodiaceae*)

Lycopus

ly-KOH-pus

From Greek *lykos* meaning 'wolf' and *pous* meaning 'foot', alluding to the shape of the leaves (*Lamiaceae*)

Lycoris

ly-KOR-is

After Lycoris (aka Cytheris), a Roman actress and lover of Mark Anthony (*Amaryllidaceae*)

lydius

LID-ee-us

lydia, lydium

Connected with Lydia, now part of Turkey, as in *Genista lydia*

Lygodium

ly-GOH-dee-um

From Greek *lygodes* meaning 'flexible', like the stems of this climbing fern (*Lygodiaceae*)

Lyonia

ly-OH-nee-uh

Named after John Lyon (1765–1814), Scottish-born American botanist (*Ericaceae*)

Lyonothamnus

ly-on-oh-THAM-nus

Named after William Scrugham Lyon (1851–1916), American botanist, plus Greek *thamnos* meaning 'shrub' (*Rosaceae*)

Lysichiton

ly-si-KY-ton

From Greek *lysis* meaning 'to dissolve' and *chiton* meaning 'tunic', referring to the prominent spathe that soon withers (*Araceae*)

Lysimachia

ly-si-MAK-ee-uh

From Greek *lysis* meaning 'to dissolve' and *mache* meaning 'strife', alluding to its medicinal properties, as in 'loosestrife'; alternatively, after Lysimachus (c. 360–281 BC), King of Thrace, Macedonia and Asia Minor or Lysimachus of Kos, a 4th/5th century BC physician (*Primulaceae*)

lysimachioides

ly-see-mak-ee-OY-deez

Resembling loosestrife (*Lysimachia*), as in *Hypericum lysimachioides*

Lythrum

LITH-rum

From Greek *lythron* meaning 'blood', a reference to flower colour (*Lythraceae*)

Lycopersicon

The tomato (*Solanum lycopersicum*) was initially described in the same genus as the potato (*S. tuberosum*), but quickly moved into its own genus (as *Lycopersicon esculentum*). However, just as old styles come back into fashion, so DNA data has suggested that tomato should rejoin potato. The word *lycopersicon* is derived from Greek, meaning 'wolf-peach', and is a name endowed with suspicion. Though indigenous South Americans have long eaten the fruits, Europeans were initially sceptical of them. Tomatoes are members of a family that includes henbane (*Hyoscyamus*), deadly nightshade (*Atropa*) and mandrake (*Mandragora*), so they had reason to worry. Thankfully, tomatoes have shaken off their poisonous reputation.

Solanum lycopersicum, **tomato**

A
B
C
D
E
F
G
H
I
J
K
L
M
N
O
P
Q
R
S
T
U
V
W
X
Y
Z
i

Maackia [1]

MAH-kee-uh
Named after Richard Otto Maack (1825–86), Russian naturalist and anthropologist (*Fabaceae*)

Macadamia

mak-uh-DAME-ee-uh
Named after John Macadam (1827–65), Scottish-born Australian chemist and politician (*Proteaceae*)

macedonicus

mas-eh-DON-ih-kus
macedonica, macedonicum
Connected with Macedonia, as in *Knautia macedonica*

Machaeranthera

mak-uh-RAN-thu-ruh
From Greek *macha* meaning 'sword' and *anthera* meaning 'anther' (*Asteraceae*)

macilentus

mas-il-LEN-tus
macilenta, macilentum
Thin; lean, as in *Justicia macilenta*

Mackaya

muh-KY-uh
Named after James Townsend Mackay (1775–1862), Scottish botanist (*Acanthaceae*)

Macleania

muh-KLAY-nee-uh
Named after John Maclean (18th century), British merchant in Peru (*Ericaceae*)

Macleaya

muh-KLAY-uh
Named after Alexander Macleay (1767–1848), Scottish colonial official in New South Wales and entomologist (*Papaveraceae*)

Maclura

ma-KLUR-uh
Named after William Maclure (1763–1840), Scottish-born American geologist (*Moraceae*)

macro-

Used in compound words to denote either long or large

macracanthus

mak-ra-KAN-thus
macracantha, macracanthum
With large spines, as in *Acacia macracantha*

macrandrus

mak-RAN-drus
macrandra, macrandrum
With large anthers, as in *Eucalyptus macrandra*

macranthus

mak-RAN-thus
macrantha, macranthum
With large flowers, as in *Hebe macrantha*

macrobotrys

mak-roh-BOT-rees
With large grape-like clusters, as in *Strongylodon macrobotrys*

macrocarpus [2]

mak-roh-KAR-pus
macrocarpa, macrocarpum
With large fruit, as in *Cupressus macrocarpa*

1

Maackia amurensis,
Amur maackia

2

Begonia maculata,
Spotted begonia

macrocephalus

mak-roh-SEF-uh-lus

macrocephala, macrocephalum

With large heads, as in *Centaurea macrocephala*

macrodontus

mak-roh-DON-tus

macrodonta, macrodontum

With large teeth, as in *Olearia macrodonta*

macromeris

mak-roh-MER-is

With many or large parts, as in *Coryphantha macromeris*

macrophyllus

mak-roh-FIL-us

macrophylla, macrophyllum

With large or long leaves, as in *Hydrangea macrophylla*

macropodus

mak-roh-POH-dus

macropoda, macropodum

With stout stalks, as in *Daphniphyllum macropodum*

macrorrhizus

mak-roh-RY-zus

macrorrhiza, macrorrhizum

With large roots, as in *Geranium macrorrhizum*

macrospermus

mak-roh-SPERM-us

macrosperma, macrospermum

With large seeds, as in *Senecio macrospermus*

macrostachyus

mak-roh-STAH-kus

macrostachya, macrostachyum

With long or large spikes, as in *Setaria macrostachya*

Macrozamia

mak-roh-ZAY-mee-uh

From Greek *makros* meaning 'large' and *Zamia*, a related genus (*Zamiaceae*)

maculatus

mak-yuh-LAH-tus

maculata, maculatum

—

maculosus

mak-yuh-LAH-sus

maculosa, maculosum

With spots, as in *Begonia maculata*

madagascariensis

mad-uh-gas-KAR-ee-EN-sis

madagascariensis, madagascariense

From Madagascar, as in *Buddleja madagascariensis*

Magnolia

Many plant names were created to honour people and *Magnolia* is no exception. Pierre Magnol was a French botanist who is credited with creating the plant family, a unit of classification still in use today. Once rather exclusive, magnolias (note the lowercase 'm') have become ubiquitous in towns and cities, so much so that their name is now appended to one of the most popular colours of paint for UK home interiors. As *Magnolia* became magnolia, it lost some of its lustre and few people familiar with the tree (or the colour) have heard of poor Monsieur Magnol.

Magnolia campbellii,
Campbell's magnolia

maderensis

ma-der-EN-sis

maderensis, maderense

From Madeira, as in *Geranium maderense*

Madia

MAY-dee-uh

From Mapuche (Chile) name *madi*, for *M. sativa* (*Asteraceae*)

Maesa

MAY-zuh

From Arabic *maas*, the vernacular name for *M. lanceolata* (*Primulaceae*)

magellanicus

ma-jell-AN-ih-kus

megallanica, megallanicum

Connected with the Straits of Magellan, South America, as in *Fuchsia magellanica*

magellensis

mag-ah-LEN-sis

magellensis, magellense

Of the Maiella massif, Italy, as in *Sedum magellense*

magnificus

mag-NIH-fih-kus

magnifica, magnificum

Splendid, magnificent, as in *Geranium* × *magnificum*

Magnolia

mag-NOH-lee-uh

Named after Pierre Magnol (1638–1715), French botanist (*Magnoliaceae*)

magnus

MAG-nus

magna, magnum

Great; big, as in *Alberta magna*

Mahonia

muh-HOH-nee-uh

Named after Bernard McMahon (1775–1816), Irish-born American horticulturist (*Berberidaceae*)

Maianthemum

my-ANTH-uh-mum

From Greek *Maios* meaning 'May' and *anthemon* meaning 'flower', alluding to the bloom period (*Asparagaceae*)

Maihuenia

my-WEN-ee-uh

From Mapuche (Chile) name *maihuén*, for *M. poeppigii* (*Cactaceae*)

majalis

maj-AH-lis

majalis, majale

Flowering in May, as in *Convallaria majalis*

GENUS SPOTLIGHT

Mahonia

Taxonomists are often unpopular with gardeners because of their annoying habit of changing the name by which we know our favourite plant. Contrary to popular belief, such changes are enacted because new evidence arises revealing relationships that contradict current taxonomy. The popular genus *Mahonia* is a confusing case in point. Taxonomists have long disagreed as to whether it should be combined with its close relative *Berberis*. DNA evidence suggests the two should be merged, an unpopular move with many gardeners. One recently mooted solution is to hive off a handful of mahonias into new genera (*Moranothamnus*, *Alloberberis*), allowing the rest to retain their well-known name and independent status. It will be many years before we know whether the taxonomic community has embraced this option.

Mahonia napaulensis,
Nepal mahonia

major
MAY-jor
major, majus
Bigger; larger, as in *Astrantia major*

malabaricus
mal-uh-BAR-ih-kus
malabarica, malabaricum
Connected with the Malabar coast, India, as in *Bauhinia malabarica*

malacoides
mal-a-koy-deez
Soft, as in *Erodium malacoides*

malacospermus
mal-uh-ko-SPER-mus
malacosperma, malacospermum
With soft seeds, as in *Hibiscus malacospermus*

maliformis
ma-lee-for-mees
maliformis, maliforme
Shaped like an apple, as in *Passiflora maliformis*

Malope [1]
muh-LOH-pee
From Greek *malos* meaning 'tender', as the leaves are soft (*Malvaceae*)

Malpighia
mal-PIG-ee-uh
Named after Marcello Malpighi (1628–94), Italian biologist (*Malpighiaceae*)

Malus
MA-lus
From Latin *malus* meaning 'apple tree' (*Rosaceae*)

Malva
MAL-vuh
From Greek *malaco* meaning 'to soften', a reference to the use of some species as emollients (*Malvaceae*)

malvaceus
mal-VAY-see-us
malvacea, malvaceum
Like mallow (*Malva*), as in *Physocarpus malvaceus*

Malvastrum
mal-VAS-trum
From *Malva*, a related genus, plus Greek *astrum* meaning 'incomplete resemblance' (*Malvaceae*)

Malvaviscus
mal-vuh-VIS-kus
From *Malva*, a related genus plus Latin *viscidus* meaning 'sticky', like the sap (*Malvaceae*)

malviflorus
mal-VEE-flor-us
malviflora, malviflorum
With flowers like mallow (*Malva*), as in *Geranium malviflorum*

malvinus
mal-VY-nus
malvina, malvinum
Mauve, as in *Plectranthus malvinus*

Mammillaria [2]
mam-uh-LAIR-ee-uh
From Latin *mamilla* meaning 'nipple', referencing the shape of the spine-bearing tubercles, which in some species produce white latex (*Cactaceae*)

mammillatus
mam-mil-LAIR-tus
mammillata, mammillatum
—

mammillaris
mam-mil-LAH-ris
mammillaris, mammillare
—

mammosus
mam-OH-sus
mammosa, mammosum
Bearing nipple- or breast-like structures, as in *Solanum mammosum*

Malope trifida,
mallow wort

Mammillaria elongata,
ladyfinger cactus

Mandragora officinarum,
mandrake

Mangifera indica,
mango

Manihot esculenta,
cassava

Mandevilla
man-duh-VIL-uh
Named after Henry John Mandeville
(1773–1861), British diplomat
(*Apocynaceae*)

Mandragora [3]
man-druh-GOR-uh
From Greek *mandragoras* meaning
'mandrake', itself deriving from a proto-
Greek or Persian word (*Solanaceae*)

mandshuricus
mand-SHEU-rih-kus
mandshurica, mandshuricum
—
manshuricus
man-SHEU-rih-kus
manshurica, manshuricum
Connected with Manchuria, northeast Asia,
as in *Tilia mandshurica*

Manettia
muh-NET-ee-uh
Named after Saverio Manetti (1723–85),
Italian physician, ornithologist and botanist
(*Rubiaceae*)

Mangifera [4]
man-GIF-er-uh
From Tamil (India) *mangai* meaning 'unripe
mango fruit' [*manpalam* is Tamil for 'ripe
mango fruit'], adopted by Portuguese sailors,
becoming the standard word for the fruit
and plant; Latin *iferus* means 'bearing'
(*Anacardiaceae*)

manicatus
mah-nuh-KAH-tus
manicata, manicatum
With long sleeves, as in *Gunnera manicata*

Manihot [5]
MAN-ee-hot
From Brazilian indigenous *manioc*, the name
for cassava, *M. esculenta* (*Euphorbiaceae*)

Maranta
ma-RAN-tuh
Named after Bartolomea Maranti (?–1751),
Venetian botanist and physician
(*Marantaceae*)

margaritaceus
mar-gar-ee-tuh-KEE-us
margaritacea, margaritaceum
—
margaritus
mar-gar-ee-tus
margarita, margaritum
Relating to pearls, as in *Anaphalis
margaritacea*

margaritiferus
mar-guh-rih-TIH-fer-us
margaritifera, margaritiferum
With pearls, as in *Haworthia margaritifera*

marginalis
mar-gin-AH-lis
marginalis, marginale
—
marginatus
mar-gin-AH-tus
marginata, marginatum
Margined, as in *Saxifraga marginata*

Margyricarpus
mar-jir-ee-KAR-pus
From Greek *margaron* meaning 'pearl' and
karpos meaning 'fruit', as the fruits are
opalescent (*Rosaceae*)

marianus
mar-ee-AH-nus
mariana, marianum
Of the Virgin Mary (or sometimes
Maryland, USA), as in *Silybum marianum*

marilandicus
mar-i-LAND-ih-kus
marilandica, marilandicum
Connected with Maryland, USA, as in
Quercus marilandica

maritimus
muh-RIT-tim-mus
maritima, maritimum
Relating to the sea, as in *Armeria maritima*

Marrubium vulgare,
white horehound

Matthiola sinuata,
sea stock

marmoratus

mar-mor-RAH-tus

marmorata, marmoratum

—

marmoreus

mar-MOH-ree-us

marmorea, marmoreum

Marbled; mottled, as in *Kalanchoe marmorata*

maroccanus

mar-oh-KAH-nus

maroccana, maroccanum

Connected with Morocco, as in *Linaria maroccana*

Marrubium [1]

muh-ROO-bee-um

From Latin *marrubium*, the vernacular name for horehound, *M. vulgare* (*Lamiaceae*)

Marsilea

mar-si-LAY-uh

Named after Luigi Fernando Marsigli (1656–1730), Italian scholar, soldier and emissary (*Marsileaceae*)

martagon

MART-uh-gon

A word of uncertain origin, thought in *Lilium martagon* to refer to the turban-like flower

martinicensis

mar-teen-i-SEN-sis

martinicensis, martinicense

From Martinique, Lesser Antilles, as in *Trimezia martinicensis*

mas

MAS

—

masculus

MASK-yoo-lus

mascula, masculum

With masculine qualities, male, as in *Cornus mas*

Masdevallia

mas-duh-VAY-lee-uh

Named after José Masdeval (?–1801), Spanish physician and botanist (*Orchidaceae*)

Mathiasella

mu-thy-us-EL-uh

Named after Mildred Esther Mathias (1906–95), American botanist (*Apiaceae*)

Matricaria

ma-tri-KARE-ee-uh

From Latin *matrix* meaning 'womb' and *aria* meaning 'pertaining to', a reference to medicinal properties (*Asteraceae*)

matronalis

mah-tro-NAH-lis

matronalis, matronale

Relating to 1st March, the Roman Matronalia, festival of motherhood and Juno as goddess of childbirth, as in *Hesperis matronalis*

Matteuccia

ma-TOO-chee-uh

Named after Carlo Matteucci (1811–68), Italian physicist (*Onocleaceae*)

Matthiola [2]

mat-ee-OH-luh

Named after Pietro Andrea Matthioli (1500–77), Italian physician and botanist (*Brassicaceae*)

Maurandya

maw-RAN-dee-uh

Named after Catherina Pancracia Maurandy (18th century), Spanish botanist (*Plantaginaceae*)

mauritanicus

maw-rih-TAWN-ih-kus

mauritanica, mauritanicum

Connected with North Africa, especially Morocco, as in *Lavatera mauritanica*

mauritianus

maw-rih-tee-AH-nus

mauritiana, mauritianum

Connected with Mauritius, Indian Ocean, as in *Croton mauritianus*

Maxillaria

maks-i-LAIR-ee-uh

From Latin *maxilla* meaning 'jawbone', an allusion to the yawning flowers and the column base, which may resemble a jaw (*Orchidaceae*)

maxillaris

maks-ILL-ah-ris

maxillaris, maxillare

Relating to the jaw, as in *Zygopetalum maxillare*

maximus

MAKS-ih-mus

maxima, maximum

Largest, as in *Rudbeckia maxima*

Maytenus

MAY-ten-us

From Mapuche (Chile) name *mayten* for *M. boaria* (*Celastraceae*)

Mazus

MAY-zus

From Greek *mazos* meaning 'nipple', as the petals have noticeable swellings (*Phrymaceae*)

Meconopsis [3]

mek-uh-NOP-sis

From Greek *mekon* meaning 'poppy' and *opsis* meaning 'resemblance' (*Papaveraceae*)

Medeola

me-dee-OH-luh

Named after Medea, the sorceress in Greek mythology who helped Jason find the golden fleece (*Liliaceae*)

Medicago

me dee-KAH-go

From Greek *medikos* meaning 'lucerne' (aka alfalfa, *M. sativa*), a plant said to come from Media, now in northwestern Iran (*Fabaceae*)

medicus

MED-ih-kus

medica, medicum

Medicinal, as in *Citrus medica*

Medinilla

med-uh-NILL-uh

Named after José de Medinilla y Pineda (dates unknown), twice Spanish Governor of the Mariana Islands [1812–22, 1826–31] (*Melastomataceae*)

mediopictus

MED-ee-o-pic-tus

mediopicta, mediopictum

With a stripe or colour running down the middle, as in *Calathea mediopicta*

mediterraneus

med-ih-ter-RAY-nee-us

mediterranea, mediterraneum

Either from a land-locked region, or from the Mediterranean, as in *Minuartia mediterranea*

medius

MEED-ee-us

media, medium

Intermediate; middle, as in *Mahonia × media*

medullaris

med-yoo-LAH-ris

medullaris, medullare

—

medullus

med-DUL-us

medulla, medullum

Pithy, as in *Cyathea medullaris*

mega-

Used in compound words to denote big

megacanthus

meg-uh-KAN-thus

megacantha, megacanthum

With big spines, as in *Opuntia megacantha*

megacarpus

meg-uh-CAR-pus

megacarpa, megacarpum

With big fruits, as in *Ceanothus megacarpus*

megalanthus

meg-uh-LAN-thus

megalantha, megalanthum

With big flowers, as in *Potentilla megalantha*

megalophyllus

meg-uh-luh-FIL-us

megalophylla, megalophyllum

With big leaves, as in *Ampelopsis megalophylla*

megapotamicus

meg-uh-poh-TAM-ih-kus

megapotamica, megapotamicum

Connected with a big river, for instance the Amazon or Rio Grande, as in *Abutilon megapotamicum*

Megaskepasma

meg-uh-skuh-PAZ-muh

From Greek *megas* meaning 'great' and *skepasma* meaning 'covering', as the flowers are partially concealed under large, colourful bracts (*Acanthaceae*)

megaspermus

meg-uh-SPER-mus

megasperma, megaspermum

With big seeds, as in *Callerya megasperma*

megastigma

meg-uh-STIG-ma

With a big stigma, as in *Boronia megastigma*

3

Meconopsis delavayi,
Himalayan poppy

Melaleuca [1]

me-luh-LOO-kuh

From Greek *melas* meaning 'black' and *leukos* meaning 'white'; early specimens had white stems blackened by fire (*Myrtaceae*)

melanocaulon

mel-an-oh-KAW-lon

With black stems, as in *Blechnum melanocaulon*

melanocentrus

mel-an-oh-KEN-trus

melanocentra, melanocentrum

With a black centre, as in *Saxifraga melanocentra*

melanococcus

mel-an-oh-KOK-us

melanococca, melanococcum

With black berries, as in *Elaeis melanococcus*

melanoxylon

mel-an-oh-ZY-lon

With black wood, as in *Acacia melanoxylon*

Melastoma

mel-uh-STO-muh

From Greek *melas* meaning 'black' and *stoma* meaning 'mouth', as eating the fruit stains the tongue dark blue or black (*Melastomataceae*)

meleagris [3]

mel-EE-uh-gris

meleagris, meleagre

With spots like a guinea fowl, as in *Fritillaria meleagris*

Melia

ME-lee-uh

The classical Greek name for an ash tree (*Fraxinus*), which has similar leaves to *M. azedarach* (*Meliaceae*)

Melianthus

me-lee-ANTH-us

From Greek *mel* meaning 'honey' and *anthos* meaning 'flower', due to the copious nectar (*Francoaceae*)

Melica

MEL-i-kuh

From Greek *melike* meaning 'grass', or possibly derived from Latin *herba medica* meaning 'grass from Media', now in northeastern Iran (*Poaceae*)

Melicope

mel-i-KOH-pee

From Greek *mel* meaning 'honey' and *kope* meaning 'split', as the floral glands are notched (*Rutaceae*)

Melicytus [2]

mel-i-SY-tus

From Greek *mel* meaning 'honey' and *kytos* meaning 'container', because the nectar seeps from a hollow nectary (*Violaceae*)

Melilotus

mel-i-LOH-tus

From Greek *mel* meaning 'honey' and *Lotus*, a related genus, as this plant has sweet-scented foliage (*Fabaceae*)

1

Melaleuca cajuputi,
white samet

2

Melicytus crassifolius,
thick-leaved mahoe

Melinis
mel-I-nis
From Greek *mel* meaning 'honey', as some species smell of molasses, or from *melas* meaning 'black', the colour of the seeds (*Poaceae*)

Meliosma
me-lee-OZ-muh
From Greek *mel* meaning 'honey' and *osme* meaning 'fragrance', the scent of the flowers (*Sabiaceae*)

Melissa
muh-LISS-uh
From Greek *melissa* or *melitta* meaning 'honeybee', which are strongly attracted to the flowers (*Lamiaceae*)

Melittis
MEH-lit-iss
From Greek *melissa* or *melitta* meaning 'honeybee', which are strongly attracted to the flowers (*Lamiaceae*)

melliferus
mel-IH-fer-us
mellifera, melliferum
Producing honey, as in *Euphorbia mellifera*

Melliodendron
mel-ee-oh-DEN-dron
From Greek *mel* meaning 'honey' and *dendron* meaning 'tree', suggesting fragrant flowers (*Styracaceae*)

melliodorus
mel-ee-uh-do-rus
melliodora, melliodorum
With the scent of honey, as in *Eucalyptus melliodora*

mellitus
mel-IT-tus
mellita, mellitum
Sweet, like honey, as in *Iris mellita*

Melocactus
mel-oh-KAK-tus
From Greek *melon* meaning 'apple' plus cactus, alluding to the spherical shape of young plants; sometimes taken to derive from English 'melon' (*Cactaceae*)

meloformis
mel-OH-for-mis
meloformis, meloforme
Shaped like a melon, as in *Euphorbia meloforme*

Fritillaria meleagris,
snake's-head fritillary

membranaceus
mem-bran-AY-see-us
membranacea, membranaceum
Like skin or membrane, as in *Scadoxus membranaceus*

meniscifolius
men-is-ih-FOH-lee-us
meniscifolia, meniscifolium
With leaves that are crescent-shaped, as in *Serpocaulon meniscifolium*

Menispermum
men-i-SPER-mum
From Greek *mene* meaning 'moon' and *sperma* meaning 'seed', as the seeds are crescent-like (*Menispermaceae*)

Mentha [4]
MEN-thuh
From the classical Latin name for mint; also a nymph in Greek mythology, who was transformed into a mint plant (*Lamiaceae*)

Mentzelia
ment-ZEE-lee-uh
Named after Christian Mentzel (1622–1701), German botanist and physician (*Loasaceae*)

Mentha longifolia,
brook mint

Menyanthes
men-ee-ANTH-eez
From Greek *menanthos*, the name of an aquatic plant, probably the related *Nymphoides peltata*, though several other etymologies have been proposed (*Menyanthaceae*)

menziesii
menz-ESS-ee-eye
Named after Archibald Menzies (1754–1842), British naval surgeon and botanist, as in *Pseudotsuga menziesii*

Mercurialis
mer-kure-ee-AH-lis
Named after the Roman god Mercury, who is said to have discovered the plant (*Euphorbiaceae*)

meridianus
mer-id-ee-AH-nus
meridiana, meridianum
—

meridionalis
mer-id-ee-oh-NAH-lis
meridionalis, meridionale
Flowering at noon, as in *Primula × meridiana*

1

Metrosideros excelsa,
pohutukawa

2

Michauxia campanuloides,
Michaux's bellflower

Mertensia
mer-TEN-see-uh
Named after Frank Carl Mertens (1764–1831), German botanist (*Boraginaceae*)

Mesembryanthemum
mez-em-bree-ANTH-uh-mum
From Greek *mesembria* meaning 'midday' and *anthemon* meaning 'flower', as the blooms open around noon (*Aizoaceae*)

Mespilus
MES-pi-lus
From the classical Latin name for medlar, *M. germanica*; possibly derived from Greek *mesos* meaning 'half' and *pilos* meaning 'ball', an allusion to the shape of the fruits (*Rosaceae*)

metallicus
meh-TAL-ih-kus
metallica, metallicum
Metallic, as in *Begonia metallica*

Metasequoia
met-uh-seh-KWOY-uh
From Greek *metra* meaning 'after' or 'changed', plus *Sequoia*, a related genus (*Cupressaceae*)

Metrosideros [1]
met-roh-SID-ur-os
From Greek *metra* meaning 'heart/centre' and *sideron* meaning 'iron', as the heartwood is robust (*Myrtaceae*)

mexicanus
meks-sih-KAH-nus
mexicana, mexicanum
Connected with Mexico, as in *Agastache mexicana*

Michauxia [2]
mich-OH-zee-uh
Named after André Michaux (1746–1802), French botanist (*Campanulaceae*)

michauxioides
mich-OH-zee-uh-deez
Resembling *Michauxia*, as in *Campanula michauxioides*

micracanthus
mik-ra-KAN-thus
micracantha, micracanthum
With small thorns, as in *Euphorbia micracantha*

micranthus
my-KRAN-thus
micrantha, micranthum
With small flowers, as in *Heuchera micrantha*

micro-
Used in compound words to denote small

Microbiota
my-kro-by-OH-tuh
From Greek *mikros* meaning 'small' plus *Biota*, a related genus [now *Platycladus*] (*Cupressaceae*)

Microcachrys
my-kro-KAK-ris
From Greek *mikros* meaning 'small' and *cachrus* meaning 'catkin', referring to the tiny pollen cones (*Podocarpaceae*)

microcarpus
my-kro-KAR-pus
microcarpa, microcarpum
With small fruit, as in × *Citrofortunella microcarpa*

microcephalus
my-kro-SEF-uh-lus
microcephala, microcephalum
With a small head, as in *Persicaria microcephala*

microdasys
my-kro-DAS-is
Small and shaggy, as in *Opuntia microdasys*

microdon
my-kro-DON
With small teeth, as in *Asplenium × microdon*

microglossus
my-kro-GLOS-us
microglossa, microglossum
Small-tongued, as in *Ruscus × microglossum*

micropetalus
my-kro-PET-uh-lus
micropetala, micropetalum
With small petals, as in *Cuphea micropetala*

microphyllus
my-kro-FIL-us
microphylla, microphyllum
With small leaves, as in *Sophora microphylla*

micropterus
my-krop-TER-us
microptera, micropterum
With small wings, as in *Promenaea microptera*

Promenaea microptera

microsepalus

my-kro-SEP-a-lus

microsepala, microsepalum

With small sepals, as in *Pentadenia microsepala*

Mikania

my-KAY-nee-uh

Named after Josef Gottfried Mikan (1743–1814), Czech botanist (*Asteraceae*)

miliaceus

mil-ee-AY-see-us

miliacea, miliaceum

Relating to millet, as in *Panicum miliaceum*

militaris

mil-ih-TAH-ris

militaris, militare

Relating to soldiers; like a soldier, as in *Orchis militaris*

Milium

MIL-ee-um

From Greek *meline* meaning 'millet' (*Poaceae*)

millefoliatus

mil-le-foh-lee-AH-tus

millefoliata, millefoliatum

—

millefolius

mil-le-FOH-lee-us

millefolia, millefolium

With many leaves (literally a thousand leaves), as in *Achillea millefolium*

Millettia

mil-ETT-ee-uh

Named after Charles Millett (1792–1873) of the East India Company (*Fabaceae*)

Miltonia

mil-TOH-nee-uh

Named after Charles William Wentworth-Fitzwilliam (1786–1857), formerly Viscount Milton, British politician (*Orchidaceae*)

Miltoniopsis

mil-toh-nee-OP-sis

Resembling the related genus *Miltonia* (*Orchidaceae*)

Mimosa [1]

mim-OH-suh

From Greek *mimos*, an 'imitator', as the sensitive plant (*M. pudica*) appears to mimic the movements of animals (*Fabaceae*)

mimosoides

mim-yoo-SOY-deez

Resembling *Mimosa*, as in *Caesalpinia mimosoides*

Mimulus

MIM-ew-lus

From Greek *mimos*, an 'imitator', or *mimo*, a 'monkey', as the flowers of some species (especially *M. guttatus*) resemble faces (*Phrymaceae*)

miniatus

min-ee-AH-tus

miniata, miniatum

Cinnabar-red, as in *Clivia miniata*

minimus

MIN-eh-mus

minima, minimum

Smallest, as in *Myosurus minimus*

minor

MY-nor

minor, minus

Smaller, as in *Vinca minor*

Minuartia

min-ew-ART-ee-uh

Named after Joan Minuart i Parets (1693–1768), Spanish/Catalan botanist and pharmacist (*Caryophyllaceae*)

minutiflorus

min-yoo-tih-FLOR-us

minutiflora, minutiflorum

With minute flowers, as in *Narcissus minutiflorus*

1

Mimosa pudica, **sensitive plant**

minutifolius

min-yoo-tih-FOH-lee-us

minutifolia, minutifolium

With minute leaves, as in *Rosa minutifolia*

minutissimus

min-yoo-TEE-sih-mus

minutissima, minutissimum

The most minute, as in *Primula minutissima*

minutus

min-YOO-tus

minuta, minutum

Very small, as in *Tagetes minuta*

Mirabilis

mi-RAB-il-is

From Latin *mirabilis* meaning 'wonderful' (*Nyctaginaceae*)

Miscanthus

mis-KAN-thus

From Greek *miskos* meaning 'stalk' and *anthos* meaning 'flower', as the spikelets are stalked (*Poaceae*)

missouriensis

miss-oor-ee-EN-sis

missouriensis, missouriense

From Missouri, USA, as in *Iris missouriensis*

Mitchella

mi-CHEL-uh

Named after John Mitchell (1711–1768), American botanist and cartographer (*Rubiaceae*)

Mitella

my-TEL-uh

From Greek *mitra* meaning 'cap' and the diminutive *ella*, as the fruits resemble small hats (*Saxifragaceae*)

mitis

MIT-is

mitis, mite

Mild; gentle; without spines, as in *Caryota mitis*

Mitraria

my-TRAIR-ee-uh

From Greek *mitra* meaning 'cap', in reference to the hat-shaped bracts enclosing the calyx (*Gesneriaceae*)

mitratus

my-TRAH-tus

mitrata, mitratum

With a turban or mitre, as in *Mitrophyllum mitratum*

mitriformis

my-tri-FOR-mis

mitriformis, mitriforme

Like a cap, as in *Aloe mitriformis*

2

Hamamelis mollis,
Chinese witch hazel

mixtus

MIKS-tus

mixta, mixtum

Mixed, as in *Potentilla* × *mixta*

modestus

mo-DES-tus

modesta, modestum

Modest, as in *Aglaonema modestum*

moesiacus

mee-shee-AH-kus

moesiaca, moesiacum

Connected with Moesia, the Balkans, as in *Campanula moesiaca*

moldavicus

mol-DAV-ih-kus

moldavica, moldavicum

From Moldavia, eastern Europe, as in *Dracocephalum moldavica*

Molinia

muh-LIN-ee-uh

Named after Juan Ignacio Molina (1740–1829), Chilean cleric and botanist (*Poaceae*)

mollis [2]

MO-lis

mollis, molle

Soft; with soft hairs, as in *Alchemilla mollis*

mollissimus

maw-LISS-ih-mus

mollissima, mollissimum

Very soft, as in *Passiflora mollissima*

Moltkia

MOLT-kee-uh

Named after Joachim Gadske Moltke
(1746–1818), Danish politician
(*Boraginaceae*)

moluccanus

mol-oo-KAH-nus

moluccana, moluccanum

Connected with the Moluccas or Spice
Islands, Indonesia, as in *Pittosporum
moluccanum*

Moluccella

mol-oo-KEL-uh

Named after the Molucca Islands of
Indonesia, in the mistaken belief that this
was their point of origin; actually distributed
from Mediterranean to northwest India
(*Lamiaceae*)

monacanthus

mon-ah-KAN-thus

monacantha, monacanthum

With one spine, as in *Rhipsalis monacantha*

monadelphus

mon-ah-DEL-fus

monadelpha, monadelphum

With filaments united, as in *Dianthus
monadelphus*

monandrus

mon-AN-drus

monandra, monandrum

With one stamen, as in *Bauhinia monandra*

Monanthes

mon-ANTH-eez

From Greek *monos* meaning 'single' and
anthos meaning 'flower', as unlike related
genera, flowers are typically solitary, not in
inflorescences (*Crassulaceae*)

Monarda [1]

mon-AR-duh

Named after Nicolás Bautista Monardes
(1493–1588), Spanish physician and
botanist (*Lamiaceae*)

Monardella

mon-ar-DEL-uh

Resembling the related genus *Monarda*,
though smaller (diminutive *ella*)
(*Lamiaceae*)

monensis

mon-EN-sis

monensis, monense

From Mona, either the Isle of Man or
Anglesey, as in *Coincya monensis*

mongolicus

mon-GOL-ih-kus

mongolica, mongolicum

Connected with Mongolia, as in *Quercus
mongolica*

moniliferus

mon-ih-LIH-fer-us

monilifera, moniliferum

With a necklace, as in *Chrysanthemoides
monilifera*

moniliformis

mon-il-lee-FOR-mis

moniliformis, moniliforme

Like a necklace; with structures resembling
strings of beads, as in *Melpomene
moniliformis*

mono-

Used in compound words to denote single

monogynus

mon-OH-gy-nus

monogyna, monogynum

With one pistil, as in *Crataegus monogyna*

monopetalus

mon-OH-PET-uh-lus

monopetala, monopetalum

With a single petal, as in *Limoniastrum
monopetalum*

monophyllus

mon-oh-FIL-us

monophylla, monophyllum

With one leaf, as in *Pinus monophylla*

monopyrenus

mon-OH-py-ree-nus

monopyrena, monopyrenum

With a single stone, as in *Cotoneaster
monopyrenus*

monostachyus

mon-oh-STAK-ee-us

monostachya, monostachyum

With one spike, as in *Guzmania
monostachya*

1

Monarda didyma,
bergamot

2

Clematis montana,
mountain clematis

monspessulanus
monz-pess-yoo-LAH-nus
monspessulana, monspessulanum
Connected with Montpellier, France, as in
Acer monspessulanum

Monstera
mon-STEER-uh
From Latin *monstrosus* meaning 'abnormal',
because the leaves of many species are
perforated (*Araceae*)

monstrosus
mon-STROH-sus
monstrosa, monstrosum
Abnormal, as in *Gypsophila* × *monstrosa*

montanus [2]
MON-tah-nus
montana, montanum
Relating to mountains, as in *Clematis
montana*

montensis
mont-EN-sis
montensis, montense
—

monticola
mon-TIH-koh-luh
Growing on mountains, as in *Halesia
monticola*

Montia
MON-tee-uh
Named after Giuseppe Monti (1682–1760),
Italian botanist and chemist (*Montiaceae*)

montigenus
mon-TEE-gen-us
montigena, montigenum
Born of the mountains, as in *Picea
montigena*

Moraea
MORE-ee-uh
Originally named *Morea* after Robert More
(1703–80), British botanist, Linnaeus had a
change of heart and re-christened it *Moraea*,
after Sara Elisabeth Moraea (1716–1806),
his wife (*Iridaceae*)

Morella
mo-REL-uh
Resembling the mulberry, *Morus*, though
smaller (diminutive *ella*) (*Myricaceae*)

morifolius
mor-ee-FOH-lee-us
morifolia, morifolium
With leaves like the mulberry (*Morus*), as in
Passiflora morifolia

Morina
mo-REE-nuh
Named after Louis Morin de Saint-Victor
(1635–1715), French botanist and physician
(*Caprifoliaceae*)

Morus
MO-russ
From Latin *morum*, the vernacular name for
M. nigra (*Moraceae*)

moschatus
MOSS-kuh-tus
moschata, moschatum
Musky, as in *Malva moschata*

mucosus
moo-KOZ-us
mucosa, mucosum
Slimy, as in *Rollinia mucosa*

mucronatus
muh-kron-AH-tus
mucronata, mucronatum
With a point, as in *Gaultheria mucronata*

mucronulatus
muh-kron-yoo-LAH-tus
mucronulata, mucronulatum
With a sharp, hard point, as in
Rhododendron mucronulatum

Muehlenbeckia
moo-lun-BEK-ee-uh
Named after Henri Gustav Mühlenbeck
(1798–1845), French physician and
botanist (*Polygonaceae*)

Muhlenbergia
moo-lun-BERG-ee-uh
Named after Gotthilf Heinrich Ernst
Muhlenberg (1753–1815), American cleric
and botanist (*Poaceae*)

Mukdenia
muk-DEEN-ee-uh
Named for Mukden (now Shenyang), the
capital of China's Liaoning Province
(*Saxifragaceae*)

multi-
Used in compound words to denote many

multibracteatus
mul-tee-brak-tee-AH-tus
multibracteata, multibracteatum
With many bracts, as in *Rosa multibracteata*

multicaulis
mul-tee-KAW-lis
multicaulis, multicaule
With many stems, as in *Salvia multicaulis*

multiceps
MUL-tee-seps
With many heads, as in *Gaillardia multiceps*

multicolor
mul-tee-kol-or
Multicoloured, as in *Echeveria multicolor*

multicostatus
mul-tee-koh-STAH-tus
multicostata, multicostatum
With many ribs, as in *Echinofossulocactus multicostatus*

multifidus
mul-TIF-id-us
multifida, multifidum
With many divisions, usually of leaves with many tears, as in *Helleborus multifidus*

multiflorus
mul-tee-FLOR-us
multiflora, multiforum
With many flowers, as in *Cytisus multiflorus*

multilineatus
mul-tee-lin-ee-AH-tus
multilineata, multilineatum
With many lines, as in *Hakea multilineata*

multinervis
mul-tee-NER-vis
multinervis, multinerve
With many nerves, as in *Quercus multinervis*

multiplex
MUL-tih-pleks
With many folds, as in *Bambusa multiplex*

multiradiatus
mul-tee-rad-ee-AH-tus
multiradiata, multiradiatum
With many rays, as in *Pelargonium multiradiatum*

multisectus
mul-tee-SEK-tus
multisecta, multisectum
With many cuts, as in *Geranium multisectum*

mundulus
mun-DYOO-lus
mundula, mundulum
Trim; neat, as in *Gaultheria mundula*

muralis [1]
mur-AH-lis
muralis, murale
Growing on walls, as in *Cymbalaria muralis*

muricatus
mur-ee-KAH-tus
muricata, muricatum
With rough and hard points, as in *Solanum muricatum*

Murraya
MUR-ee-uh
Named after Johan Andreas Murray (1740–91), Swedish physician and botanist (*Rutaceae*)

Musa
MOO-suh
From Arabic *mouz*, the vernacular name for banana (*Musaceae*)

musaicus
muh-ZAY-ih-kus
musaica, musaicum
Like a mosaic, as in *Guzmania musaica*

Muscari
mus-KAR-ee
From Greek *moschos* meaning 'musk', referring to the scent of the flowers, via the Turkish name (*Asparagaceae*)

muscipula
musk-IP-yoo-luh
Catches flies, as in *Dionaea muscipula*

muscivorus
mus-SEE-ver-us
muscivora, muscivorum
Appearing to eat flies, as in *Helicodiceros muscivorus*

muscoides
mus-COY-deez
Resembling moss, as in *Saxifraga muscoides*

muscosus
mus-KOH-sus
muscosa, muscosum
Like moss, as in *Selaginella muscosa*

Musella
moo-ZEL-uh
Resembling the related genus *Musa*, though smaller (diminutive *ella*) (*Musaceae*)

Mussaenda
moos-ay-EN-duh
From Sinhalese (Sri Lanka) *mussenda*, the vernacular name (*Rubiaceae*)

mutabilis [2]
mew-TAH-bih-lis
mutabilis, mutabile
Changeable, particularly relating to colour, as in *Hibiscus mutabilis*

mutatus
mew-TAH-tus
mutata, mutatum
Changed, as in *Saxifraga mutata*

muticus
MEW-tih-kus
mutica, muticum
Blunt, as in *Pycnanthemum muticum*

mutilatus
mew-til-AH-tus
mutilata, mutilatum
Divided as though by tearing, as in *Peperomia mutilata*

Mutisia
mew-TIZ-ee-uh
Named after José Celestino Mutis (1732–1808), Spanish cleric, botanist and mathematician (*Asteraceae*)

Myoporum
my-oh-POR-um
From Greek *myein* meaning 'to close' and *poros* meaning 'pore', a reference to the arid habit of many species, where leaf pores are closed to save water (*Scrophulariaceae*)

Myosotis [3]
my-oh-SOH-tis
From Greek *mus* meaning 'mouse' and *otis* meaning 'ear', to which the leaves are said to resemble (*Boraginaceae*)

myri-
Used in compound words to denote very many

1

Cymbalaria muralis,
ivy-leaved toadflax

2

Hibiscus mutabilis,
Confederate rose

3

Myosotis scorpioides,
water forget-me-not

Myrica
MI-ri-kuh
From Greek *myrike*, the vernacular name for
tamarisk, *Tamarix* (*Myricaceae*)

myriacanthus
mir-ee-uh-KAN-thus
myriacantha, myriacanthum
With very many thorns, as in *Aloe
myriacantha*

myriocarpus
mir-ee-oh-KAR-pus
myriocarpa, myriocarpum
With very many fruits, as in *Schefflera
myriocarpa*

Myriophyllum
mi-ree-oh-FIL-um
From Greek *myrios* meaning 'many' and
phyllon meaning 'leaf', as the finely-divided
foliage appears plentiful (*Haloragaceae*)

myriophyllus
mir-ee-oh-FIL-us
myriophylla, myriophyllum
With very many leaves, as in *Acaena
myriophylla*

myriostigma
mir-ee-oh-STIG-muh
With many spots, as in *Astrophytum
myriostigma*

Myrmecodia
mir-meh-KOH-dee-um
From Greek *myrmekodes* meaning 'full of
ants', as the swollen stem provides nesting
space for ants (*Rubiaceae*)

myrmecophilus
mir-meh-koh-FIL-us
myrmecophila, myrmecophilum
Ant-loving, as in *Aeschynanthus
myrmecophilus*

Myrrhis
MUR-iss
From Greek *murrha* meaning 'myrrh-
scented'; also the name of this plant and the
resin extracted from trees of the genus
Commiphora, the true myrrh (*Apiaceae*)

Myrsine
mir-SY-nee
From Greek *myrsine* meaning 'myrtle'
(*Primulaceae*)

myrsinifolius
mir-sin-ee-FOH-lee-us
myrsinifolia, myrsinifolium
With leaves like *Myrsine*, often referring to
myrtle for which this is an ancient Greek
name, as in *Salix myrsinifolia*

myrsinites
mir-SIN-ih-teez
—

myrsinoides
mir-SIN-OY-deez
Resembling *Myrsine*, as in *Gaultheria
myrsinoides*

myrtifolius
mir-tih-FOH-lee-us
myrtifolia, myrtifolium
With leaves like *Myrsine*, as in
Leptospermum myrtifolium

Myrtillocactus
mir-til-oh-KAK-tus
A cactus whose fruits have been likened to
those of true myrtle (*Myrtus communis*) or
bilberry (*Vaccinium myrtillus*) (*Cactaceae*)

Myrtus
MIR-tus
From Greek *myrtos*, the vernacular name for
M. communis (*Myrtaceae*)

Nandina

nan-DEEN-nuh

From Japanese *nanten*, the vernacular name for *N. domestica* (*Berberidaceae*)

nanellus

nan-EL-lus

nanella, nanellum

Very dwarf, as in *Lathyrus odoratus* var. *nanellus*

nankingensis

nan-king-EN-sis

nankingensis, nankingense

From Nanking (Nanjing), China, as in *Chrysanthemum nankingense*

nanus

NAH-nus

nana, nanum

Dwarf, as in *Betula nana*

napaulensis

nap-awl-EN-sis

napaulensis, napaulense

From Nepal, as in *Meconopsis napaulensis*

napellus

nap-ELL-us

napella, napellum

Like a little turnip, referring to the roots, as in *Aconitum napellus*

napifolius

nap-ih-FOH-lee-us

napifolia, napifolium

With leaves shaped like a turnip (*Brassica rapa*), i.e. a flattened sphere, as in *Salvia napifolia*

narbonensis

nar-bone-EN-sis

narbonensis, narbonense

From Narbonne, France, as in *Linum narbonense*

narcissiflorus

nar-sis-si-FLOR-us

narcissiflora, narcissiflorum

With flowers like daffodil (*Narcissus*), as in *Iris narcissiflora*

Narcissus

nar-SIS-us

Named after Narcissus of Greek mythology, a hunter who saw his reflection in a forest pool and fell in love with it, but upon realising that the love could not be reciprocated, melted away and turned into a flower (*Amaryllidaceae*)

Nassella

nas-EL-uh

From Latin *nassa* meaning 'basket with narrow neck', a reference to the overlapping lemmas (*Poaceae*)

Nasturtium

nuh-STUR-shum

From Latin *nasus* meaning 'nose' and *tortus* meaning 'twisted', alluding to the strong scent of the foliage; not to be confused with *Tropaeolum* (*Brassicaceae*)

natalensis

nuh-tal-EN-sis

natalensis, natalense

From Natal, South Africa, as in *Tulbaghia natalensis*

natans

NAT-anz

Floating, as in *Trapa natans*

nauseosus

naw-see-OH-sus

nauseosa, nauseosum

Causing nausea, as in *Chrysothamnus nauseosus*

navicularis

nav-ik-yoo-LAH-ris

navicularis, naviculare

Shaped like a boat, as in *Callisia navicularis*

neapolitanus

nee-uh-pol-ih-TAH-nus

neapolitana, neapolitanum

Connected with Naples, Italy, as in *Allium neapolitanum*

nebulosus

neb-yoo-LOH-sus

nebulosa, nebulosum

Like a cloud, as in *Aglaonema nebulosum*

Nectaroscordum

nek-tuh-roh-SKOR-dum

From Greek *nektar* meaning 'drink of the gods' and *skordion* meaning 'garlic', a reference to the heavy nectar production in this garlic relative (*Amaryllidaceae*)

neglectus

nay-GLEK-tus

neglecta, neglectum

Previously neglected, as in *Muscari neglectum*

Neillia

NEE-lee-uh

Named after Patrick Neill (1776–1851), Scottish botanist (*Rosaceae*)

nelumbifolius

nel-um-bee-FOH-lee-us

nelumbifolia, nelumbifolium

With leaves like lotus (*Nelumbo*), as in *Ligularia nelumbifolia*

Nelumbo [1]

ne-LUM-boh

From Sinhalese (Sri Lanka) *nelum*, the vernacular name for lotus flower, from *N. nucifera* (*Nelumbonaceae*)

Nematanthus

nem-uh-TAN-thus

From Greek *nema* meaning 'thread' and *anthos* meaning 'flower', as the blooms of some species hang from thread-like pedicels (*Gesneriaceae*)

Nemesia

nuh-ME-shuh

From Greek *nemesion*, the vernacular name for a similar plant (*Scrophulariaceae*)

Nemophila

nem-OF-il-uh

From Greek *nemos* meaning 'woodland glade' and *phileo* meaning 'to love', a reference to habitat of some species (*Boraginaceae*)

nemoralis

nem-or-RAH-lis

nemoralis, nemorale

—

nemorosus

nem-or-OH-sus

nemorosa, nemorosum

Of woodland, as in *Anemone nemorosa*

Neolitsea

ne-oh-LIT-see-uh

From Greek *neos* meaning 'new', plus the related genus *Litsea* (*Lauraceae*)

Neolloydia

ne-oh-LOY-dee-uh

Named after Francis Ernest Lloyd (1868–1947), American botanist, plus Greek *neos* meaning 'new', to differentiate the genus from *Lloydia* (*Cactaceae*)

Neomarica

ne-oh-MAR-i-kuh

From Greek *neos* meaning 'new', plus the related genus *Marica*, an illegitimate name; species of *Marica* are now distributed amongst nine other genera, including this one (*Iridaceae*)

Neoregelia

ne-oh-reg-EE-lee-uh

Named after Eduard August von Regel (1815–92), German botanist, plus Greek *neos* meaning 'new', to differentiate the genus from *Regelia* (*Bromeliaceae*)

nepalensis

nep-al-EN-sis

nepalensis, nepalense

—

nepaulensis

nep-al-EN-sis

nepaulensis, nepaulense

From Nepal, as in *Hedera nepalensis*

Nepenthes

nuh-PEN-theez

From Greek *ne* meaning 'not' and *penthes* meaning 'mourning'; in Greek mythology, the potion *nepenthes pharmakon* was given to Helen of Troy to dispel her grief (*Nepenthaceae*)

Nepeta

ne-PEE-tuh

From Latin *nepeta*, the vernacular name for an aromatic plant, possibly derived from Nepete (now Nepi), a city in central Italy (*Lamiaceae*)

nepetoides

nep-et-OY-deez

Resembling catmint (*Nepeta*), as in *Agastache nepetoides*

Nephrolepis

nef-roh-LEE-pis

From Greek *nephros* meaning 'kidney' and *lepis* meaning 'scale', alluding to the shape of the membrane over the sporangia (*Polypodiaceae*)

neriifolius

ner-ih-FOH-lee-us

neriifolia, neriifolium

With leaves like oleander (*Nerium*), as in *Podocarpus neriifolius*

Nerine [2]

nuh-RY-nee

Named after a sea nymph from Greek mythology (*Amaryllidaceae*)

Nerium

NEER-ee-um

From Greek *nerion*, the vernacular name for *N. oleander* (*Apocynaceae*)

Nelumbo nucifera, sacred lotus

Nertera

NER-tuh-ruh

From Greek *nerteros* meaning 'low down', a reference to the dainty, creeping habit (*Rubiaceae*)

nervis

NERV-is

nervis, nerve

—

nervosus

ner-VOH-sus

nervosa, nervosum

With visible nerves, as in *Astelia nervosa*

nicaeensis

ny-see-EN-sis

nicaeensis, nicaeense

From Nice, France, as in *Acis nicaeensis*

Nicandra [3]

NY-kan-druh

Named after Nicander, a Greek poet from Colophon in modern-day Turkey (*Solanaceae*)

Nicotiana

ni-koh-tee-AH-nuh

Named after Jean Nicot (1530–1604), French diplomat who introduced tobacco to France (*Solanaceae*)

nictitans

NIC-tih-tanz

Blinking; moving, as in *Chamaecrista nictitans*

Nerine humilis,
dwarf nerine

Nicandra physalodes,
shoo-fly

Galanthus nivalis,
snowdrop

Nidularium
ny-dew-LAIR-ee-um
From Greek *nidus* meaning 'nest' and *aria* meaning 'pertaining to'; the leaves are arranged in a nest-like rosette (*Bromeliaceae*)

nidus
NID-us
Like a nest, as in *Asplenium nidus*

Nierembergia
near-um-BERG-ee-uh
Named after Juan Eusebio Nieremberg (1595–1658), Spanish cleric (Solanaceae)

Nigella
ny-JEL-uh
From Latin *niger* meaning 'black' and diminutive *ella*, referring to the small black seeds (*Ranunculaceae*)

niger
NY-ger
nigra, nigrum
Black, as in *Phyllostachys nigra*

nigratus
ny-GRAH-tus
nigrata, nigratum
Blackened, blackish, as in *Oncidium nigratum*

nigrescens
ny-GRESS-enz
Turning black, as in *Silene nigrescens*

nigricans
ny-GRIH-kanz
Blackish, as in *Salix nigricans*

nikoensis
nik-o-EN-sis
nikoensis, nikoense
From Nike, Japan, as in *Adenophora nikoensis*

niloticus
nil-OH-tih-kus
nilotica, niloticum
Connected with the Nile Valley, as in *Salvia nilotica*

Nipponanthemum
nip-on-ANTH-uh-mum
From Japanese *Nippon* meaning 'Japan', plus Greek *anthemon* meaning 'flower' (*Asteraceae*)

nipponicus
nip-PON-ih-kus
nipponica, nipponicum
Connected with Japan (Nippon), as in *Phyllodoce nipponica*

nitens
NI-tenz
—
nitidus
NI-ti-dus
nitida, nitidum
Shining, as in *Lonicera nitida*

nivalis [4]
niv-VAH-lis
nivalis, nivale
—
niveus
NIV-ee-us
nivea, niveum

nivosus
niv-OH-sus
nivosa, nivosum
As white as snow, or growing near snow, as in *Galanthus nivalis*

nobilis
NO-bil-is
nobilis, nobile
Noble; renowned, as in *Laurus nobilis*

noctiflorus
nok-tee-FLOR-us
noctiflora, noctiflorum
—
nocturnus
NOK-ter-nus
nocturna, nocturnum
Flowering at night, as in *Silene noctiflora*

nodiflorus
no-dee-FLOR-us
nodiflora, nodiflorum
Flowering at the nodes, as in *Eleutherococcus nodiflorus*

2   3   4

A B C D E F G H I J K L M N O P Q R S T U V W X Y Z i

1

Nolana spathulata,
Chilean bellflower

2

Hyacinthoides non-scripta,
English bluebell

3

Symphyotrichum novi-belgii,
Michaelmas daisy

nodosus
nod-OH-sus
nodosa, nodosum
With conspicuous joints or nodes, as in
Geranium nodosum

nodulosus
no-du-LOH-sus
nodulosa, nodulosum
With small nodes, as in *Echeveria nodulosa*

Nolana [1]
noh-LAH-nuh
From Latin *nola* meaning 'small bell', like the
flowers (*Solanaceae*)

noli-tangere
NO-lee TAN-ger-ee
'Touch not' (because the seed pods burst), as
in *Impatiens noli-tangere*

Nomocharis
noh-MOK-ur-is
From Greek *nomos* meaning 'meadow' and
charis meaning 'grace', graceful plants from
meadows (*Liliaceae*)

non-scriptus [2]
non-SKRIP-tus
non-scripta, non-scriptum
Without any markings, as in *Hyacinthoides
non-scripta*

norvegicus
nor-VEG-ih-kus
norvegica, norvegicum
Connected with Norway, as in *Arenaria
norvegica*

notatus
no-TAH-tus
notata, notatum
With spots or marks, as in *Glyceria notata*

Nothofagus
noh-toh-FAY-gus
From Greek *nothos* meaning 'false' and
Fagus, another genus (*Nothofagaceae*)

Notholirion
noh-toh-LIR-ee-on
From Greek *nothos* meaning 'false' and *lirion*
meaning 'lily' (*Liliaceae*)

Notholithocarpus
noh-tho-lith-oh-KAR-pus
From Greek *nothos* meaning 'false' and
Lithocarpus, a related genus (*Fagaceae*)

Nothoscordum
noh-toh-SKOR-dum
From Greek *nothos* meaning 'false' and
skordion meaning 'garlic' (*Amaryllidaceae*)

novae-angliae
NO-vay ANG-lee-a
Connected with New England, USA, as in
Aster novae-angliae

novae-zelandiae
NO-vay zee-LAN-dee-ay
Connected with New Zealand, as in *Acaena
novae-zelandiae*

novi-
Used in compound words to denote new

novi-belgii [3]
NO-vee BEL-jee-eye
Connected with New York, USA, as in *Aster
novi-belgii*

nubicola
new-BIH-koh-luh
Growing up in the clouds, as in *Salvia
nubicola*

nubigenus
new-bee-GEE-nus
nubigena, nubigenum
Born up in the clouds, as in *Kniphofia
nubigena*

nucifer
NEW-siff-er
nucifera, nuciferum
Producing nuts, as in *Cocos nucifera*

nudatus

new-DAH-tus

nudata, nudatum

nudus

NEW-dus

nuda, nudum

Bare; naked, as in *Nepeta nuda*

nudicaulis

new-dee-KAW-lis

nudicaulis, nudicaule

With bare stems, as in *Papaver nudicaule*

nudiflorus

new-dee-FLOR-us

nudiflora, nudiflorum

With flowers that appear before the leaves, as in *Jasminum nudiflorum*

numidicus

nu-MID-ih-kus

numidica, numidicum

Connected with Algeria, as in *Abies numidica*

nummularius

num-ew-LAH-ree-us

nummularia, nummularium

Like coins, as in *Lysimachia nummularia*

Nuphar

NEW-far

From Arabic or Persian *nenufar*, meaning water lily (*Nymphaeaceae*)

nutans

NUT-anz

Nodding, as in *Billbergia nutans*

nyctagineus

nyk-ta-JEE-nee-us

nyctaginea, nyctagineum

Flowering at night, as in *Mirabilis nyctaginea*

Nymphaea

nim-FAY-uh

From Greek *nymphaia* meaning 'water lily', derived from the nymphs of Greek mythology (*Nymphaeaceae*)

Nymphoides (also nymphoides)

nim-FOY-deez

Resembling the genus *Nymphaea* (*Menyanthaceae*)

Nyssa

NIS-uh

The classical Latin name for a water nymph, alluding to the aquatic habitat of *N. aquatica* (*Nyssaceae*)

Nymphaea

Water lilies are aquatic perennials with floating leaves and elaborate flowers. This description, though accurate, fails to convey the romance of these plants, a romance that inspired French Impressionist Claude Monet to paint them so frequently. They are important to biologists, too, as one of the first families of flowering plants to diverge. Their beautiful blooms reveal characteristics considered by some as primitive, such as having numerous petals (most flowers have three, four or five petals) and stamens where the anther and filament can be difficult to tell apart. Observing these characteristics can help us understand how flowers first evolved.

Nymphaea alba, white water lily

obconicus

ob-KON-ih-kus

obconica, obconicum

In the shape of an inverted cone, as in *Primula obconica*

obesus

oh-BEE-sus

obesa, obesum

Fat, as in *Euphorbia obesa*

oblatus

ob-LAH-tus

oblata, oblatum

With flattened ends, as in *Syringa oblata*

obliquus

oh-BLIK-wus

obliqua, obliquum

Lopsided, as in *Nothofagus obliqua*

oblongatus

ob-long-GAH-tus

oblongata, oblongatum

—

oblongus

ob-LONG-us

oblonga, oblongum

Oblong, as in *Passiflora oblongata*

oblongifolius

ob-long-Ih-FOH-lee-us

oblongifolia, oblongifolium

With oblong leaves, as in *Asplenium oblongifolium*

obovatus

ob-oh-VAH-tus

obovata, obovatum

In the shape of an inverted egg, as in *Paeonia obovata*

Obregonia

oh-bre-GOH-nee-uh

Named after Álvaro Obregón Salido (1880–1928), 39th President of Mexico (*Cactaceae*)

obscurus

ob-SKEW-rus

obscura, obscurum

Not clear or certain, as in *Digitalis obscura*

obtectus

ob-TEK-tus

obtecta, obtectum

Covered; protected, as in *Cordyline obtecta*

obtusatus

ob-tew-SAH-tus

obtusata, obtusatum

Blunt, as in *Asplenium obtusatum*

obtusifolius

ob-too-sih-FOH-lee-us

obtusifolia, obtusifolium

With blunt leaves, as in *Peperomia obtusifolia*

obtusus

ob-TOO-sus

obtusa, obtusum

Blunt, as in *Chamaecyparis obtusa*

obvallatus

ob-val-LAH-tus

obvallata, obvallatum

Enclosed, within a wall, as in *Saussurea obvallata*

occidentalis

ok-sih-den-TAH-lis

occidentalis, occidentale

Relating to the west, as in *Thuja occidentalis*

occultus

ock-ULL-tus

occulta, occultum

Hidden, as in *Huernia occulta*

ocellatus

ock-ell-AH-tus

ocellata, ocellatum

With an eye; with a spot surrounding a smaller spot of a different colour, as in *Convolvulus ocellatus*

Ochagavia

ok-uh-GAH-vee-uh

Named after Sylvestris Ochagavia (19th century), Chilean education minister (*Bromeliaceae*)

Ochna

OK-nuh

From Greek *ochne* meaning 'pear tree', in reference to the shape of the fruit or possibly the leaves (*Ochnaceae*)

ochraceus

oh-KRA-see-us

ochracea, ochraceum

Ochre-coloured, as in *Hebe ochracea*

ochroleucus

ock-roh-LEW-kus

ochroleuca, ochroleucum

Yellowish white, as in *Crocus ochroleucus*

Ocimum

OS-i-mum

From Greek *okimom*, the vernacular name for an aromatic plant (*Lamiaceae*)

oct-

Used in compound words to denote eight

octandrus

ock-TAN-drus

octandra, octandrum

With eight stamens, as in *Phytolacca octandra*

octopetalus

ock-toh-PET-uh-lus

octopetala, octopetalum

With eight petals, as in *Dryas octopetala*

oculatus

ock-yoo-LAH-tus

oculata, oculatum

With an eye, as in *Haworthia oculata*

oculiroseus

ock-yoo-lee-ROH-sus

oculirosea, oculiroseum

With a rose-coloured eye, as in *Hibiscus palustris* f. *oculiroseus*

ocymoides

ok-kye-MOY-deez

Resembling basil (*Ocimum*), as in *Halimium ocymoides*

Odontoglossum

oh-don-toh-GLOS-um

From Greek *odontos* meaning 'tooth' and *glossos* meaning 'tongue', as the floral lip has tooth-like projections (*Orchidaceae*)

odoratissimus

oh-dor-uh-TISS-ih-mus

odoratissima, odoratissimum

With a very fragrant scent, as in *Viburnum odoratissimum*

odoratus

oh-dor-AH-tus

odorata, odoratum

—

odoriferus

oh-dor-IH-fer-us

odorifera, odoriferum

—

odorus

oh-DOR-us

odora, odorum

With a fragrant scent, as in *Lathyrus odoratus*

Oemleria

oom-LEER-ee-uh

Named after Augustus Gottlieb Oemler (1773–1852), German naturalist (*Rosaceae*)

Oenanthe

ee-NAN-thee

From Greek *oinos* meaning 'wine' and *anthos* meaning 'flower', as the blooms have a vinous scent (*Apiaceae*)

Oenothera

ee-NOTH-ur-uh

Etymology uncertain, though perhaps from Greek *oinotheras*, a plant added to wine to induce sleep, or improve the taste of wine; alternatively from Latin *onotheras*, a toxic plant given to animals so they can be caught (*Onagraceae*)

officinalis

oh-fiss-ih-NAH-lis

officinalis, officinale

Sold in shops, hence denoting a useful plant (vegetable, culinary or medicinal herb), as in *Rosmarinus officinalis*

officinarum

off-ik-IN-ar-um

From a shop, usually an apothecary, as in *Mandragora officinarum*

olbius

OL-bee-us

olbia, olbium

Connected with the Îles d'Hyères, France, as in *Lavatera olbia*

Olea [1]

OH-lee-uh

From classical Latin name for olive, *O. europaea* (*Oleaceae*)

Olea europaea,
common olive

Olearia

oh-LEAR-ee-uh

Named after Adam Ölschläger (c. 1603–71), German scholar [Adam Olearius in Latin] (*Asteraceae*)

oleiferus

oh-lee-IH-fer-us

oleifera, oleiferum

Producing oil, as in *Elaeis oleifera*

oleifolius

oh-lee-ih-FOH-lee-us

oleifolia, oleifolium

With leaves like olive (*Olea*), as in *Lithodora oleifolia*

oleoides

oh-lee-OY-deez

Resembling olive (*Olea*), as in *Daphne oleoides*

oleraceus

awl-lur-RAY-see-us

oleracea, oleraceum

Used as a vegetable, as in *Spinacia oleracea*

oliganthus

ol-ig-AN-thus

oligantha, oliganthum

With few flowers, as in *Ceanothus oliganthus*

oligocarpus

ol-ig-oh-KAR-pus

oligocarpa, oligocarpum

With few fruits, as in *Cayratia oligocarpa*

oligophyllus

ol-ig-oh-FIL-us

oligophylla, oligophyllum

With few leaves, as in *Senna oligophylla*

oligospermus

ol-ig-oh-SPERM-us

oligosperma, oligospermum

With few seeds, as in *Draba oligosperma*

olitorius

ol-ih-TOR-ee-us

olitoria, olitorium

Relating to culinary herbs, as in *Corchorus olitorius*

olivaceus

oh-lee-VAY-see-us

olivacea, olivaceum

Olive; green-brown, as in *Lithops olivacea*

Olsynium

ol-SY-nee-um

From Greek *ol* meaning 'little' and *syn* meaning 'joined', as the stamens are only partially fused together (*Iridaceae*)

2

Oncidium leucochilum,
white-lipped orchid

olympicus

oh-LIM-pih-kus

olympica, olympicum

Connected with Mount Olympus, Greece, as in *Hypericum olympicum*

Omphalodes

om-fah-LOH-deez

From Greek *omphalos* meaning 'navel', as the fruits are dimpled like the human navel (*Boraginaceae*)

Omphalogramma

om-fah-loh-GRAM-uh

From Greek *omphalos* meaning 'navel' and *gramme* meaning 'line', perhaps an allusion to lines of dimples on the seeds? (*Primulaceae*)

Oncidium [2]

on-SID-ee-um

From Greek *oncos* meaning 'swelling or tumour', referring to calluses on the floral lip (*Orchidaceae*)

Onoclea

on-OK-lee-uh

From Greek *onos* meaning 'vessel and *kleiein* meaning 'to close', as the leaf edge is folded over to enclose the sporangia (*Onocleaceae*)

Ononis

o-NOH-nis

From Greek *onos* meaning 'donkey' and *oninemi* meaning 'useful', perhaps because only a donkey can safely eat from spiny *O. spinosa* (*Fabaceae*)

Onopordum

o-noh-POR-dum

From Greek *onos* meaning 'donkey' and *perdo* meaning 'to break wind', though the reasons for this name are obscure (*Asteraceae*)

Onosma

uh-NOZ-muh

From Greek *onos* meaning 'donkey' and *osme* meaning 'fragrance', either because some part of the plant smells or because donkeys consume it (*Boraginaceae*)

Onychium

on-IK-ee-um

From Greek *onychion* meaning 'little claw', referring to the shape of the leaflets (*Pteridaceae*)

opacus

oh-PAH-kus

opaca, opacum

Dark; dull; shaded, as in *Crataegus opaca*

operculatus

oh-per-koo-LAH-tus

operculata, operculatum

With a cover or lid, as in *Luffa operculata*

ophioglossifolius

oh-fee-oh-gloss-ih-FOH-lee-us

ophioglossifolia, ophioglossifolium

With leaves like adder's tongue fern (*Ophioglossum*), as in *Ranunculus ophioglossifolius*

Ophiopogon

oh-fee-oh-POH-gon

From Greek *ophis* meaning 'snake' and *pogon* meaning 'beard', a translation of the Japanese name 'snake's-beard', perhaps referring to the tufted habit (*Asparagaceae*)

Ophrys

OF-ris

From Greek *ophyras* meaning 'eyebrow', as several species have a fringe of hairs on the edge of the flower lip (*Orchidaceae*)

Ophthalmophyllum

of-thal-moh-FIL-um

From Greek *ophthalmos* meaning 'eye' and *phyllon* meaning 'leaf', as each leaf has a lens-like tip (*Aizoaceae*)

Oplismenus

op-lis-MEN-us

From Greek *oplisma* meaning 'armament' and *menos* meaning 'courage', as the flower spikelets have spear-like awns (*Poaceae*)

oppositifolius

op-po-sih-tih-FOH-lee-us

oppositifolia, oppositifolium

With leaves that grow opposite each other from the stem, as in *Chiastophyllum oppositifolium*

Opuntia

oh-POON-tee-uh

From Greek, the name for a spiny plant found near the ancient Greek city of Opus (*Cactaceae*)

Orbea

OR-bee-uh

From Latin *orbis* meaning 'ring', as the flowers have a prominent ring-like annulus in the centre (*Apocynaceae*)

orbicularis

or-bik-yoo-LAH-ris

orbicularis, orbiculare

—

orbiculatus

or-bee-kul-AH-tus

orbiculata, orbiculatum

In the shape of a disc; flat and round, as in *Cotyledon orbiculata*

orchideus

or-KI-de-us

orchidea, orchideum

—

orchioides

or-ki-OY-deez

Like an orchid (*Orchis*), as in *Veronica orchidea*

orchidiflorus

or-kee-dee-FLOR-us

orchidiflora, orchidiflorum

With flowers like an orchid (*Orchis*), as in *Gladiolus orchidiflorus*

Orchis
OR-kis
From Greek *orkhis* meaning 'testicle', alluding to the shape of the tubers (*Orchidaceae*)

oreganus
or-reh-GAH-nus
oregana, oreganum
Connected with Oregon, USA, as in *Sidalcea oregana*

Oreocereus
or-ee-oh-SER-ee-us
From Greek *oros* meaning 'mountain', plus *Cereus*, a related genus; these cacti hail from the Andes (*Cactaceae*)

oreophilus
or-ee-O-fil-us
oreophila, oreophilum
Mountain-loving, as in *Sarracenia oreophila*

oresbius
or-ES-bee-us
oresbia, oresbium
Growing on mountains, as in *Castilleja oresbia*

orientalis
or-ee-en-TAH-lis
orientalis, orientale
Relating to the Orient; eastern, as in *Thuja orientalis*

origanifolius
or-ih-gan-ih-FOH-lee-us
origanifolia, origanifolium
With leaves like marjoram (*Origanum*), as in *Chaenorhinum origanifolium*

origanoides
or-ig-an-OY-deez
Resembling marjoram (*Origanum*), as in *Dracocephalum origanoides*

Origanum
o-ri-GAH-num
From Greek *origanon*, an acrid herb; derived from *oros* meaning 'mountain' and *ganos* meaning 'beauty' (*Lamiaceae*)

Orixa
o-RIKS-uh
From Japanese vernacular name for *O. japonica* (*Rutaceae*)

Orlaya
or-LAY-uh
Named after Johann Orlay (c. 1770–1827), Hungarian physician and botanist (*Apiaceae*)

ornans
OR-nanz
—

ornatus
or-NA-tus
ornata, ornatum
Ornamental; showy, as in *Musa ornata*

ornatissimus
or-nuh-TISS-ih-mus
ornatissima, ornatissimum
Very showy, as in *Bulbophyllum ornatissimum*

Ornithogalum [1]
or-ni-THO-gal-um
From Greek *ornithos* meaning 'bird' and *gala* meaning 'milk', on account of the white flowers of some species, though Romans are said to have used the term 'bird's milk' to refer to something wonderful or rare, as with 'hen's teeth' (*Asparagaceae*)

ornithopodus
or-nith-OP-oh-dus
ornithopoda, ornithopodum
—

ornithopus
or-nith-OP-pus
Like a bird's foot, as in *Carex ornithopoda*

Orobanche
or-oh-BAN-kee
From Greek *orobos* meaning a type of vetch, plus *ankho* meaning 'to strangle', referring to the parasitic habit (*Orobanchaceae*)

Orontium
o-RON-tee-um
From Greek name for a plant that grew by/in the River Orontes, which flows through Lebanon, Syria and Turkey; this aquatic plant is native to the eastern United States (*Araceae*)

Orostachys
or-oh-STAK-is
From Greek *oros* meaning 'mountain' and *stachys* meaning 'ear of grain', as these are alpine plants with wheat-like flower spikes (*Crassulaceae*)

Oroya
uh-ROY-uh
Named after La Oroya, a city in central Peru, where the plant was first discovered (*Cactaceae*)

Ortegocactus
or-TAY-goh-kak-tus
Named after the Ortega family of San José Lachiguirí in Oaxaca, Mexico, who helped discover this cactus (*Cactaceae*)

ortho-
Used in compound words to denote straight or upright

1

Ornithogalum pyrenaicum,
Bath asparagus

2

Oryza sativa,
rice

orthobotrys

or-THO-bot-ris

With upright clusters, as in *Berberis orthobotrys*

orthocarpus

or-tho-KAR-pus

orthocarpa, orthocarpum

With upright fruit, as in *Malus orthocarpa*

orthoglossus

or-tho-GLOSS-us

orthoglossa, orthoglossum

With a straight tongue, as in *Bulbophyllum orthoglossum*

Orthophytum

or-tho-FY-tum

From Greek *orthos* meaning 'straight' and *phyton* meaning 'plant', as the tall, straight inflorescences bear leaves (*Bromeliaceae*)

orthosepalus

or-tho-SEP-a-lus

orthosepala, orthosepalum

With straight sepals, as in *Rubus orthosepalus*

Oryza [2]

or-EYE-zuh

From Greek *oryza* meaning 'rice', both words deriving from Arabic *eruz* (*Poaceae*)

Osmanthus

oz-MAN-thus

From Greek *osme* meaning 'fragrant' and *anthos* meaning 'flower' (*Oleaceae*)

3

Osmunda regalis,
royal fern

Osmunda [3]

oz-MOON-duh

Many possible etymologies have been suggested for this Linnean name, which he did not explain. Osmunder was the Saxon name for the Norse god Thor, while Osmund the Waterman, also from Saxon mythology, hid his family in a clump of ferns; bog iron, an iron deposit found in marshland where these ferns grew, was reduced in a furnace called an osmund (*Osmundaceae*)

Osmundastrum

oz-moon-DAS-trum

Referring to *Osmunda*, a related genus (*Osmundaceae*)

Osteomeles

oss-tee-oh-ME-leez

From Greek *osteon* meaning 'bone' and *melon* meaning 'apple', as the seeds within the apple-like fruits have hard outer coats (*Rosaceae*)

Osteospermum

oss-tee-oh-SPER-mum

From Greek *osteon* meaning 'bone' and *sperma* meaning 'seed', as the small, seed-like fruits are hard (*Asteraceae*)

Ostrowskia

oss-TROH-skee-uh

Named after Michael Nicolajewitsch von Ostrowski (dates unknown), Russian Imperial government minister (*Campanulaceae*)

Ostrya

oss-TRY-uh

From Greek *ostryos* meaning 'scale' as each seed is enclosed within a scale-like bract (*Betulaceae*)

Ostryopsis

oss-try-OP-sis

Resembling the related genus *Ostrya* (*Betulaceae*)

Othonna

oth-ON-uh

From Greek *othonne* meaning 'linen', as some species have soft hairs on their leaves (*Asteraceae*)

ovalis

oh-VAH-lis

ovalis, ovale

Oval, as in *Amelanchier ovalis*

ovatus

oh-VAH-tus

ovata, ovatum

Shaped like an egg; ovate, as in *Lagurus ovatus*

ovinus

oh-VIN-us

ovina, ovinum

Relating to sheep or sheep feed, as in *Festuca ovina*

Oxalis

oks-AH-lis

From Greek *oxys* meaning 'acid', referring to the sharp taste of the leaves caused by oxalic acid (*Oxalidaceae*)

oxyacanthus

oks-ee-a-KAN-thus

oxyacantha, oxyacanthum

With sharp spines, as in *Asparagus oxyacanthus*

Oxydendrum

oks-ee-DEN-drum

From Greek *oxys* meaning 'acid' and *dendron* meaning 'tree', as the leaves taste sharp when eaten (*Ericaceae*)

oxygonus

ok-SY-goh-nus

oxygona, oxygonum

With sharp angles, as in *Echinopsis oxygona*

oxyphilus

oks-ee-FIL-us

oxyphila, oxyphilum

Growing in acid soils, as in *Allium oxyphilum*

oxyphyllus

oks-ee-FIL-us

oxyphylla, oxyphyllum

With sharp-pointed leaves, as in *Euonymus oxyphyllus*

Ozothamnus

oh-zoh-THAM-nus

From Greek *ozo* meaning 'to smell' and *thamnus* meaning 'shrub', due to aromatic foliage (*Asteraceae*)

pachy-
Used in compound words to denote thick

pachycarpus
pak-ee-KAR-pus
pachycarpa, pachycarpum
With a thick pericarp, as in *Angelica pachycarpa*

Pachycereus
pak-ee-SER-ee-us
From Greek *pachys* meaning 'thick' plus *Cereus*, a related genus (*Cactaceae*)

Pachycormus
pak-ee-KOR-mus
From Greek *pachys* meaning 'thick' and *kormos* meaning 'stump', as this shrub has a thickened stem (*Anacardiaceae*)

Pachycymbium
pak-ee-SIM-bee-um
From Greek *pachys* meaning 'thick' and *kumbivon* meaning 'small cup', alluding to the flower shape (*Apocynaceae*)

Pachyphragma
pak-ee-FRAG-muh
From Greek *pachys* meaning 'thick' and *phragma* meaning 'fence', as the chambers within the fruits are divided by a thick wall (*Brassicaceae*)

pachyphyllus
pak-ih-FIL-us
pachyphylla, pachyphyllum
Thick-leaved, as in *Callistemon pachyphyllus*

Pachyphytum
pak-ee-FY-tum
From Greek *pachys* meaning 'thick' and *phyton* meaning 'plant', alluding to the thick, succulent leaves and stems (*Crassulaceae*)

Pachypodium [1]
pak-ee-POH-dee-um
From Greek *pachys* meaning 'thick' and *podion* meaning 'foot', as these succulents have swollen trunks (*Apocynaceae*)

pachypodus
pak-ih-POD-us
pachypoda, pachypodum
With a fat stem, as in *Actaea pachypoda*

pachypterus
pak-IP-ter-us
pachyptera, pachypterum
With thick wings, as in *Rhipsalis pachyptera*

Pachysandra
pak-ee-SAN-druh
From Greek *pachys* meaning 'thick' and *andros* meaning 'male', referencing the thick, white stamen filaments (*Buxaceae*)

pachysanthus
pak-ee-SAN-thus
pachysantha, pachysanthum
With thick flowers, as in *Rhododendron pachysanthum*

Pachystachys
pak-ee-STAK-iss
From Greek *pachys* meaning 'thick' and *stachys* meaning 'ear of grain', as the flowers are arranged in sturdy, upright inflorescences (*Acanthaceae*)

Pachystegia
pak-ee-STEE-jee-uh
From Greek *pachys* meaning 'thick' and *stegos* meaning 'cover', alluding to the thick, woolly coating on the stems and leaf undersides (*Asteraceae*)

pacificus
pa-SIF-ih-kus
pacifica, pacificum
Connected with the Pacific Ocean, as in *Chrysanthemum pacificum*

Packera
PAK-er-uh
Named after John G. Packer (1929-), Canadian botanist (*Asteraceae*)

1

Pachypodium succulentum,
thickfoot

1

Paeonia suffruticosa,
Chinese tree peony

padus
PAD-us
Ancient Greek name for a kind of wild cherry, as in *Prunus padus*

Paeonia [1]
pee-OH-nee-uh
Named after Paeon, physician to the gods in Greek mythology, alluding to the medicinal properties of peony (*Paeoniaceae*)

paganus
PAG-ah-nus
pagana, paganum
From wild or country regions, as in *Rubus paganus*

palaestinus
pal-ess-TEEN-us
palaestina, palaestinum
Connected with Palestine, as in *Iris palaestina*

Paliurus
pal-ee-EW-rus
From Greek *paliouros*, the classical name for *P. spina-christi* or the related *Ziziphus spina-christi* (*Rhamnaceae*)

pallens
PAL-lenz
—

pallidus
PAL-lid-dus
pallida, pallidum
Pale, as in *Tradescantia pallida*

pallescens
pa-LESS-enz
Rather pale, as in *Sorbus pallescens*

pallidiflorus
pal-id-uh-FLOR-us
pallidiflora, pallidiflorum
With pale flowers, as in *Eucomis pallidiflora*

palmaris
pal-MAH-ris
palmaris, palmare
A hand's breadth wide, as in *Limonium palmare*

palmatus
pahl-MAH-tus
palmata, palmatum
Palmate, as in *Acer palmatum*

palmensis
pal-MEN-sis
palmensis, palmense
From Las Palmas, Canary Islands, as in *Aichryson palmense*

palmeri
PALM-er-ee
Named after Ernest Jesse Palmer (1875–1962), British explorer and plant collector in the United States, as in *Agave palmeri*

palmetto
pahl-MET-oh
A small palm, as in *Sabal palmetto*

palmifolius
palm-ih-FOH-lee-us
palmifolia, palmifolium
With palm-like leaves, as in *Sisyrinchium palmifolium*

paludosus
pal-oo-DOH-sus
paludosa, paludosum
—

palustris
pal-US-tris
palustris, palustre
Of marshland, as in *Quercus palustris*

Pamianthe
pam-ee-ANTH-ee
Named after Albert Samuel Pam (1875–1955), British soldier and banker (*Amaryllidaceae*)

Panax
PA-nax
From Greek *panakes* meaning 'all-healing' or 'panacea', for its medicinal properties (*Araliaceae*)

Pancratium
pan-KRAT-ee-um
From Greek *pan* meaning 'all' and *kratos* meaning 'strength', as many of these bulbous plants tolerate extreme drought (*Amaryllidaceae*)

pandanifolius
pan-dan-uh-FOH-lee-us
pandanifolia, pandanifolium
With leaves like *Pandanus*, as in *Eryngium pandanifolium*

Pandanus

pan-DAN-us

From Malay *pandan*, the name for the edible *P. amaryllifolius* (*Pandanaceae*)

Pandorea

pan-DOR-ee-uh

Named after Pandora of Greek mythology; the fruits are said to resemble her famous jar, often mistranslated as a box (*Apocynaceae*)

panduratus

pand-yoor-RAH-tus

pandurata, panduratum

Shaped like a fiddle, as in *Coelogyne pandurata*

paniculatus

pan-ick-yoo-LAH-tus

paniculata, paniculatum

With flowers arranged in panicles, as in *Koelreuteria paniculata*

Panicum

PAN-ik-um

From Latin *panicum*, the classical name for millet (*Poaceae*)

pannonicus

pa-NO-nih-kus

pannonica, pannonicum

Of Pannonia, a Roman region, as in *Lathyrus pannonicus*

pannosus

pan-OH-sus

pannosa, pannosum

Tattered, as in *Helianthemum pannosum*

Papaver [2]

puh-PAH-ver

From Latin *papaver*, the classical name for poppy (*Papaveraceae*)

Paphiopedilum

paf-ee-oh-PED-uh-lum

Named after the city of Paphos in Cyprus, the site of the temple of Aphrodite, plus the Greek *pedilon* meaning 'slipper' [see *Cypripedium*] (*Orchidaceae*)

papilio

pap-ILL-ee-oh

A butterfly, as in *Hippeastrum papilio*

papilionaceus

pap-il-ee-on-uh-SEE-us

papilionacea, papilionaceum

Like a butterfly, as in *Pelargonium papilionaceum*

papyraceus

pap-ih-REE-see-us

papyracea, papyraceum

Like paper, as in *Narcissus papyraceus*

papyrifer

pap-IH-riff-er

—

papyriferus

pap-ih-RIH-fer-us

papyrifera, papyriferum

Producing paper, as in *Tetrapanax papyrifer*

papyrus

pa-PY-rus

Ancient Greek word for paper, as in *Cyperus papyrus*

Paradisea

par-uh-DIZ-ee-uh

Named after Giovanni Paradisi (1760–1820), Italian botanist and politician (*Asparagaceae*)

paradisi

par-uh-DEE-see

—

paradisiacus

par-uh-DEE-see-cus

paradisiaca, paradisiacum

From parks or gardens, as in *Citrus × paradisi*

paradoxus

par-uh-DOKS-us

paradoxa, paradoxum

Unexpected or paradoxical, as in *Acacia paradoxa*

paraguayensis

par-uh-gway-EN-sis

paraguayensis, paraguayense

From Paraguay, as in *Ilex paraguayensis*

Paraquilegia

par-ak-wi-LEE-juh

From Greek *para* meaning 'near', plus *Aquilegia*, a related genus (*Ranunculaceae*)

Paraserianthes

par-uh-ser-ee-ANTH-eez

From Greek *para* meaning 'near', plus *Serianthes*, a related genus (*Fabaceae*)

parasiticus

par-uh-SIT-ih-kus

parasitica, parasiticum

Parasitic, as in *Agalmyla parasitica*

2

***Papaver somniferum*, opium poppy**

Parthenocissus

As its name suggests, Virginia creeper (*Parthenocissus quinquefolia*) is native to the US state of Virginia, and much of eastern North America. The genus name originates in the French common name *vigne-vierge*, or 'virgin vine', which was translated into Latinised Greek as *Parthenocissus* (or 'virgin-ivy'). The virgin is, of course, the Virgin Queen, Elizabeth I, after whom the original colony was named. The Greek *kissos* meaning 'ivy' has been used in Latin names for several other vines, including *Cissus*, *Ampelocissus* and *Rhoicissus*. However, all are members of the grape family (*Vitaceae*), while true ivy (*Hedera*) belongs elsewhere (*Araliaceae*).

Parthenocissus tricuspidata,
Boston ivy

pardalinus
par-da-LEE-nus
pardalina, pardalinum
—
pardinus
par-DEE-nus
pardina, pardinum
With spots like a leopard, as in *Hippeastrum pardinum*

pari-
Used in compound words to denote equal

Parietaria
par-ee-uh-TAIR-ee-uh
From Latin *paries* meaning 'wall', a common habitat for pellitory-of-the-wall, *P. officinalis* (*Urticaceae*)

Paris
PA-ris
From Latin *par* meaning 'equal', alluding to *P. quadrifolia*, which typically has four symmetrically arranged leaves (*Melanthiaceae*)

Parkinsonia
par-kin-SOWN-ee-uh
Named after John Parkinson (1567–1650), British botanist and apothecary (*Fabaceae*)

Parnassia
par-NASS-ee-uh
Named after Mount Parnassus in Greece, which was sacred to the gods Dionysus and Apollo and home to the Muses (*Celastraceae*)

parnassicus
par-NASS-ih-kus
parnassica, parnassicum
Connected with Mount Parnassus, Greece, as in *Thymus parnassicus*

parnassifolius
par-nass-ih-FOH-lee-us
parnassifolia, parnassifolium
With leaves like the grass-of-Parnassus (*Parnassia*), as in *Saxifraga parnassifolia*

Parochetus
par-oh-KEE-tus
From Greek *para* meaning 'near' and *ochetos* meaning 'stream', a reference to habitat (*Fabaceae*)

Parodia
puh-ROH-dee-uh
Named after Domingo Parodi (1823–90), Italian pharmacist and botanist (*Cactaceae*)

Paronychia
par-oh-NY-kee-uh
From Greek *para* meaning 'near' and *onyx* meaning 'nail', as the plant was used to treat paronychia, or inflammation around the fingernails (*Caryophyllaceae*)

Parrotia
puh-ROT-ee-uh
Named after Johann Jacob Friedrich Wilhelm Parrot (1791–1841), Baltic German physician and explorer (*Hamamelidaceae*)

Parrotiopsis
puh-roh-tee-OP-sis
Resembling the related genus *Parrotia* (*Hamamelidaceae*)

parryae
PAR-ee-eye
—
parryi
PAIR-ree
Named after Dr Charles Christopher Parry (1823–90), British-born botanist and plant collector. The form *parryae* commemorates his wife, Emily Richmond Parry (1821–1915), as in *Linanthus parryae*

Passiflora

Passionflowers (*Passiflora*) were named by early Catholic missionaries in South America. To them, the intricate blooms were highly symbolic, with the ten petals representing the apostles (minus Peter, who denied Christ, and Judas, who betrayed him), the corona was the crown of thorns, the five stamens were the five wounds, and the three stigmas, the nails. Only a handful of species are suitable for cultivation outside in frost-prone regions, but the best of these, the blue passionflower (*P. caerulea*), clearly demonstrates this religious imagery. Edible passionfruit also come from *Passiflora*, from *P. edulis* and a few other species.

Passiflora caerulea,
blue passionflower

Parthenium (also parthenium)
par-THEE-nee-um
From Greek *parthenos* meaning 'virgin' or *parthenion*, the name of an unidentified plant; the etymology is unclear (*Asteraceae*)

Parthenocissus
parth-en-oh-SIS-us
From Greek *parthenos* meaning 'virgin' and *kissos* meaning 'ivy', as Virginia creeper, *P. quinquefolia*, is an ivy-like plant from Virginia (*Vitaceae*)

partitus
par-TY-tus
partita, partitum
Parted, as in *Hibiscus partitus*

parvi-
Used in compound words to denote small

parviflorus
par-vih-FLOR-us
parviflora, parviflorum
With small flowers, as in *Aesculus parviflora*

parvifolius
par-vih-FOH-lee-us
parvifolia, parvifolium
With small leaves, as in *Eucalyptus parvifolia*

parvus
PAR-vus
parva, parvum
Small, as in *Lilium parvum*

Passiflora
pas-i-FLAW-ruh
From Latin *passio* meaning 'passion' and *flos* meaning 'flower', as the parts of the flower were thought to symbolise the crucifixion of Christ (*Passifloraceae*)

Pastinaca
pas-tin-AH-kuh
From Latin *pastinaca*, vernacular name for parsnips and carrots (*Apiaceae*)

patagonicus
pat-uh-GOH-nih-kus
patagonica, patagonicum
Connected with Patagonia, as in *Sisyrinchium patagonicum*

patavinus
pat-uh-VIN-us
patavina, patavinum
Connected with Padua (previously Patavium), Italy, as in *Haplophyllum patavinum*

patens
PAT-enz
—

patulus
PAT-yoo-lus
patula, patulum
With a spreading habit, as in *Salvia patens*

Patersonia
pat-ur-SOH-nee-uh
Named after William Paterson (1755–1810), Scottish soldier and botanist (*Iridaceae*)

Patrinia
puh-TRIN-ee-uh
Named after Eugène Louis Melchior Patrin (1742–1815), French naturalist and mineralogist (*Caprifoliaceae*)

pauci-
Used in compound words to denote few

pauciflorus
PAW-si-flor-us
pauciflora, pauciflorum
With few flowers, as in *Corylopsis pauciflora*

i

227

paucifolius
paw-se-FOH-lee-us
paucifolia, paucifolium
With few leaves, as in *Scilla paucifolia*

paucinervis
paw-se-NER-vis
paucinervis, paucinerve
With few nerves, as in *Cornus paucinervis*

Paulownia
paw-LOH-nee-uh
Named after Anna Pavlovna (1795–1865), daughter of Czar Paul I of Russia and wife of King William II of the Netherlands (*Paulowniaceae*)

pauperculus
paw-PER-yoo-lus
paupercula, pauperculum
Poor, as in *Alstroemeria paupercula*

Pavetta
puh-VET-uh
From Sinhalese (Sri Lanka) *pawetta*, the vernacular name for *P. indica* (*Rubiaceae*)

pavia
PAH-vee-uh
Named after Peter Paaw (1564–1617), Dutch physician, as in *Aesculus pavia*

Pavonia
puh-VOH-nee-uh
Named after José Antonio Pavón Jiménez (1754–1840), Spanish botanist (*Malvaceae*)

pavoninus
pav-ON-ee-nus
pavonina, pavoninum
Peacock blue, as in *Anemone pavonina*

Paxistima
paks-i-STEEM-uh
From Greek *pachys* meaning 'thick' and stigma (*Celastraceae*)

pectinatus
pek-tin-AH-tus
pectinata, pectinatum
Like a comb, as in *Euryops pectinatus*

pectoralis
pek-TOR-ah-lis
pectoralis, pectorale
Of the chest, as in *Justicia pectoralis*

peculiaris
pe-kew-lee-AH-ris
peculiaris, peculiare
Peculiar or special, as in *Cheiridopsis peculiaris*

pedatifidus
ped-at-ee-FEE-dus
pedatifida, pedatifidum
Divided like a bird's foot, as in *Viola pedatifida*

pedatus
ped-AH-tus
pedata, pedatum
Shaped like a bird's foot, often in reference to the shape of a palmate leaf, as in *Adiantum pedatum*

pedemontanus
ped-ee-MON-tah-nus
pedemontana, pedemontanum
Connected with Piedmont, Italy, as in *Saxifraga pedemontana*

Pedilanthus
ped-i-LAN-thus
From Greek *pedilon* meaning 'slipper' and *anthos* meaning 'flower', as the flowers are sometimes enclosed within shoe-shaped bracts (*Euphorbiaceae*)

Pediocactus
pee-dee-oh-KAK-tus
From Greek *pedion* meaning 'plain' (the geographical feature), plus cactus; a reference to preferred habitat (*Cactaceae*)

peduncularis
ped-unk-yoo-LAH-ris
peduncularis, pedunculare
—

pedunculatus
ped-unk-yoo-LA-tus
pedunculata, pedunculatum
With a flower stalk, as in *Lavandula pedunculata*

pedunculosus
ped-unk-yoo-LOH-sus
pedunculosa, pedunculosum
With many or particularly well-developed flower stems, as in *Ilex pedunculosa*

pekinensis
pee-keen-EN-sis
pekinensis, pekinense
From Peking (Beijing), China, as in *Euphorbia pekinensis*

Pelargonium
pel-ur-GOH-nee-um
From Greek *pelargos* meaning 'stork'; the fruits resemble storks' bills (*Geraniaceae*)

pelegrina
pel-e-GREE-nuh
Local name for *Alstroemeria pelegrina*

Pellaea
PEL-ay-uh
From Greek *pellos* meaning 'dark-coloured', referring to the fronds (*Pteridaceae*)

Pellionia
pel-ee-OH-nee-uh
Named after Marie Joseph Alphonse Pellion (1796–1868), French naval officer (*Urticaceae*)

pellucidus
pel-LOO-sid-us
pellucida, pellucidum
Transparent; clear, as in *Conophytum pellucidum*

peloponnesiacus
pel-uh-pon-ee-see-AH-kus
peloponnesiaca, peloponnesiacum
Connected with the Peloponnese, Greece, as in *Colchicum peloponnesiacum*

Peltandra
pel-TAN-druh
From Greek *pelte* meaning 'small shield' and *andros* meaning 'male', as the male flowers appear shield-shaped (*Araceae*)

peltatus
pel-TAH-tus
peltata, peltatum
Shaped like a shield, as in *Darmera peltata*

Peltoboykinia
pel-toh-boy-KIN-ee-uh
From Greek *pelte* meaning 'small shield' and *Boykinia*, a related genus; this perennial with shield-like leaves used to belong in *Boykinia* (*Saxifragaceae*)

Peltophorum
pel-toh-FOR-um
From Greek *pelte* meaning 'small shield' and *phorus* meaning 'bearing', as the stigma is shield-shaped (*Fabaceae*)

Paulownia tomentosa,
foxglove tree

pelviformis
pel-vih-FORM-is
pelviformis, pelviforme
In the shape of a shallow cup, as in
Campanula pelviformis

pendulinus
pend-yoo-LIN-us
pendulina, pendulinum
Hanging, as in *Salix × pendulina*

pendulus
PEND-yoo-lus
pendula, pendulum
Hanging, as in *Betula pendula*

1

Penstemon rupicola,
cliff beardtongue

penicillatus
pen-iss-sil-LAH-tus
penicillata, penicillatum
—

penicillius
pen-iss-SIL-ee-us
penicillia, penicillium
With a tuft of hair, as in *Parodia penicillata*

peninsularis
pen-in-sul-AH-ris
peninsularis, peninsulare
From peninsular regions, as in *Allium peninsulare*

Peniocereus
pen-ee-oh-SER-ee-us
From Greek *penios* meaning 'thread' and *Cereus*, a related genus; the stems are long, narrow and sprawling (*Cactaceae*)

penna-marina
PEN-uh mar-EE-nuh
Sea feather, as in *Blechnum penna-marina*

pennatus
pen-AH-tus
pennata, pennatum
With feathers, pinnate, as in *Stipa pennata*

pennigerus
pen-NY-ger-us
pennigera, pennigerum
With leaves like feathers, as in *Thelypteris pennigera*

Pennisetum
pen-uh-SEE-tum
From Latin *penna* meaning 'feather' and *seta* meaning 'bristle', as the inflorescences may contain bristles covered in plume-like hairs (*Poaceae*)

pennsylvanicus
pen-sil-VAN-ih-kus
pennsylvanica, pennsylvanicum
—

pensylvanicus
pensylvanica, pensylvanicum
Connected with Pennsylvania, USA, as in *Acer pensylvanicum*

pensilis
PEN-sil-is
pensilis, pensile
Hanging, as in *Glyptostrobus pensilis*

Penstemon [1]
pen-STEM-on, PEN-stem-on
From Greek *pente* meaning 'five' and *stemon* meaning 'stamen', as each flower has five stamens (*Plantaginaceae*)

penta-
Used in compound words to denote five

Pentaglottis
pen-tuh-GLOT-iss
From Greek *pente* meaning 'five' and *glottis* meaning 'tongue', referring to the five white scales in the flower centre (*Boraginaceae*)

pentagonius
pen-ta-GON-ee-us
pentagonia, pentagonium
—

pentagonus
pen-ta-GON-us
pentagona, pentagonum
With five angles, as in *Rubus pentagonus*

pentagynus
pen-ta-GY-nus
pentagyna, pentagynum
With five pistils, as in *Crataegus pentagyna*

pentandrus
pen-TAN-drus
pentandra, pentandrum
With five stamens, as in *Ceiba pentandra*

pentapetaloides
pen-ta-pet-al-OY-deez
Appearing to possess five petals, as in
Convolvulus pentapetaloides

pentaphyllus
pen-tuh-FIL-us
pentaphylla, pentaphyllum
With five leaves or leaflets, as in *Cardamine pentaphylla*

Pentas
PEN-tass
From Greek *pente* meaning 'five', as the
petals and other flower parts are arranged in
whorls of five, unlike many related genera
where they are in whorls of four (*Rubiaceae*)

Peperomia
pep-uh-ROH-mee-uh
From Greek *peperi* meaning 'pepper' and
homoios meaning 'similar', as some species
resemble the related black pepper, *Piper
nigrum* (*Piperaceae*)

pepo
PEP-oh
Latin word for a large melon or pumpkin, as
in *Cucurbita pepo*

perbellus
per-BELL-us
perbella, perbellum
Very beautiful, as in *Mammillaria perbella*

peregrinus
per-uh-GREE-nus
peregrina, peregrinum
To wander, as in *Delphinium peregrinum*

perennis
per-EN-is
perennis, perenne
Perennial, as in *Bellis perennis*

Pereskia [2]
puh-RES-kee-uh
Named after Nicolas-Claude Fabri de
Peiresc (1580–1637), French astronomer
(*Cactaceae*)

perfoliatus
per-foh-lee-AH-tus
perfoliata, perfoliatum
With the leaf surrounding the stem, as in
Parahebe perfoliata

perforatus
per-for-AH-tus
perforata, perforatum
With, or appearing to have, small holes, as in
Hypericum perforatum

pergracilis
per-GRASS-il-is
pergracilis, pergracile
Very slender, as in *Scleria pergracilis*

Pericallis
per-i-KAL-iss
From Greek *peri* meaning 'around' and *kallos*
meaning 'beautiful' (*Asteraceae*)

Perilla
puh-RIL-uh
From Greek *pera* meaning 'pouch', plus
diminutive *ella*, possibly referring to the
shape of the calyx, though derivation unclear
(*Lamiaceae*)

Periploca
per-i-PLOK-uh
From Greek *periplokos* meaning 'entwined',
as this climber has twining stems
(*Apocynaceae*)

Peritoma
per-i-TOH-muh
From Greek *peri* meaning 'around' and *tome*
meaning 'to cut', referring to the fruits,
which split all the way round (*Cleomaceae*)

pernyi
PERN-yee-eye
Named after Paul Hubert Perny (1818–
1907), French missionary and botanist, as in
Ilex pernyi

Perovskia
per-OV-ski-uh
Named after Vasily Alekseevich Perovsky
(1794–1857), Russian soldier (*Lamiaceae*)

Persea
PER-see-uh
The classical Greek name for a fruiting tree,
possibly *Mimusops laurifolia*, as used by
Dioscorides (*Lauraceae*)

Persicaria
per-si-KAIR-ee-uh
Named after the peach, *Prunus persica*,
whose leaves resemble those of some
Persicaria species (*Polygonaceae*)

2

Pereskia grandifolia,
rose cactus

Euphorbia petiolaris,
manchineel berry

Petrocallis pyrenaica,
rock beauty

persicifolius
per-sik-ih-FOH-lee-us
persicifolia, persicifolium
With leaves like the peach (*Prunus persica*), as in *Campanula persicifolia*

persicus
PER-sih-kus
persica, persicum
Connected with Persia (Iran), as in *Parrotia persica*

persistens
per-SIS-tenz
Persistent, as in *Elegia persistens*

persolutus
per-sol-YEW-tus
persoluta, persolutum
Very loose, as in *Erica persoluta*

perspicuus
PER-spic-kew-us
perspicua, perspicuum
Transparent, as in *Erica perspicua*

pertusus
per-TUS-us
pertusa, pertusum
Perforated; pierced, as in *Listrostachys pertusa*

perulatus
per-uh-LAH-tus
perulata, perulatum
With perules (bud scales), as in *Enkianthus perulatus*

peruvianus
per-u-vee-AH-nus
peruviana, peruvianum
Connected with Peru, as in *Scilla peruviana*

petaloideus
pet-a-LOY-dee-us
petaloidea, petaloideum
Like a petal, as in *Thalictrum petaloideum*

Petasites
pet-uh-SY-teez
From Greek *petasos* meaning 'broad-brimmed hat', alluding to the large parasol-like leaves (*Asteraceae*)

petiolaris [1]
pet-ee-OH-lah-ris
petiolaris, petiolare
—

petiolatus
pet-ee-oh-LAH-tus
petiolata, petiolatum
With a leaf stalk, as in *Helichrysum petiolare*

petraeus
pet-RAY-us
petraea, petraeum
Connected with rocky regions, as in *Quercus petraea*

Petrea
peh-TRAY-uh
Named after Robert James Petre (1713–42), British peer and horticulturist (*Verbenaceae*)

Petrocallis [2]

pet-roh-KAL-iss

From Greek *petros* meaning 'rock' and *kallos* meaning 'beautiful', an apt description of this attractive alpine (*Brassicaceae*)

Petrocosmea

pet-roh-KOS-mee-uh

From Greek *petros* meaning 'rock' and *kosmo* meaning 'ornamental', an allusion to its beauty and preferred habitat (*Gesneriaceae*)

Petrophytum

pet-roh-FY-tum

From Greek *petros* meaning 'rock' and *phyton* meaning 'plant', as these prostrate shrubs occupy rocky outcrops (*Rosaceae*)

Petrorhagia

pet-roh-RAJ-ee-uh

From Greek *petros* meaning 'rock' and *rhagas* meaning 'fissure', a native of rock crevices (*Caryophyllaceae*)

Petroselinum [3]

pet-roh-SEL-in-um

From Greek *petros* meaning 'rock' and *selinon* meaning 'celery'; the British word 'parsley' (for *P. crispum*) has the same root (*Apiaceae*)

Petunia

puh-TEW-nee-uh

From Tupi-Guarani (Brazil) *petun*, vernacular name for the related tobacco (*Solanaceae*)

Peucedanum

pew-SED-uh-num

From Greek *peuke* meaning 'pine', a reference to the bitter taste (*Apiaceae*)

Phacelia

fuh-SEE-lee-uh

From Greek *phakelos* meaning a 'bundle', a reference to the clustered flowers (*Boraginaceae*)

phaeacanthus

fay-uh-KAN-thus

phaeacantha, phaeacanthum

With grey thorns, as in *Opuntia phaeacantha*

Phaedranassa

fee-druh-NAS-uh

From Greek *phaidros* meaning 'bright' and *anassa* meaning 'queen', an allusion to the attractive and brightly coloured blooms (*Amaryllidaceae*)

phaeus

FAY-us

phaea, phaeum

Dusky, as in *Geranium phaeum*

Phaius

FY-us

From Greek *phaios* meaning 'dusky', as some species have dark-coloured flowers (*Orchidaceae*)

Phalaenopsis [4]

fal-uh-NOP-sis

From Greek *phalaina* meaning 'moth' and *opsis* ('resembling'), as the flowers look like moths (*Orchidaceae*)

3

Petroselinum crispum,
parsley

4

Phalaenopsis × *intermedia,*
moth orchid

1

Philadelphus
'Belle Étoile', mock orange

Phalaris
fuh-LAR-iss
From Greek *phalara* meaning 'white-crested',
a reference to the inflorescence (*Poaceae*)

Phaseolus
faz-ee-OH-lus
From Greek *phaselos* meaning 'bean'
(*Fabaceae*)

Phellodendron
fel-oh-DEN-dron
From Greek *phellos* meaning 'cork' and
dendron meaning 'tree', a reference to the
bark (*Rutaceae*)

philadelphicus
fil-uh-DEL-fih-kus
philadelphica, philadelphicum
Connected with Philadelphia, as in *Lilium
philadelphicum*

Philadelphus [1]
fil-uh-DELF-us
From Greek *philos* meaning 'loving' and
adelphus meaning 'brother', for reasons
unknown; alternatively, named after
Ptolemy Philadelphus (309–246 BC), King
of Egypt (*Hydrangeaceae*)

Philesia
fy-LEE-zee-uh
Etymology uncertain, but probably from
Greek *philos* meaning 'loving', as the flowers
are attractive (*Philesiaceae*)

philippensis
fil-lip-EN-sis
philippensis, philippense
—

philippianus
fil-lip-ee-AH-nus
philippiana, philippianum
—

philippii
fil-LIP-ee-eye
—

philippinensis
fil-ip-ee-NEN-sis
philippinensis, philippinense
From the Philippines, as in *Adiantum
philippense*

Phillyrea
fil-uh-RAY-uh
From Greek *philyrea*, the vernacular name
for *P. latifolia* (*Oleaceae*)

Philodendron
fil-oh-DEN-dron
From Greek *philos* meaning 'loving' and
dendron meaning 'tree', a reference to the
many species of climbers and epiphytes in
this genus (*Araceae*)

Philotheca
fil-oh-THEE-kuh
From Greek *philos* meaning 'loving' and
theke meaning 'container', probably referring
to the capsular fruits (*Rutaceae*)

Phlebodium
fluh-BOH-dee-um
From Greek *phlebos* meaning 'vein', as the
fronds have prominent venation
(*Polypodiaceae*)

phleoides
flee-OY-deez
Resembling *Phleum* (cat's tail grass), as in
Phleum phleoides

Phleum
FLEE-um
From Greek *phleos* meaning 'woolly reed',
probably referring to another grass species
(*Poaceae*)

phlogiflorus
flo-GIF-flor-us
phlogiflora, phlogiflorum
With flame-coloured flowers or flowers like
Phlox, as in *Verbena phlogiflora*

Phlomis

FLOH-mis

From Greek *phlogmos* meaning 'flame', as the leaves of some species were used as lamp wicks (*Lamiaceae*)

Phlox

FLOX

From Greek *phlogmos* meaning 'flame'; used as the vernacular name for a red-flowered plant, possibly a *Silene* (*Polemoniaceae*)

Phoebe

FEE-bee

From Greek *phoibos* meaning 'bright, radiant' (*Lauraceae*)

phoeniceus

feen-ih-KEE-us

phoenicea, phoeniceum

Purple/red, as in *Juniperus phoenicea*

phoenicolasius

fee-nik-oh-LASS-ee-us

phoenicolasia, phoenicolasium

With purple hairs, as in *Rubus phoenicolasius*

Phoenix

FEE-niks

From Greek *phoinix*, the vernacular name for date palm, *P. dactylifera*; perhaps originating in the Phoenician culture of the Mediterranean (*Arecaceae*)

Phormium

FOR-mee-um

From Greek *phormion* meaning 'mat', as fibres from this plant were used for weaving (*Asphodelaceae*)

Photinia

foh-TIN-ee-uh

From Greek *photeinos* meaning 'shining', alluding to the glossy leaves (*Rosaceae*)

Phragmipedium

frag-mi-PEE-dee-um

From Greek *phragma* meaning 'fence' and *pedilon* meaning 'slipper'; this orchid's flowers have a slipper-like lip and an ovary divided into chambers (*Orchidaceae*)

Phragmites

frag-MY-teez

From Greek *phragma* meaning 'fence' or 'hedge', as this reed forms large banks and is also collected for construction (*Poaceae*)

phrygius

FRIJ-ee-us

phrygia, phrygium

Connected with Phrygia, Anatolia, as in *Centaurea phrygia*

Phygelius

fy-JEE-lee-us

From Greek *phyge* meaning 'avoidance' and *helios* meaning 'sun', as plants were said to prefer shade (*Scrophulariaceae*)

Phylica

FY-lik-uh

From Greek *phyllikos* meaning 'leafy', as the foliage is dense (*Rhamnaceae*)

Phyllodoce

fy-loh-DOH-see

Named after a sea nymph in Greek mythology, though as these plants typically occur in arctic or alpine areas, the etymology is obscure (*Ericaceae*)

Phyllostachys

fy-loh-STAK-is

From Greek *phyllon* meaning 'leaf' and *stachys* meaning 'ear of grain', referring to the presence of leaves on flowering shoots (*Poaceae*)

phyllostachyus

fy-lo-STAY-kee-us

phyllostachya, phyllostachyum

With a leaf spike, as in *Hypoestes phyllostachya*

Physalis [2]

fis-AH-lis

From Greek *physa* meaning 'bladder' as the fruits are surrounded by inflated sepals (*Solanaceae*)

Physaria

fy-SAIR-ee-uh

From Greek *physa* meaning 'bladder', as some species have inflated fruits (*Brassicaceae*)

2

Physalis alkekengi,
Chinese lantern

Pieris formosa,
Chinese pieris

Physocarpus
(also **physocarpus**)

fy-soh-KAR-pus

From Greek *physa* meaning 'bladder' and *karpos* meaning 'fruit', as the fruits of some species are inflated (*Rosaceae*)

Physostegia

fy-soh-STEE-jee-uh

From Greek *physa* meaning 'bladder' and *stegos* meaning 'cover', as the calyx covering the fruit is inflated (*Lamiaceae*)

Phyteuma (also **phyteuma**)

fy-TEW-muh

From Greek *phuteuma* meaning 'that which is planted' (*Campanulaceae*)

Phytolacca

fy-toh-LAK-uh

From Greek *phyton* meaning 'plant' and Latin *lacca*, a red dye, as the fruits yield a dye (*Phytolaccaceae*)

Picea

py-SEE-uh

From Latin *picis* meaning 'pitch-producing pine' (*Pinaceae*)

Picrasma

pi-KRAS-muh

From Greek *picros* meaning 'bitter', as the bark yields a bitter flavouring (*Simaroubaceae*)

picturatus

pik-tur-AH-tus

picturata, picturatum

With variegated leaves, as in *Calathea picturata*

pictus

PIK-tus

picta, pictum

Painted; highly coloured, as in *Acer pictum*

Picris

PEER-iss

Named after the Muses of Greek mythology, who were worshipped at Pieria in Macedonia (*Ericaceae*)

Pilea

py-LEE-uh

From Greek *pilos* meaning 'felt cap', as the calyx covers the fruit (*Urticaceae*)

pileatus

py-lee-AH-tus

pileata, pileatum

With a cap, as in *Lonicera pileata*

Pileostegia

pil-ee-oh-STEE-jee-uh

From Greek *pilos* meaning 'felt cap' and *stegos* meaning 'cover', as the corolla is cap-like (*Hydrangeaceae*)

piliferus

py-LIH-fer-us

pilifera, piliferum

With short, soft hairs, as in *Ursinia pilifera*

pillansii

pil-AN-see-eye

Named after Neville Stuart Pillans (1884–1964), South African botanist, as in *Watsonia pillansii*

Pilosella

py-loh-SEL-uh

From Latin *pilosa* meaning 'hairy', plus diminutive *ella*, as these are small, often woolly plants (*Asteraceae*)

Pilosocereus

py-loss-oh-SER-ee-us

From Latin *pilosa* meaning 'hairy' and *Cereus*, a related genus (*Cactaceae*)

pilosus

pil-OH-sus

pilosa, pilosum

With long, soft hairs, as in *Aster pilosus*

pilularis

pil-yoo-LAH-ris

pilularis, pilulare

—

piluliferus

pil-yoo-LIH-fer-us

pilulifera, piluliferum

With globular fruit, as in *Urtica pilulifera*

Pimelea

pim-EE-lee-uh

From Greek *pimele* meaning 'fat', as the seeds are oily (*Thymelaeaceae*)

pimeleoides

py-mee-lee-OY-deez

Resembling *Pimelea*, as in *Pittosporum pimeleoides*

Pimpinella

pimp-i-NEL-uh

From Latin *pimpinella*, a medicinal herb (*Apiaceae*)

pimpinellifolius

pim-pi-nel-ih-FOH-lee-us

pimpinellifolia, pimpinellifolium

With leaves like anise (*Pimpinella*), as in *Rosa pimpinellifolia*

Pinellia

py-NEE-lee-uh

Named after Giovanni Vincenzo Pinelli (1535–1601), Italian botanist (*Araceae*)

pinetorum

py-net-OR-um

Connected with pine forests, as in *Fritillaria pinetorum*

pineus

PY-nee-us

pinea, pineum

Relating to pine (*Pinus*), as in *Pinus pinea*

Pinguicula

pin-GWIK-ew-luh

From Latin *pinguis* meaning 'fat' as the glistening leaves appear oily (*Lentibulariaceae*)

pinguifolius

pin-gwih-FOH-lee-us

pinguifolia, pinguifolium

With fat leaves, as in *Hebe pinguifolia*

pinifolius

pin-ih-FOH-lee-us

pinifolia, pinifolium

With leaves like pine (*Pinus*), as in *Penstemon pinifolius*

pininana

pin-in-AH-nuh

A dwarf pine, as in *Echium pininana*

pinnatifidus

pin-nat-ih-FY-dus

pinnatifida, pinnatifidum

Cut in the form of a feather, as in *Eranthis pinnatifida*

pinnatifolius

pin-nat-ih-FOH-lee-us

pinnatifolia, pinnatifolium

With leaves like feathers, as in *Meconopsis pinnatifolia*

pinnatifrons

pin-NAT-ih-fronz

With fronds like feathers, as in *Chamaedorea pinnatifrons*

pinnatus

pin-NAH-tus

pinnata, pinnatum

With leaves that grow from each side of a stalk; like a feather, as in *Santolina pinnata*

Pinus

PY-nus

The classical Latin name for pine trees (*Pinaceae*)

Piper

PY-per

From Greek *peperi* meaning 'pepper'; black pepper comes from *P. nigrum* (*Piperaceae*)

piperitus

pip-er-EE-tus

piperita, piperitum

With a pepper-like taste, as in *Mentha × piperita*

Piptanthus

pip-TAN-thus

From Greek *pipto* meaning 'to fall' and *anthos* meaning 'flower', as the sepals, petals and stamens fall as one unit (*Fabaceae*)

pisiferus

pih-SIH-fer-us

pisifera, pisiferum

Bearing peas, as in *Chameacyparis pisifera*

Pisonia

py-SOH-nee-uh

Named after Willem Pies (1611–78), Dutch physician and botanist (*Nyctaginaceae*)

Pistacia

pi-STAS-ee-uh

From Greek *pistakia*, the pistachio tree, *P. vera* (*Anacardiaceae*)

Pistia

PIS-tee-uh

From Greek *pistra* meaning 'watertrough', a reference to the aquatic habitat (*Araceae*)

Pisum [1]

PY-sum

From Greek *pison*, the vernacular name for pea, *P. sativum* (*Fabaceae*)

pitardii

pit-ARD-ee-eye

Named after Charles-Joseph Marie Pitard-Briau, 20th-century French plant collector and botanist, as in *Camellia pitardii*

Pitcairnia

pit-KAIR-nee-uh

Named after William Pitcairn (1711–91), British physician and gardener (*Bromeliaceae*)

pittonii

pit-TON-ee-eye

Named after Josef Claudius Pittoni, 19th-century Austrian botanist, as in *Sempervivum pittonii*

Pittosporum

pit-OS-po-rum

From Greek *pitta* meaning 'pitch' and *spora* meaning 'seed', as the seeds have a sticky coating (*Pittosporaceae*)

Pityrogramma

pit-ay-roh-GRAM-uh

From Greek *pityros* meaning 'bran' and *gramme* meaning 'line', as the sporangia appear dust-like (*Pteridaceae*)

planiflorus

plan-ih-FLOR-us

planiflora, planiflorum

With flat flowers, as in *Echidnopsis planiflora*

planifolius

plan-ih-FOH-lee-us

planifolia, planifolium

With flat leaves, as in *Iris planifolia*

planipes

PLAN-ee-pays

With a flat stalk, as in *Euonymus planipes*

plantagineus

plan-tuh-JIN-ee-us

plantaginea, plantagineum

Like plantain (*Platago*), as in *Hosta plantaginea*

Pisum sativum, pea

Platycarya strobilacea

Platycodon grandifloras,
balloon flower

Plantago
plan-TAY-goh
From Latin *planta* meaning 'sole of the foot', as in some species the leaves lie flat along the ground; also, common weeds of well-trodden lawns (*Plantaginaceae*)

planus
PLAH-nus
plana, planum
Flat, as in *Eryngium planum*

platanifolius
pla-tan-ih-FOH-lee-us
platanifolia, platanifolium
With leaves like a plane tree (*Platanus*), as in *Begonia platanifolia*

platanoides
pla-tan-OY-deez
Resembling a plane tree (*Platanus*), as in *Acer platanoides*

Platanus
PLAT-ah-nus
From Greek *platanos*, the vernacular name for *P. orientalis* (*Platanaceae*)

platy-
Used in compound words to denote broad (or sometimes flat)

platycanthus
plat-ee-KAN-thus
platycantha, platycanthum
With broad spines, as in *Acaena platycantha*

platycarpus
plat-ee-KAR-pus
platycarpa, platycarpum
With broad fruit, as in *Thalictrum platycarpum*

Platycarya [2]
pla-tee-KAR-ee-uh
From Greek *platys* meaning 'broad' and *karyon* meaning 'nut', as the seeds are winged (*Junglandaceae*)

platycaulis
plat-ee-KAWL-is
platycaulis, platycaule
With a broad stem, as in *Allium platycaule*

Platycerium
pla-tee-SEER-ee-um
From Greek *platys* meaning 'broad' and *keras* meaning 'horn', relating to the antler-like fronds (*Polypodiaceae*)

Platycladus
pla-tee-KLAY-dus
From Greek *platys* meaning 'broad' and *klados* meaning 'branch', alluding to the flattened, spray-like branchlets (*Cupressaceae*)

Platycodon [3]
pla-tee-KOH-don
From Greek *platys* meaning 'broad' and *codon* meaning 'bell', referring to the inflated, balloon-like flowers (*Campanulaceae*)

1

Plumeria rubra,
frangipani

platyglossus
plat-ee-GLOSS-us
platyglossa, platyglossum
With a broad tongue, as in *Phyllostachys platyglossa*

platypetalus
plat-ee-PET-uh-lus
platypetala, platypetalum
With broad petals, as in *Epimedium platypetalum*

platyphyllos
plat-tih-FIL-los
—
platyphyllus
pla-tih-FIL-us
platyphylla, platyphyllum
With broad leaves, as in *Betula platyphylla*

platypodus
pah-tee-POD-us
platypoda, platypodum
With a broad stalk, as in *Fraxinus platypoda*

platyspathus
plat-ees-PATH-us
platyspatha, platyspathum
With a broad spathe, as in *Allium platyspathum*

platyspermus
plat-ee-SPER-mus
platysperma, platyspermum
With broad seeds, as in *Hakea platysperma*

Plectranthus
plek-TRAN-thus
From Greek *plektron* meaning 'spur' and *anthos* meaning 'flower', as some species have spurs at the base of their blooms (*Lamiaceae*)

Pleioblastus
ply-oh-BLAST-us
From Greek *pleios* meaning 'more' and *blastos* meaning 'bud', as this bamboo produces numerous shoots at each node (*Poaceae*)

Pleione
plee-OH-nee
Named after Pleione, wife of Atlas in Greek mythology (*Orchidaceae*)

Pleiospilos
ply-os-PIE-los
From Greek *pleios* meaning 'more' and *spilos* meaning 'spot', as the succulent leaves mimic pebbles and are spotted, but hard to spot (*Aizoaceae*)

pleniflorus
plen-ee-FLOR-us
pleniflora, pleniflorum
With double flowers, as in *Kerria japonica* 'Pleniflora'

plenissimus
plen-ISS-i-mus
plenissima, plenissimum
Very double-flowered, as in *Eucalyptus kochii* subsp. *plenissima*

plenus
plen-US
plena, plenum
Double; full, as in *Felicia plena*

Pleurothallis
plew-roh-THAL-us
From Greek *pleuron* meaning 'rib' and *thallos* meaning 'branch', perhaps alluding to the narrow stems of many species (*Orchidaceae*)

plicatus
ply-KAH-tus
plicata, plicatum
Pleated, as in *Thuja plicata*

plumarius
ploo-MAH-ree-us
plumaria, plumarium
With feathers, as in *Dianthus plumarius*

plumbaginoides
plum-bah-gih-NOY-deez
Resembling *Plumbago*, as in *Ceratostigma plumbaginoides*

Plumbago

plum-BAY-goh

From Greek *plumbago* meaning 'galena', a type of lead ore; the name was used for a herb that cured lead poisoning, though it may not have been this plant (*Plumbaginaceae*)

plumbeus

plum-BEY-us

plumbea, plumbeum

Relating to lead, as in *Alocasia plumbea*

Plumeria [1]

plew-MEER-ee-uh

Named after Charles Plumier (1646–1704), French botanist (*Apocynaceae*)

plumosus

plum-OH-sus

plumosa, plumosum

Feathery, as in *Libocedrus plumosa*

pluriflorus

plur-ee-FLOR-us

pluriflora, pluriflorum

With many flowers, as in *Erythronium pluriflorum*

pluvialis

ploo-VEE-uh-lis

pluvialis, pluviale

Relating to rain, as in *Calendula pluvialis*

Poa

POH-uh

From Greek *poa* meaning 'grass' (*Poaceae*)

pocophorus

po-KO-for-us

pocophora, pocophorum

Fleece-bearing, as in *Rhododendron pocophorum*

podagraria

pod-uh-GRAR-ee-uh

From *podagra*, Latin for 'gout', as in *Aegopodium podagraria*

Podalyria

pod-uh-LIR-ee-uh

Named after Podalirius, son of Asklepios, Greek god of medicine (*Fabaceae*)

Podocarpus

pod-oh-KARP-us

From Greek *podion* meaning 'foot' and *karpos* meaning 'fruit', as some species have a fleshy stalk below the seed (*Podocarpaceae*)

Podophyllum

pod-oh-FIL-um

From Greek *podion* meaning 'foot' and *phyllon* meaning 'leaf', due to the leaves resembling a duck's webbed foot (*Berberidaceae*)

podophyllus

po-do-FIL-us

podophylla, podophyllum

With stout-stalked leaves, as in *Rodgersia podophylla*

Podranea

pod-RAH-nee-uh

An anagram of the related genus *Pandorea* (*Bignoniaceae*)

GENUS SPOTLIGHT

Plumbago

Plumbago as a common name applies to two different groups of plants. The first are members of the genus *Plumbago*, tender shrubs and vines that make excellent conservatory plants. The best known is *P. auriculata*, or Cape leadwort, a sprawling South African plant with vibrant blue blooms. The second group comprises hardy (or half-hardy) shrubs with striking blue flowers and often attractive autumn foliage colour. *Ceratostigma plumbaginoides*, named for its similarity to *Plumbago*, is a suckering shrub suitable for ground cover, while the more upright *C. willmottianum* is an unassuming shrub that grows to around 1 metre tall.

Ceratostigma plumbaginoides, hardy blue-flowered leadwort

poeticus
po-ET-ih-kus
poetica, poeticum
Relating to poets, as in *Narcissus poeticus*

polaris
po-LAH-ris
polaris, polare
Connected with the North Pole, as in *Salix polaris*

Polemonium
pol-uh-MOH-nee-um
From Greek *polemonion*, a medicinal herb associated with Polemon I, or his son Polemon II, rulers of regions in modern-day Turkey; may also derive from Greek *polemos* meaning 'war' (*Polemoniaceae*)

Polianthes
poh-lee-ANTH-eez
From Greek *polios* meaning 'grey' and *anthos* meaning 'flower', a somewhat deprecating etymology for these attractive blooms; sometimes interpreted as deriving from Greek *polys* meaning 'many' (*Asparagaceae*)

polifolius
po-lih-FOH-lee-us
polifolia, polifolium
With grey leaves, as in *Andromeda polifolia*

Ranunculus polyanthemos,
multiflowered buttercup

Poliothyrsis
poh-lee-oh-THUR-sis
From Greek *polios* meaning 'grey' and *thyrsus* meaning 'panicle', referring to the panicles of white flowers (*Salicaceae*)

politus
POL-ee-tus
polita, politum
Polished, as in *Saxifraga × polita*

polonicus
pol-ON-ih-kus
polonica, polonicum
Connected with Poland, as in *Cochlearia polonica*

poly-
Used in compound words to denote many

polyacanthus
pol-lee-KAN-thus
polyacantha, polyacanthum
With many thorns, as in *Acacia polyacantha*

polyandrus
pol-lee-AND-rus
polyandra, polyandrum
With many stamens, as in *Conophytum polyandrum*

polyanthemos [1]
pol-lee-AN-them-os
—
polyanthus
pol-ee-AN-thus
polyantha, polyanthum
With many flowers, as in *Jasminum polyanthum*

polyblepharus
pol-ee-BLEF-ar-us
polyblephara, polyblepharum
With many fringes or eyelashes, as in *Polystichum polyblepharum*

polybotryus
pol-lee-BOT-ree-us
polybotrya, polybotryum
With many clusters, as in *Acacia polybotrya*

polybulbon [2]
pol-lee-BUL-bun
With many bulbs, as in *Dinema polybulbon*

polycarpus
pol-ee-KAR-pus
polycarpa, polycarpum
With many fruits, as in *Fatsia polycarpa*

polycephalus
pol-ee-SEF-a-lus
polycephala, polycephalum
With many heads, as in *Cordia polycephala*

polychromus
pol-ee-KROW-mus
polychroma, polychromum
With many colours, as in *Euphorbia polychroma*

Polygala
poh-LIG-uh-luh
From Greek *polys* meaning 'many' and *gala* meaning 'milk', as they've been variously promoted to increase milk yield in cattle and humans (*Polygalaceae*)

polygaloides
pol-ee-gal-OY-deez
Resembling milkwort (*Polygala*), as in *Osteospermum polygaloides*

Polygonatum [3]
po-lig-oh-NAY-tum
From Greek *polys* meaning 'many' and *gonia* meaning 'knee', referring to the jointed rhizome (*Asparagaceae*)

polygonoides
pol-ee-gon-OY-deez
Resembling *Polygonum*, as in *Alternanthera polygonoides*

Polygonum
po-LIG-oh-num
From Greek *polys* meaning 'many' and either *gonia* meaning 'knee', referring to the jointed stems, or *gone* meaning 'seed', which are profuse (*Polygonaceae*)

Polylepis
pol-ee-LEE-pis
From Greek *polys* meaning 'many' and *lepis* meaning 'scale', alluding to the peeling, many-layered bark (*Rosaceae*)

polymorphus
pol-ee-MOR-fus
polymorpha, polymorphum
With many or variable forms, as in *Acer polymorphum*

polypetalus
pol-ee-PET-uh-lus
polypetala, polypetalum
With many petals, as in *Caltha polypetala*

2

Dinema polybulbon,
many-bulbed dinema

Polygonatum hirtum,
hairy Solomon's seal

polyphyllus
pol-ee-FIL-us
polyphylla, polyphyllum
With many leaves, as in *Paris polyphylla*

polypodioides
pol-ee-pod-ee-OY-deez
Resembling *Polypodium*, as in *Blechnum polypodioides*

Polypodium
po-lee-POH-dee-um
From Greek *polys* meaning 'many' and *podion* meaning 'foot', referring to the branched rhizome (*Polypodiaceae*)

polyrhizus
pol-ee-RY-zus
polyrhiza, polyrhizum
—

polyrrhizus
polyrrhiza, polyrrhizum
With many roots, as in *Allium polyrrhizum*

Polyscias
po-lee-SKY-us
From Greek *polys* meaning 'many' and *skias* meaning 'canopy', as the leaves are often compound and numerous (*Araliaceae*)

polysepalus
pol-ee-SEP-a-lus
polysepala, polysepalum
With many sepals, as in *Nuphar polysepala*

Polyspora
po-lee-SPOR-uh
From Greek *polys* meaning 'many' and *spora* meaning 'seed', so presumably the fruits contain numerous seeds, though possibly a reference to the fruits, which have five valves in *Polyspora*, but only three in related *Camellia* (*Theaceae*)

polystachyus
pol-ee-STAK-ee-us
polystachya, polystachyum
With many spikes, as in *Ixia polystachya*

polystichoides
pol-ee-stik-OY-deez
Resembling *Polystichum*, as in *Woodsia polystichoides*

Polystichum
pol-IS-ti-kum
From Greek *polys* meaning 'many' and *stichos* meaning 'row', as the sori are in rows under the fronds (*Dryopteridaceae*)

polytrichus
pol-ee-TRY-kus
polytricha, polytrichum
With many hairs, as in *Thymus politrichus*

pomeridianus
pom-er-id-ee-AHN-us
pomeridiana, pomeridanium
Flowering in the afternoon, as in *Carpanthea pomeridiana*

pomiferus
pom-IH-fer-us
pomifera, pomiferum
Bearing apples, as in *Maclura pomifera*

pomponius
pomp-OH-nee-us
pomponia, pomponium
With a tuft or pompon, as in *Lilium pomponium*

ponderosus

pon-der-OH-sus

ponderosa, ponderosum

Heavy, as in *Pinus ponderosa*

Pontederia

pon-tuh-DEER-ee-uh

Named after Giulio Pontedera (1688–1757), Italian botanist (*Pontederiaceae*)

ponticus

PON-tih-kus

pontica, ponticum

Connected with Pontus, Asia Minor, as in *Daphne pontica*

populifolius

pop-yoo-lih-FOH-lee-us

populifolia, populifolium

With leaves like poplar (*Populus*), as in *Cistus populifolius*

populneus

pop-ULL-nee-us

populnea, populneum

Relating to poplar (*Populus*), as in *Brachychiton populneus*

Populus

POP-ew-lus

From Latin *arbor populi* meaning 'tree of the people', though reasons unknown (*Salicaceae*)

porophyllus

po-ro-FIL-us

porophylla, porophyllum

With leaves with (apparent) holes, as in *Saxifraga porophylla*

porphyreus

por-FY-ree-us

porphyrea, porphyreum

Purple-red, as in *Epidendrum porphyreum*

porrifolius

po-ree-FOH-lee-us

porrifolia, porrifolium

With leaves like leek (*Allium porrum*), as in *Tragopogon porrifolius*

porrigens

por-RIG-enz

Spreading, as in *Schizanthus porrigens*

portenschlagianus

port-en-shlag-ee-AH-nus

portenschlagiana, portenschlagianum

Named after Franz von Portenschlag-Leydermayer (1772–1822), Austrian naturalist, as in *Campanula portenschlagiana*

Portulaca

por-tew-LAH-kuh

From Latin *portula* meaning 'little door', as the fruiting capsule initially opens like a door (*Portulacaceae*)

Portulacaria

por-tew-lak-AIR-ee-uh

Resembling the related genus *Portulaca* (*Didiereaceae*)

poscharskyanus

po-shar-skee-AH-nus

poscharskyana, poscharskyanum

Named after Gustav Poscharsky (1832–1914), German horticulturist, as in *Campanula poscharskyana*

Potamogeton

pot-am-oh-GEE-ton

From Greek *potamos* meaning 'river' and *geiton* meaning 'neighbour', referring to the aquatic habit (*Potamogetonaceae*)

potamophilus

pot-am-OH-fil-us

potamophila, potomaphilum

River-loving, as in *Begonia potamophila*

potaninii

po-tan-IN-ee-eye

Named after Grigory Nikolaevich Potanin (1835–1920), Russian plant collector, as in *Indigofera potaninii*

potatorum

poh-tuh-TOR-um

Relating to drinking and brewing, as in *Agave potatorum*

Potentilla [1]

poh-ten-TIL-uh

From Latin *potens* meaning 'powerful', plus diminutive *ella*, alluding to medicinal properties (*Rosaceae*)

Poterium

pot-EER-ee-um

From Greek *poterion* meaning 'goblet', referring to the cup-like hypanthium at the base of the flower (*Rosaceae*)

pottsii

POT-see-eye

Named after John Potts or C.H. Potts, 19th-century British horticulturists and plant collectors, as in *Crocosmia pottsii*

powellii

pow-EL-ee-eye

Named after John Wesley Powell (1834–1902), American explorer, as in *Crinum × powellii*

praealtus

pray-AL-tus

praealta, praealtum

Very tall, as in *Aster praealtus*

praecox

pray-koks

Very early, as in *Stachyurus praecox*

praemorsus

pray-MOR-sus

praemorsa, praemorsum

With the appearance of bitten tips, as in *Banksia praemorsa*

praeruptorum

pray-rup-TOR-um

Growing in rough ground, as in *Peucedanum praeruptorum*

praestans

PRAY-stanz

Distinguished, as in *Tulipa praestans*

Potentilla × macnabiana,
Macnab's cinquefoil

praetextus

pray-TEX-tus

praetexta, praetextum

With a border, as in *Oncidium praetextum*

prasinus

pra-SEE-nus

prasina, prasinum

The colour of leeks, as in *Dendrobium prasinum*

pratensis

pray-TEN-sis

pratensis, pratense

From the meadow, as in *Geranium pratense*

Pratia

PRAH-tee-uh

Named after L. Prat-Bernon (?–1817), French midshipman who died on Louis de Freycinet's circumnavigation of the world (*Campanulaceae*)

prattii

PRAT-tee-eye

Named after Antwerp E. Pratt, 19th-century British zoologist, as in *Anemone prattii*

pravissimus

prav-ISS-ih-mus

pravissima, pravissimum

Very crooked, as in *Acacia pravissima*

Primula

PRIM-yew-luh

From Latin *primus* meaning 'first', as primrose flowers are some of the first to appear in spring (*Primulaceae*)

primula [2]

PRIM-yew-luh

First flowering, as in *Rosa primula*

primuliflorus

prim-yew-LIF-flor-us

primuliflora, primuliflorum

With flowers like primrose (*Primula*), as in *Rhododendron primuliflorum*

primulifolius

prim-yew-lih-FOH-lee-us

primulifolia primulifolium

With leaves like primrose (*Primula*), as in *Campanula primulifolia*

Primulina

prim-yew-LEE-nuh

Resembling the genus *Primula* (*Gesneriaceae*)

primulinus

prim-yew-LEE-nus

primulina, primulinum

—

primuloides

prim-yew-LOY-deez

Like primrose (*Primula*), as in *Paphiopedilum primulinum*

princeps

PRIN-keps

Most distinguished, as in *Centaurea princeps*

pringlei

PRING-lee-eye

Named after Cyrus Guernesey Pringle (1838–1911), American botanist and plant collector, as in *Monarda pringlei*

Prinsepia

prin-SEEP-ee-uh

Named for James Prinsep (1799–1840), British scholar and colonial administrator (*Rosaceae*)

prismaticus

priz-MAT-ih-kus

prismatica, prismaticum

In the shape of a prism, as in *Rhipsalis prismatica*

Pritchardia

prit-CHARD-ee-uh

Named after William Thomas Pritchard (1829–1907), British consul in Fiji (*Arecaceae*)

proboscideus

pro-bosk-ee-DEE-us

proboscidea, proboscideum

Shaped like a snout, as in *Arisarum proboscideum*

procerus

PRO-ker-us

procera, procerum

Tall, as in *Abies procera*

procumbens

pro-KUM-benz

Prostrate, as in *Gaultheria procumbens*

procurrens

pro-KUR-enz

Spreading underground, as in *Geranium procurrens*

prodigiosus

pro-dij-ee-OH-sus

prodigiosa, prodigiosum

Wonderful; enormous; prodigious, as in *Tillandsia prodigiosa*

productus

pro-DUK-tus

producta, productum

Lengthened, as in *Costus productus*

2

Primula auricula,
auricula

prolifer
PRO-leef-er
—
proliferus
pro-LIH-fer-us
prolifera, proliferum
Increasing by the production of side shoots, as in *Primula prolifera*

prolificus
pro-LIF-ih-kus
prolifica, prolificum
Producing many fruits, as in *Echeveria prolifica*

propinquus
prop-IN-kwus
propinqua, propinquum
Related to, near, as in *Myriophyllum propinquum*

Prosartes
pro-SAR-teez
From Greek *prosarto* meaning 'to hang', due to the pendulous ovules inside the ovary of some species (*Liliaceae*)

Prostanthera
pros-TAN-thu-ruh
From Greek *prostheke* meaning 'appendix' and *anthera*, as the anthers have spur-like appendages (*Lamiaceae*)

prostratus
prost-RAH-tus
prostrata, prostratum
Growing flat on the ground, as in *Veronica prostrata*

Protea
PRO-tee-uh
Named after the Greek god Proteus, who could change his shape; an allusion to the great diversity of form in this genus (*Proteaceae*)

protistus
pro-TISS-tus
protista, protistum
The first, as in *Rhododendron protistum*

provincialis
pro-VIN-ki-ah-lis
provincialis, provinciale
Connected with Provence, France, as in *Arenaria provincialis*

pruinatus
proo-in-AH-tus
pruinata, pruinatum
—
pruinosus
proo-in-NOH-sus
pruinosa, pruinosum
Glistening like frost, as in *Cotoneaster pruinosus*

Prumnopitys
prum-NOP-it-iss
From Greek *prymnos* meaning 'hindmost' and *pitys* meaning 'pine', as the resin duct is below the midvein in the leaf (*Podocarpaceae*)

Prunella
proo-NEL-uh
From Latin *prunum* meaning 'plum', referring to flower colour, though many other etymologies have been proposed for this name (*Lamiaceae*)

prunelloides
proo-nel-LOY-deez
Resembling self-heal (*Prunella*), as in *Haplopappus prunelloides*

prunifolius
proo-ni-FOH-lee-us
prunifolia, prunifolium
With leaves like plum (*Prunus*), as in *Malus prunifolia*

Prunus [1, 2]
PROO-nus
From Latin *prunum* meaning 'plum', though this genus also includes cherries, peaches and almonds (*Rosaceae*)

przewalskianus
prez-WAL-skee-ah-nus
przewalskiana, przewalskianum
—
przewalskii
prez-WAL-skee
Named after Nicolai Przewalski, 19th-century Russian naturalist, as in *Ligularia przewalskii*

pseud-
Used in compound words to denote false

pseudacorus
soo-DA-ko-rus
Deceptively like *Acorus* or sweet flag, as in *Iris pseudacorus*

Pseuderanthemum
soo-der-ANTH-uh-mum
From Greek *pseudes* meaning 'false', plus *Eranthemum*, a related genus (*Acanthaceae*)

pseudocamellia
soo-doh-kuh-MEE-lee-uh
Deceptively like a camellia, as in *Stewartia pseudocamellia*

Prunus armeniaca,
apricot

Prunus domestica,
plum

pseudochrysanthus

soo-doh-kris-AN-thus

pseudochrysantha, pseudochrysanthum

Resembling a *chrysanthus* species in the same genus, as in *Rhododendron pseudochrysanthum*, which means resembling *R. chrysanthum*

Pseudocydonia

soo-doh-sy-DOH-nee-uh

From Greek *pseudes* meaning 'false', plus *Cydonia*, a related genus (*Rosaceae*)

pseudodictamnus

soo-do-dik-TAM-nus

Deceptively like *Dictamnus*, as in *Ballota pseudodictamnus*

Pseudofumaria

soo-doh-foo-MAIR-ee-uh

From Greek *pseudes* meaning 'false', plus *Fumaria*, a related genus (*Papaveraceae*)

Pseudogynoxys

soo-doh-jy-NOKS-iss

From Greek *pseudes* meaning 'false', plus *Gynoxys*, a related genus (*Asteraceae*)

Pseudolarix

soo-doh-LAR-iks

From Greek *pseudes* meaning 'false', plus *Larix*, a related genus (*Pinaceae*)

pseudonarcissus

soo-doh-nar-SIS-us

Deceptively like *Narcissus*; in *N. pseudonarcissus*, it means like *N. poeticus*

Pseudopanax

soo-doh-PAN-aks

From Greek *pseudes* meaning 'false', plus *Panax*, a related genus (*Araliaceae*)

Pseudosasa

soo-doh-SAS-uh

From Greek *pseudes* meaning 'false', plus *Sasa*, a related genus (*Poaceae*)

Pseudotsuga

soo-doh-SOO-guh

From Greek *pseudes* meaning 'false', plus *Tsuga*, a related genus (*Pinaceae*)

Pseudowintera

soo-doh-WIN-ter-uh

From Greek *pseudes* meaning 'false', plus *Wintera* (=*Drimys*), a related genus (*Winteraceae*)

Psidium

SID-ee-um

From Greek *psidion* meaning 'pomegranate', as the fruits of many species resemble their namesake (*Myrtaceae*)

psilostemon

sigh-loh-STEE-mon

With smooth stamens, as in *Geranium psilostemon*

Psilotum

sy-LOH-tum

From Greek *psilos* meaning 'naked' as the stems are leafless (*Psilotaceae*)

psittacinus

sit-uh-SIGN-us

psittacina, psittacinum

—

psittacorum

sit-a-KOR-um

Like a parrot, relating to parrots, as in *Hippeastrum psittacinum*

Psychotria

sy-KOH-tre-uh

From Greek *psychro* meaning 'cold' and *trophe* meaning 'food', together meaning to refresh, as the plant has medicinal properties (*Rubiaceae*)

ptarmica

TAR-mik-uh

ptarmica, ptarmicum

Ancient Greek name for a plant (probably sneezewort) that caused sneezing, as in *Achillea ptarmica*

Ptelea

TEE-lee-uh

From Greek *ptelea*, the vernacular name for elm (*Ulmus*), as the winged fruits are similar (*Rutaceae*)

Pteridium

te-RID-ee-um

From Greek *pteridion* meaning 'small fern' (*Dennstaedtiaceae*)

pteridoides

ter-id-OY-deez

Resembling *Pteris*, as in *Coriaria pteridioides*

Pteris

TE-ris

From Greek *pteris* meaning 'fern', derived from *pteron* meaning 'wing' as fern fronds can resemble bird wings (*Pteridaceae*)

PTERIS AND PTERIDOLOGY

The Greek word *pteris* means 'fern' and it's a component of many generic names (*Pteris*, *Dryopteris*, *Cystopteris*). Indeed, the study of ferns is known as pteridology. Fern Latin names often refer to details of fern morphology that are confusing to gardeners, so here's a quick primer. Ferns reproduce using spores, produced by sporangia. In most garden ferns, sporangia are arranged in distinct clusters called sori (sing. sorus) on the leaf (frond) underside, though they can be distributed across the leaf or on separate, fertile fronds. In many ferns, the sori are protected by a membrane (indusium). The location and arrangement of sporangia and indusia are often critical for fern identification.

Pterocarya

te-roh-KAR-ee-uh

From Greek *pteron* meaning 'wing' and *karyon* meaning 'nut', as the fruits are winged (*Juglandaceae*)

Pteroceltis

te-roh-KEL-tis

From Greek *pteron* meaning 'wing' and *Celtis*, a related genus (*Cannabaceae*)

pteroneurus

ter-OH-new-rus

pteroneura, pteroneurum

With nerves that have wings, as in *Euphorbia pteroneura*

Pterostyrax
tair-oh-STY-raks
From Greek *pteron* meaning 'wing' and *Styrax*, a related genus (*Styracaceae*)

Ptilotus
ty-LOH-tus
From Greek *ptilon* meaning 'feather', as the hairy flowers are arranged in feather-like spikes (*Amaranthaceae*)

pubens
PEW-benz
—

pubescens
pew-BESS-enz
Downy, as in *Primula* × *pubescens*

pubigerus
pub-EE-ger-us
pubigera, pubigerum
Producing down, as in *Schefflera pubigera*

pudicus
pud-IH-kus
pudica, pudicum
Shy, as in *Mimosa pudica*

pugioniformis
pug-ee-oh-nee-FOR-mis
pugioniformis, pugioniforme
Shaped like a dagger, as in *Celmisia pugioniformis*

pulchellus
pul-KELL-us
pulchella, pulchellum
—

pulcher
PUL-ker
pulchra, pulchrum
Pretty, beautiful, as in *Correa pulchella*

pulcherrimus
pul-KAIR-ih-mus
pulcherrima, pulcherrimum
Very beautiful, as in *Dierama pulcherrimum*

pulegioides
pul-eg-ee-OY-deez
Like *Mentha pulegium* (pennyroyal), as in *Thymus pulegioides*

pulegium
pul-ee-GEE-um
Latin for pennyroyal, reputed to be a flea-repellent, as in *Mentha pulegium*

pullus
PULL-us
pulla, pullum
Dark-coloured, as in *Campanula pulla*

Pulmonaria
pul-mon-AIR-ee-uh
From Latin *pulmo* meaning 'lung', as the mottled leaves resemble lungs and were therefore said to be effective at treating chest conditions (*Boraginaceae*)

Pulsatilla
pul-su-TIL-uh
From Latin *pulsare* meaning 'to pulsate', a reference to the way the flowers or seed heads move in the wind; however, it could also originate as a corruption of Hebrew *paschal* meaning 'passion', a reference to Easter flowering (*Ranunculaceae*)

Pultenaea
pul-ten-AY-uh
Named after Richard Pulteney (1730–1801), British physician and botanist (*Fabaceae*)

GENUS SPOTLIGHT

Pulmonaria

Many medieval herbalists believed that God would guide them to the correct plant to cure a specific illness by shaping the plant like the ailing organ. This philosophy, known as the doctrine of signatures, was initially developed by Greek physicians, but gained widespread acceptance. Liverwort (*Hepatica*), birthwort (*Aristolochia*), eyebright (*Euphrasia*) and spleenwort (*Asplenium*) all derive their English and Latin names from their supposed medicinal properties. Lungworts (*Pulmonaria*) have crescent-shaped leaves mottled with white, said to resemble ulcerated lungs. However, the presence of toxic pyrrolizidine alkaloids suggests these herbs may be harmful.

Pulmonaria officinalis,
lungwort

pulverulentus

pul-ver-oo-LEN-tus

pulverulenta, pulverulentum

Appearing to be covered in dust, as in *Primula pulverulenta*

pulvinatus

pul-vin-AH-tus

pulvinata, pulvinatum

Like a cushion, as in *Echeveria pulvinata*

pumilio

poo-MIL-ee-oh

Small, dwarf; as in *Edraianthus pumilio*

pumilus

POO-mil-us

pumila, pumilum

Dwarf, as in *Trollius pumilus*

punctatus

punk-TAH-tus

punctata, punctatum

With spots, as in *Anthemis punctata*

pungens

PUN-genz

With a sharp point, as in *Elymus pungens*

Punica

PEW-ni-kuh

From Latin *punicum malum* meaning 'apple of Carthage' (*Lythraceae*)

puniceus

pun-IK-ee-us

punicea, puniceum

Red-purple, as in *Clianthus puniceus*

purpurascens

pur-pur-ASS-kenz

Becoming purple, as in *Bergenia purpurascens*

purpuratus

pur-pur-AH-tus

purpurata, purpuratum

Made purple, as in *Phyllostachys purpurata*

purpureus

pur-PUR-ee-us

purpurea, purpureum

Purple, as in *Digitalis purpurea*

purpusii

pur-PUSS-ee-eye

Named after Carl Purpus (1851–1941) or his brother Joseph Purpus (1860–1932), German plant collectors, as in *Lonicera × purpusii*

Purshia

PUR-shee-uh

Named after Friedrich Traugott Pursch (1774–1820), German botanist (*Rosaceae*)

Puschkinia

push-KIN-ee-uh

Named after Apollos Apollosovich Musin-Pushkin (1760–1805), Russian chemist and botanist (*Asparagaceae*)

pusillus

pus-ILL-us

pusilla, pusillum

Very small, as in *Soldanella pusilla*

pustulatus

pus-tew-LAH-tus

pustulata, pustulatum

Appearing to be blistered, as in *Lachenalia pustulata*

Puya

POO-yuh

From Mapuche (Chile) word meaning 'pointed' and the vernacular name for *P. chilensis* (*Bromeliaceae*)

pycnacanthus

pik-na-KAN-thus

pycnacantha, pycnacanthum

Densely spined, as in *Coryphantha pycnacantha*

pycnanthus

pik-NAN-thus

pycnantha, pycnanthum

With densely crowded flowers, as in *Acer pycnanthum*

Pycnostachys

pik-noh-STAK-is

From Greek *pyknos* meaning 'dense' and *stachys* meaning 'ear of grain', as the flowers are tightly clustered (*Lamiaceae*)

pygmaeus

pig-MAY-us

pygmaea, pygmaeum

Dwarf; pygmy, as in *Erigeron pygmaeus*

Pyracantha

py-ruh-KAN-thuh

From Greek *pyr* meaning 'fire' and *akantha* meaning 'thorn', referring to the sharp thorns and scarlet fruits (*Rosaceae*)

pyramidalis

peer-uh-mid-AH-lis

pyramidalis, pyramidale

Shaped like a pyramid, as in *Ornithogalum pyramidale*

pyrenaeus

py-ren-AY-us

pyrenaea, pyrenaeum

—

pyrenaicus

py-ren-AY-ih-kus

pyrenaica, pyrenaicum

Connected with the Pyrenees, as in *Fritillaria pyrenaica*

pyrifolius

py-rih-FOH-lee-us

pyrifolia, pyrifolium

With leaves like pear (*Pyrus*), as in *Salix pyrifolia*

pyriformis

py-rih-FOR-mis

pyriformis, pyriforme

Shaped like a pear, as in *Rosa pyriformis*

Pyrostegia

py-roh-STEE-jee-uh

From Greek *pyr* meaning 'fire' and *stegos* meaning 'cover', as the flame-coloured flowers can coat this climber (*Bignoniaceae*)

Pyrrosia

py-ROH-see-uh

From Greek *pyrrhos* meaning 'flame-coloured', a reference to the tawny frond undersides in some species (*Polypodiaceae*)

Pyrus

PY-rus

From Latin *pirum*, the vernacular name for pear, *P. communis* (*Rosaceae*)

quadr-
Used in compound words to denote four

quadrangularis
kwad-ran-gew-LAH-ris
quadrangularis, quadrangulare
—

quadrangulatus
kwad-ran-gew-LAH-tus
quadrangulata, quadrangulatum
With four angles, as in *Passiflora quadrangularis*

quadratus
kwad-RAH-tus
quadrata, quadratum
In fours, as in *Restio quadratus*

quadriauritus
kwad-ree-AWR-ry-tus
quadriaurita, quadriauritum
With four ears, as in *Pteris quadriaurita*

quadrifidus
kwad-RIF-ee-dus
quadrifida, quadrifidum
Cut into four, as in *Calothamnus quadrifidus*

quadrifolius
kwad-rih-FOH-lee-us
quadrifolia, quadrifolium
With four leaves, as in *Marsilea quadrifolia*

quadrivalvis
kwad-rih-VAL-vis
quadrivalvis, quadrivalve
With four valves, as in *Nicotiana quadrivalvis*

quamash
KWA-mash
Nex Perce (Native American) word for *Camassia*, especially *C. quamesh*

quamoclit
KWAM-oh-klit
Old generic name, possibly meaning kidney bean, as in *Ipomoea quamoclit*

quercifolius
kwer-se-FOH-lee-us
quercifolia, quercifolium
With leaves like oak (*Quercus*), as in *Hydrangea quercifolia*

Quercus
KWER-kus
From classical Latin name for English oak, *Q. robur*; the name may derive from an unknown early European language or from Greek *kerkhaleos* ('rough', like the bark), or *kakhrus* meaning 'acorn' (*Fagaceae*)

Quesnelia
kes-NEE-lee-uh
Named after D. Quesnel (dates unknown), who grew plants then known as *Billbergia quesneliana* in Paris (*Bromeliaceae*)

quin-
Used in compound words to denote five

quinatus
kwi-NAH-tus
quinata, quinatum
In fives, as in *Akebia quinata*

quinoa
KEEN-oh-a
A Spanish word for *Chenopodium quinoa*, from Quechua, *kinua*

quinqueflorus
kwin-kway-FLOR-rus
quinqueflora, quinqueflorum
With five flowers, as in *Enkianthus quinqueflorus*

quinquefolius
kwin-kway-FOH-lee-us
quinquefolia, quinquefolium
With five leaves, often referring to leaflets, as in *Parthenocissus quinquefolia*

quinquevulnerus
kwin-kway-VUL-ner-us
quinquevulnera, quinquevulnerum
With five wounds (i.e. marks), as in *Aerides quinquevulnerum*

Quisqualis
KWIS-kwuh-lis
From Malay *udani*, converted to Dutch *hoedanig* meaning 'how, what?', then translated to Latin *quis* ('who') and *qualis* ('what') (*Combretaceae*)

GENUS SPOTLIGHT

Quercus

The English oak (*Quercus robur*) is one of Europe's most familiar trees. The common name is a bit misleading as England actually has two native oaks (the other is *Q. petraea*), while *Q. robur*'s range stretches east to the Caucasus. One of the easiest ways to distinguish the two British oaks is to look at their acorns. In *Q. robur*, they sit at the end of a stalk (or peduncle) and an alternative common name is pedunculate oak, while in *Q. petraea*, the acorns lack a stalk and so are said to be sessile, thus 'sessile oak'.

Quercus robur,
English oak

racemiflorus
ray-see-mih-FLOR-us
racemiflora, racemiflorum
—

racemosus
ray-see-MOH-sus
racemosa, racemosum
With flowers that appear in racemes, as in *Nepeta racemosa*

raddianus
rad-dee-AH-nus
raddiana, raddianum
Named after Giuseppe Raddi (1770–1829), Italian botanist, as in *Adiantum raddianum*

Radermachera
ray-der-MAK-er-uh
Named after Jacob Cornelis Matthieu Radermacher (1741–83), Dutch botanist and artist (*Bignoniaceae*)

radiatus
rad-ee-AH-tus
radiata, radiatum
With rays, as in *Pinus radiata*

radicans
RAD-ee-kanz
With stems that take root, as in *Campsis radicans*

radicatus
rad-ee-KAH-tus
radicata, radicatum
With conspicuous roots, as in *Papaver radicatum*

radicosus
ray-dee-KOH-sus
radicosa, radicosum
With many roots, as in *Silene radicosa*

radiosus
ray-dee-OH-sus
radiosa, radiosum
With many rays, as in *Masdevallia radiosa*

radula
RAD-yoo-luh
From Latin *radula*, a scraper, as in *Silphium radula*

ramentaceus
ra-men-TA-see-us
ramentacea, ramentaceum
Covered with scales, as in *Begonia ramentacea*

ramiflorus
ram-ee-FLOR-us
ramiflora, ramiflorum
With flowers on the older branches, as in *Romulea ramiflora*

Ramonda
ray-MON-duh
Named after Louis-Francois Èlisabeth Ramon de Carbonnières (1755–1827), French politician, botanist and geologist (*Gesneriaceae*)

ramondioides
ram-on-di-OY-deez
Resembling *Ramonda*, as in *Conandron ramondoides*

ramosissimus
ram-oh-SIS-ih-mus
ramosissima, ramosissimum
Much branched, as in *Lonicera ramosissima*

ramosus
ram-OH-sus
ramosa, ramosum
Branched, as in *Anthericum ramosum*

ramulosus
ram-yoo-LOH-sus
ramulosa, ramulosum
Twiggy, as in *Celmisia ramulosa*

ranunculoides
ra-nun-kul-OY-deez
Resembling buttercup (*Ranunculus*), as in *Anemone ranunculoides*

Ranunculus [1, 2]
ruh-NUNK-ew-lus
From Latin *rana* meaning 'frog' and diminutive *unculus*, as some species, especially water-crowfoots, are aquatic (*Ranunculaceae*)

Ranzania
ran-ZAH-nee-uh
Named after Ono Ranzan (1729–1810), Japanese botanist and herbalist (*Berberidaceae*)

Raoulia
rah-OOL-ee-uh
Named after Étienne Fiacre Louis Raoul (1815–52), French naval surgeon and naturalist (*Asteraceae*)

Raphanus
RAF-uh-nus
From Greek *raphanos*, the vernacular name for radish, *R. sativus* (*Brassicaceae*)

1
Ranunculus aconitifolius,
aconite buttercup

2
Ranunculus asiaticus,
Persian buttercup

1

2

3

Raphia farinifera,
raffia palm

Ravenala madagascariensis,
traveller's palm

Phoenix reclinata,
Senegal date palm

Raphia [1]
RAF-ee-uh
From Malagasy (Madagascar) *rofia*, the vernacular name for
R. farinifera (*Arecaceae*)

rariflorus
rar-ee-FLOR-us
rariflora, rariflorum
With scattered flowers, as in *Carex rariflora*

Ravenala [2]
rav-uh-NAH-luh
From Malagasy (Madagascar) *ravinala* meaning 'forest leaves'
(*Strelitziaceae*)

re-
Used in compound words to denote back or again

Rebutia
ruh-BEW-tee-uh
Named after Pierre Rebut (c. 1828–98), French horticulturist
(*Cactaceae*)

reclinatus [3]
rek-lin-AH-tus
reclinata, reclinatum
Bent backwards, as in *Phoenix reclinata*

rectus
REK-tus
recta, rectum
Upright, as in *Phygelius* × *rectus*

recurvatus
rek-er-VAH-tus
recurvata, recurvatum

recurvus
re-KUR-vus
recurva, recurvum
Curved backward, as in *Beaucarnea recurvata*

redivivus
re-div-EE-vus
rediviva, redivivum
Revived; brought back to life (e.g. after drought) as in *Lunaria
rediviva*

reductus
red-UK-tus
reducta, reductum
Dwarf, as in *Sorbus reducta*

reflexus
ree-FLEKS-us
reflexa, reflexum
—

refractus
ray-FRAK-tus
refracta, refractum
Bent sharply backwards, as in *Correa reflexa*

refulgens
ref-FUL-genz
Shining brightly, as in *Bougainvillea refulgens*

Reseda luteola,
weld

regalis
re-GAH-lis
regalis, regale
Regal; of exceptional merit, as in *Osmunda regalis*

reginae
ree-JIN-ay-ee
Relating to a queen, as in *Strelitzia reginae*

reginae-olgae
ree-JIN-ay-ee OL-gy
Named after Queen Olga of Greece (1851–1926), as in *Galanthus reginae-olgae*

regius
REE-jee-us
regia, regium
Royal, as in *Juglans regia*

rehderi
RAY-der-eye
—

rehderianus
ray-der-ee-AH-nus
rehderiana, rehderianum
Named after Alfred Rehder (1863–1949), German-born dendrologist who worked at the Arnold Arboretum, Massachusetts, USA, as in *Clematis rehderiana*

Rehderodendron
ray-der-oh-DEN-dron
Named after Alfred Rehder (1863–1949), German-born American botanist (*Styracaceae*)

Rehmannia
ray-MAN-ee-uh
Named after Joseph Rehmann (?–1831), German physician (*Orobanchaceae*)

rehmannii
ray-MAN-ee-eye
Named after Joseph Rehmann (?–1831), German physician, or Anton Rehmann (1840–1917), Polish botanist, as in *Zantedeschia rehmannii*

reichardii
ri-KAR-dee-eye
Named after Johann Jakob Reichard, (1743–1782), German botanist, as in *Erodium reichardii*

reichenbachiana
rike-en-bak-ee-AH-nuh
—

reichenbachii
ry-ken-BAHK-ee-eye
Named after Heinrich Gottlieb Ludwig Reichenbach (1793–1879) or Heinrich Gustav Reichenbach, as in *Echinocereus reichenbachii*

Reineckea
ry-NEK-ee-uh
Named after Joseph Heinrich Julius Reinecke (1799–1871), German horticulturist (*Asparagaceae*)

Reinwardtia
rine-WARD-tee-uh
Named after Caspar Georg Carl Reinwardt (1773–1854), Dutch botanist (*Linaceae*)

religiosus
re-lij-ee-OH-sus
religiosa, religiosum
Relating to religious ceremonies; sacred, as in *Ficus religiosa*, under which the Buddha attained enlightenment

remotus
ree-MOH-tus
remota, remotum
Scattered, as in *Carex remota*

Renanthera
ray-NAN-thu-ruh
From Latin *renis* meaning 'kidney' and anther, as some species have anthers of this shape (*Orchidaceae*)

renardii
ren-AR-dee-eye
Named after Charles Claude Renard (1809–86), as in *Geranium renardii*

reniformis
ren-ih-FOR-mis
reniformis, reniforme
Shaped like a kidney, as in *Begonia reniformis*

repandus
REP-an-dus
repanda, repandum
With wavy margins, as in *Cyclamen repandum*

repens
REE-penz
With a creeping habit, as in *Gypsophila repens*

replicatus
rep-lee-KAH-tus
replicata, replicatum
Doubled; folded back, as in *Berberis replicata*

reptans
REP-tanz
With a creeping habit, as in *Ajuga reptans*

requienii
re-kwee-EN-ee-eye
Named after Esprit Requien (1788–1851), French naturalist, as in *Mentha requienii*

Reseda [4]
RES-uh-duh
From Latin *resedare* meaning 'to assuage' or 'to heal', due to its medicinal properties (*Resedaceae*)

resiniferus
res-in-IH-fer-us
resinifera, resiniferum

resinosus
res-in-OH-sus
resinosa, resinosum
Producing resin, as in *Euphorbia resinifera*

Rhinanthus

Yellow rattle (*Rhinanthus minor*) gets its common name from the dry, papery seed pods, which contain numerous small seeds that rattle in the breeze. Those seeds have an important role to play in meadows, boosting the diversity of wildflowers by reining in the grasses. *Rhinanthus* is a parasite and, while it can survive on its own, it prefers to connect to the root system of a vigorous grass and steal water and nutrients. This weakens the grass, allowing other non-parasitic wildflowers such as orchids to successfully compete and thrive.

Rhinanthus minor, yellow rattle

Restio
RES-tee-oh
From Latin *restis* meaning 'rope', as the plant is a source of cordage (*Restionaceae*)

reticulatus
reh-tick-yoo-LAH-tus
reticulata, reticulatum
Netted, as in *Iris reticulata*

retortus
re-TOR-tus
retorta, retortum
—

retroflexus
re-troh-FLEKS-us
retroflexa, retroflexum
—

retrofractus
re-troh-FRAK-tus
retrofracta, retrofractum
Twisted or turned backwards, as in *Helichrysum retortum*

retusus
re-TOO-sus
retusa, retusum
With a rounded and notched tip, *Coryphantha retusa*

reversus
ree-VER-sus
reversa, reversum
Reversed, as in *Rosa × reversa*

revolutus
re-vo-LOO-tus
revoluta, revolutum
Rolled backwards (e.g. of leaves), as in *Cycas revoluta*

rex
REKS
King; with outstanding qualities, as in *Begonia rex*

rhamnifolius
ram-nih-FOH-lee-us
rhamnifolia, rhamnifolium
With leaves like buckthorn (*Rhamnus*), as in *Rubus rhamnifolius*

rhamnoides
ram-NOY-deez
Resembling buckthorn (*Rhamnus*), as in *Hippophae rhamnoides*

Rhamnus
RAM-nus
From Greek *rhamnos*, the name of a spiny shrub (*Rhamnaceae*)

Rhaphidophora
raf-id-oh-FOR-uh
From Greek *rhaphis* meaning 'needle' and *phoreus* meaning 'bearer', as sharp crystals can be found within the tissues (*Araceae*)

Rhaphiolepis
raf-ee-oh-LEE-pis
From Greek *rhaphis* meaning 'needle' and *lepis* meaning 'scale', referring to the slender bracts below the flower clusters (*Rosaceae*)

Rhapidophyllum
rap-id-oh-FIL-um
From *Rhapis*, a related genus, and *phyllon* meaning leaf; the two genera have similar foliage (*Arecaceae*)

Rhapis
RAH-pis
From Greek *rhapis* meaning 'rod', an allusion to the cane-like stems (*Arecaceae*)

Rheum
REE-um
From Greek *rheon*, the vernacular name for rhubarb (*Polygonaceae*)

Rhinanthus

ry-NAN-thus

From Greek *rhis* meaning 'nose' and *anthos* meaning 'flower', referring to the snout-like upper petal (*Orobanchaceae*)

Rhipsalis

RIP-suh-lis

From Greek *rhips* meaning 'wickerwork', a reference to the often entangled, many-branched stems (*Cactaceae*)

rhizophyllus

ry-zo-FIL-us

rhizophylla, rhizophyllum

With leaves that take root, as in *Asplenium rhizophyllum*

Rhodanthe

roh-DAN-thee

From Greek *rhodon* meaning 'rose' and *anthos* meaning 'flower' (*Asteraceae*)

Rhodanthemum

roh-DAN-thuh-mum

From Greek *rhodon* meaning 'rose' and *anthos* meaning 'flower' (*Asteraceae*)

rhodanthus

rho-DAN-thus

rhodantha, rhodanthum

With rose-coloured flowers, as in *Mammillaria rhodantha*

Rhodiola

roh-dee-OH-luh

From Greek *rhodon* meaning 'rose', as the roots of *R. rosea* are floral-scented (*Crassulaceae*)

Rhodochiton

roh-doh-KY-ton

From Greek *rhodon* meaning 'rose' and *chiton* meaning 'tunic', referring to the red calyx (*Plantaginaceae*)

Rhodocoma

roh-doh-KOH-muh

From Greek *rhodon* meaning 'rose' and *kome* meaning 'hair', an allusion to the rufous hair-like inflorescences (*Restionaceae*)

Rhododendron [1]

roh-doh-DEN-dron

From Greek *rhodon* meaning 'rose' and *dendron* meaning 'tree'; the name *rhododendron* was applied to oleander (*Nerium oleander*) by the Greeks (*Ericaceae*)

Rhodohypoxis

roh-doh-hy-POX-iss

From Greek *rhodon* meaning 'rose' and *Hypoxis*, a related genus that typically has yellow flowers (*Hypoxidaceae*)

rhodopensis

roh-doh-PEN-sis

rhodopensis, rhodopense

From the Rhodope Mountains, Bulgaria, as in *Haberlea rhodopensis*

Rhodophiala

roh-doh-FEE-ah-luh

From Greek *rhodon* meaning 'rose' and *phiali* meaning 'drinking vessel', referring to the shape and colour of the flowers (*Amaryllidaceae*)

Rhodotypos

roh-doh-TY-pos

From Greek *rhodon* meaning 'rose' and *typos* meaning 'model', as the flowers are rose-like (*Rosaceae*)

rhoeas

RE-as

Ancient Greek *rhoias*, name for *Papaver rhoeas*

Rhoicissus

roh-i-SIS-us

From Latin *rhoicus*, referring to the genus *Rhus*, and Greek *kissos* meaning 'ivy', as the leaves of this climber vaguely resemble those of *Rhus* (*Vitaceae*)

rhombifolius

rom-bih-FOH-lee-us

rhombifolia, rhombifolium

With diamond-shaped leaves, as in *Cissus rhombifolia*

rhomboideus

rom-BOY-dee-us

rhomboidea, rhomboideum

Shaped like a diamond, as in *Rhombophyllum rhomboideum*

Rhopalostylis

roh-pay-loh-STY-lis

From Greek *rhopalos* meaning 'cudgel' and *stylis* meaning 'style', as in the centre of male flowers is an infertile, club-like style (*Arecaceae*)

1

Rhododendron cuffeanum,
Wheeler-Cuffe's rhododendron

Rhus
ROOS
From Greek *rhous*, the vernacular name for *R. coriaria* (*Anacardiaceae*)

Rhyncholaelia
rin-koh-LAY-lee-uh
From Greek *rhynchos* meaning 'snout' and *Laelia*, a related genus, referring to the beak that separates the ovary from the rest of the flower (*Orchidaceae*)

rhytidophyllus
ry-ti-do-FIL-us
rhytidophylla, rhytidophyllum
With wrinkled leaves, as in *Viburnum rhytidophyllum*

Ribes
RY-beez
From Arabic *ribas* meaning 'acidic' pertaining to the sharp-tasting fruits; *ribas* also refers to the unrelated rhubarb, *Rheum × hybridum* (*Grossulariaceae*)

richardii
rich-AR-dee-eye
Named after various persons with the forename or surname Richard; thus *Cortaderia richardii* commemorates the French botanist Achille Richard (1794–1852)

richardsonii
rich-ard-SON-ee-eye
Named after Sir John Richardson, 19th-century Scottish explorer, as in *Heuchera richardsonii*

Richea
RICH-ee-uh
Named after Claude Antoine Gaspard Riche (1762–97), French botanist and entomologist (*Ericaceae*)

Ricinus [1]
RIS-in-us
From Latin *ricinus* meaning 'tick', as the seeds resemble these parasites (*Euphorbiaceae*)

rigens
RIG-enz
—

rigidus
RIG-ih-dus
rigida, rigidum
Rigid; inflexible; stiff, as in *Verbena rigida*

rigescens
rig-ES-enz
Rather rigid, as in *Diascia rigescens*

ringens
RIN-jenz
Gaping; open, as in *Arisaema ringens*

riparius
rip-AH-ree-us
riparia, riparium
Of riverbanks, as in *Ageratina riparia*

ritro
RIH-tro
Probably from the Greek for globe thistle, *rhytros*, as in *Echinops ritro*

ritteri
RIT-ter-ee
ritterianus rit-ter-ee-AH-nus
—

ritteriana, ritterianum
Named after Friedrich Ritter (1898–1989), German cactus collector, as in *Cleistocactus ritteri*

rivalis
riv-AH-lis
rivalis, rivale
Growing by the side of streams, as in *Geum rivale*

riversleaianum
riv-ers-lee-i-AY-num
Named after Riverslea Nursery, Hampshire, England, as in *Geranium × riversleaianum*

riviniana
riv-in-ee-AH-nuh
Named after Augustus Quirinus Rivinus (August Bachmann; 1652–1723), German physician and botanist, as in *Viola riviniana*

rivularis
riv-yoo-LAH-ris
rivularis, rivulare
Brook-loving, as in *Cirsium rivulare*

Robinia
rob-IN-ee-uh
Named after Jean Robin (1550–1629), French botanist and horticulturist (*Fabaceae*)

robur
ROH-bur
Oak, as in *Quercus robur*

robustus
roh-BUS-tus
robusta, robustum
Growing strongly; sturdy, as in *Eremurus robustus*

rockii
ROK-ee-eye
Named after Joseph Francis Charles Rock (1884–1962), Austrian-born American plant hunter, as in *Paeonia rockii*

Rodgersia
ro-JER-zee-uh
Named after John Rodgers (1812–82), American naval officer (*Saxifragaceae*)

roebelenii
roh-bel-EN-ee-eye
Named after Carl Roebelen (1855–1927), orchid collector, as in *Phoenix roebelenii*

Rohdea
ROH-dee-uh
Named after Michael Rohde (1782–1812), German physician and botanist (*Asparagaceae*)

romanus
roh-MAHN-us
romana, romanum
Roman, as in *Orchis romana*

1

Ricinus communis,
castor oil plant

romieuxii

rom-YOO-ee-eye

Named after Henri Auguste Romieux (1857–1937), French botanist, as in *Narcissus romieuxii*

Romneya

ROM-nay-uh

Named after John Thomas Romney Robinson (1792–1882), Irish astronomer (*Papaveraceae*)

Romulea

rom-ew-LEE-uh

Named after Romulus, legendary founder of Rome, Italy, as the plants were said to be common in the Roman countryside (*Iridaceae*)

Rondeletia

ron-duh-LEE-tee-uh

Named after Guillaume Rondelet (1507–66), French physician and botanist (*Rubiaceae*)

Rosa [2]

ROH-zuh

The classical Latin name for rose (*Rosaceae*)

rosa-sinensis

RO-sa sy-NEN-sis

The rose of China, as in *Hibiscus rosa-sinensis*

rosaceus

ro-ZAY-see-us

rosacea, rosaceum

Rose-like, as in *Saxifraga rosacea*

Roscoea [3]

ros-KOH-ee-uh

Named after William Roscoe (1753–1831), British lawyer, banker and politician (*Zingiberaceae*)

roseus

RO-zee-us

rosea, roseum

Coloured like rose (*Rosa*), as in *Lapageria rosea*

rosmarinifolius

rose-ma-rih-nih-FOH-lee-us

rosmarinifolia, rosmarinifolium

With leaves like rosemary (*Rosmarinus*), as in *Santolina rosmarinifolia*

Rosmarinus

roz-MA-rin-us

From Latin *roz* meaning 'dew' and *marinus* meaning 'sea', alluding to its coastal habitat (*Lamiaceae*)

rostratus

ro-STRAH-tus

rostrata, rostratum

With a beak, as in *Magnolia rostrata*

Rosularia

roz-ew-LAIR-ee-uh

From Latin *rosula* meaning 'small rosette', the typical leaf arrangement (*Crassulaceae*)

2

Rosa × centifolia,
cabbage rose

3

Roscoea species,
roscoea

rotatus

ro-TAH-tus

rotata, rotatum

Shaped like a wheel, as in *Phlomis rotata*

Rothmannia

roth-MAN-ee-uh

Named after Göran Rothman (1739–78), Swedish physician (*Rubiaceae*)

rothschildianus

roths-child-ee-AH-nus

rothschildiana, rothschildianum

Named after Lionel Walter Rothschild (1868–1937), or other members of the House of Rothschild, as in *Paphiopedilum rothschildianum*

rotundatus

roh-tun-DAH-tus

rotundata, rotundatum

Rounded, as in *Carex rotundata*

rotundifolius

ro-tun-dih-FOH-lee-us

rotundifolia, rotundifolium

With leaves that are round, as in *Prostanthera rotundifolia*

rotundus

ro-TUN-dus

rotunda, rotundum

Rounded, as in *Cyperus rotundus*

rowleyanus

ro-lee-AH-nus

Named after Gordon Douglas Rowley, (b.1921) British botanist and succulent expert, as in *Senecio rowleyanus*

roxburghii

roks-BURGH-ee-eye

Named after William Roxburgh (1751–1815), Superintendent of Calcutta Botanic Garden, as in *Rosa roxburghii*

roxieanum

rox-ee-AY-num

Named after Roxie Hanna, 19th-century British missionary, as in *Rhododendron roxieanum*

Roystonea

roy-STOH-nee-uh

Named after Roy Stone (1836–1905), American soldier (*Arecaceae*)

Rubus idaeus, raspberry

rubellus

roo-BELL-us

rubella, rubellum

Pale red, becoming red, as in *Peperomia rubella*

rubens

ROO-benz

—

ruber

ROO-ber

rubra, rubrum

Red, as in *Plumeria rubra*

rubescens

roo-BES-enz

Becoming red, as in *Salvia rubescens*

Rubia

ROO-bee-uh

From Latin *ruber* meaning 'red', as a red dye can be extracted from the roots of madder, *R. tinctoria* (*Rubiaceae*)

rubiginosus

roo-bij-ih-NOH-sus

rubiginosa, rubiginosum

Rusty, as in *Ficus rubiginosa*

rubioides

roo-bee-OY-deez

Resembling madder (*Rubia*), as in *Bauera rubioides*

rubri-

Used in compound words to denote red

rubricaulis

roo-bri-KAW-lis

rubricaulis, rubricaule

With red stems, as in *Actinidia rubricaulis*

rubriflorus

roo-brih-FLOR-us

rubiflora, rubiflorum

With red flowers, as in *Schisandra rubriflora*

Rubus [1]

ROO-bus

From Latin *rubus* meaning 'bramble', possibly deriving from *ruber* meaning 'red', the colour of fruits in raspberry, *R. idaeus*, and others (*Rosaceae*)

Rudbeckia

rood-BEK-ee-uh

Named after father and son Olaus Johannes Rudbeck (1630–1702) and Olaus Olai Rudbeck (1660–1740), Swedish scientists (*Asteraceae*)

rudis

ROO-dis

rudis, rude

Coarse, growing on uncultivated ground, as in *Persicaria rudis*

2

Rumex scutatus,
French sorrel

3

Ruta graveolens,
rue

Ruellia
roo-EE-lee-uh
Named after Jean Ruel (1474–1537),
French physician (*Acanthaceae*)

rufinervis
roo-fi-NER-vis
rufinervis, rufinerve
With red veins, as in *Acer rufinerve*

rufus
ROO-fus
rufa, rufum
Red, as in *Prunus rufa*

rugosus
roo-GOH-sus
rugosa, rugosum
Wrinkled, as in *Rosa rugosa*

Rumex [?]
ROO-meks
From Latin *rumo* meaning 'to suck', as dock
leaves were sucked to quench the thirst
(*Polygonaceae*)

Rumohra
roo-MOH-ruh
Named after Carl Friedrich von Rumohr
(1785–1843), German writer and historian
(*Dryopteridaceae*)

rupestris
rue-PES-tris
rupestris, rupestre
Of rocky places, as in *Leptospermum rupestre*

rupicola
roo-PIH-koh-luh
Growing on cliffs and ledges, as in
Penstemon rupicola

rupifragus
roo-pee-FRAG-us
rupifraga, rupifragum
Rock-breaking, as in *Papaver rupifragum*

ruscifolius
rus-kih-FOH-lee-us
ruscifolia, ruscifolium
With leaves like butcher's broom (*Ruscus*), as
in *Sarcococca ruscifolia*

Ruscus
RUS-kus
From Latin *ruscum* meaning 'butcher's
broom', as the sharp-tipped stems were used
to clean butcher's blocks (*Asparagaceae*)

russatus
russ-AH-tus
russata, russatum
Russet, as in *Rhododendron russatum*

Russelia
rus-EL-ee-uh
Named after Alexander Russell (1715–68),
Scottish physician and naturalist
(*Plantaginaceae*)

russellianus
russ-el-ee-AH-nus
russelliana, russellianum
Named after John Russell, 6th Duke of
Bedford (1766–1839), author of numerous
botanical and horticultural works, as in
Miltonia russelliana

rusticanus
rus-tik-AH-nus
rusticana, rusticanum
—

rusticus
RUS-tih-kus
rustica, rusticum
Relating to the country, as in *Armoracia
rusticana*

Ruta [3]
ROO-tuh
From Latin *ruta* meaning 'disagreeable', in
reference to the pungent smell of the foliage
(*Rutaceae*)

ruta-muraria
ROO-tuh-mur-AY-ree-uh
Literally wall rue, as in *Asplenium ruta-
muraria*

ruthenicus
roo-THEN-ih-kus
ruthenica, ruthenicum
Connected with Ruthenia, a historial area
consisting of parts of Russia and eastern
Europe, as in *Fritillaria ruthenica*

rutifolius
roo-tih-FOH-lee-us
rutifolia, rutifolium
With leaves like rue (*Ruta*), as in *Corydalis
rutifolia*

rutilans
ROO-til-lanz
Reddish, as in *Parodia rutilans*

A
B
C
D
E
F
G
H
I
J
K
L
M
N
O
P
Q
R
S
T
U
V
W
X
Y
Z

i

sabatius

sa-BAY-shee-us

sabatia, sabatium

Connected with Savona, Italy, as in *Convolvulus sabatius*

saccatus

sak-KAH-tus

saccata, saccatum

Like a bag, or saccate, as in *Lonicera saccata*

saccharatus

sak-kah-RAH-tus

saccharata, saccharatum

—

saccharinus

sak-kah-EYE-nus

saccharina, saccharinum

Sweet or sugared, as in *Pulmonaria saccharata*

Saccharum [1]

SAK-uh-rum

From Greek *sakkharon* meaning 'sugar', extracted from sugarcane, *S. officinarum* (*Poaceae*)

sacciferus

sak-IH-fer-us

saccifera, sacciferum

Bearing bags or sacks, as in *Dactylorhiza saccifera*

sachalinensis

saw-kaw-lin-YEN-sis

sachalinensis, sachalinense

From the island Sakhalin, off the coast of Russia, as in *Abies sachalinensis*

Sadleria

sad-LEER-ee-uh

Named after Joseph Sadler (1791–1849), Hungarian physician and botanist (*Blechnaceae*)

Sageretia

sag-uh-REE-tee-uh

Named after Augustin Sageret (1763–1851), French botanist (*Rhamnaceae*)

Sagina

suh-JY-nuh

From Latin *sagina* meaning 'food' or 'fodder', as a related genus (*Spergula*) was fed to livestock (*Caryophyllaceae*)

Saccharum officinarum,
sugarcane

sagittalis

saj-ih-TAH-lis

sagittalis, sagittale

—

sagittatus

saj-ih-TAH-tus

sagittata, sagittatum

Shaped like an arrow, as in *Genista sagittalis*

Sagittaria

saj-i-TAIR-ee-uh

From Latin *sagitta* meaning 'arrow', as the leaves resemble arrowheads (*Alismataceae*)

sagittifolius

saj-it-ih-FOH-lee-us

sagittifolia, sagittifolium

With leaves shaped like arrows, as in *Sagittaria sagittifolia*

Saintpaulia

saint-PAWL-ee-uh

Named after Walter von Saint Paul-Illaire (1860–1940), German colonial administrator and botanist (*Gesneriaceae*)

salicarius

sa-lih-KAH-ree-us

salicaria, salicarium

Like willow (*Salix*), as in *Lythrum salicaria*

Salix alba,
white willow

salicariifolius

sa-lih-kar-ih-FOH-lee-us

salicariifolia, salicariifolium

—

salicifolius

sah-lis-ih-FOH-lee-us

salicifolia, salicifolium

With leaves like willow (*Salix*), as in *Magnolia salicifolia*

salicinus

sah-lih-SEE-nus

salicina, salicinum

Like willow (*Salix*), as in *Prunus salicina*

salicornioides

sal-eye-korn-ee-OY-deez

Resembling glasswort (*Salicornia*), as in *Hatiora salicornioides*

salignus

sal-LIG-nus

saligna, salignum

Like willow (*Salix*), as in *Podocarpus salignus*

salinus

sal-LY-nus

salina, salinum

Of salty regions, as in *Carex salina*

Salix [2]

SAY-liks

The classical Latin name for willow (*Salicaceae*)

1

Sambucus nigra,
common elder

2

Sambucus ebulus,
dwarf elder

3

Sandersonia aurantiaca,
Chinese lantern lily

Salpiglossis
sal-pi-GLOS-iss
From Greek *salpinx* meaning 'trumpet' and *glossa* meaning 'tongue', as the tubular flowers have tongue-like lobes (*Solanaceae*)

saluenensis
sal-WEN-en-sis
saluenensis, saluenense
From the Salween River, China, as in *Camellia saluenensis*

Salvia
SAL-vee-uh
From Latin *salvia*, the vernacular name for sage, *S. officinalis* (*Lamiaceae*)

salviifolius
sal-vee-FOH-lee-us
salviifolia, salviifolium
With leaves like salvia, as in *Cistus salviifolius*

Salvinia
sal-VIN-ee-uh
Named after Anton Maria Salvini (1633–1729), Italian botanist (*Salviniaceae*)

sambucifolius
sam-boo-kih-FOH-lee-us
sambucifolia, sambucifolium
With leaves like elder (*Sambucus*), as in *Rodgersia sambucifolia*

sambucinus
sam-byoo-ki-nus
sambucina, sambucinum
Like elder (*Sambucus*), as in *Rosa sambucina*

Sambucus [1, 2]
sam-BEW-kus
From classical Latin name for elder, *S. nigra*; a sambuca was a harp supposedly made of elder wood (*Adoxaceae*)

samius
SAM-ee-us
samia, samium
Connected with the isle of Samos, Greece, as in *Phlomis samia*

sanctus
SANK-tus
sancta, sanctum
Holy, as in *Rhododendron sanctum*

sanderi
SAN-der-eye
—
sanderianus
san-der-ee-AH-nus
sanderiana, sanderianum
Named after Henry Frederick Conrad Sander (1847–1920), German-born British plant collector, nurseryman and orchid expert, as in *Dracaena sanderiana*

Sandersonia [3]
san-der-SOH-nee-uh
Named after John Sanderson (1820–81), Scottish journalist and botanist (*Colchicaceae*)

Sanguinaria
san-gwin-AIR-ee-uh
From Latin *sanguis* meaning 'blood', as the roots exude red sap (*Papaveraceae*)

sanguineus
san-GWIN-ee-us
sanguinea, sanguineum
Blood-red, as in *Geranium sanguineum*

Sanguisorba
san-gwi-SOR-buh
From Latin *sanguis* meaning 'blood' and *sorbeo* meaning 'to absorb'; the plant was said to stop bleeding (*Rosaceae*)

Sanicula
san-IK-ew-luh
From Latin *sanus* meaning 'healthy', alluding to medicinal properties (*Apiaceae*)

Sansevieria
san-sev-EER-ee-uh
Named after Raimondo di Sangro, Prince of Sansevero (1710–71), Italian soldier and scientist (*Asparagaceae*)

Santolina
san-toh-LEE-nuh
From Latin *sanctus* meaning 'holy' and *linum* meaning 'flax', a name applied to one species that had medicinal value (*Asteraceae*)

Sanvitalia
san-vi-TAY-lee-uh
Named after Federico Sanvitali (1704–61), Italian mathematician (*Asteraceae*)

sapidus
sap-EE-dus
sapida, sapidum
With a pleasant taste, as in *Rhopalostylis sapida*

Sapindus [4]

sa-PIN-dus

From Latin *sapo* meaning 'soap' and *indicus* meaning 'from India'; the fruits are rich in saponins and have been used as soap (*Sapindaceae*)

Saponaria

sa-pon-AIR-ee-uh

From Latin *sapo* meaning 'soap' as the crushed foliage of soapwort, *S. officinalis*, produces a lather (*Caryophyllaceae*)

saponarius

sap-oh-NAIR-ee-us

saponaria, saponarium

Soapy, as in *Sapindus saponaria*

sarcocaulis

sar-koh-KAW-lis

sarcocaulis, sarcocaule

With a fleshy stem, as in *Crassula sarcocaulis*

Sarcocaulon

sar-koh-KOW-lon

From Greek *sarkos* meaning 'fleshy' and *caulon* meaning 'stem'; these are succulent shrubs (*Geraniaceae*)

Sarcococca

sar-koh-KOK-uh

From Greek *sarkos* meaning 'fleshy' and *kokkos* meaning 'berry' (*Buxaceae*)

sarcodes

sark-OH-deez

Flesh-like, as in *Rhododendron sarcodes*

sardensis

saw-DEN-sis

sardensis, sardense

Of Sardis (Sart), Turkey, as in *Chionodoxa sardensis*

sargentianus

sar-jen-tee-AH-nus

sargentiana, sargentianum

—

sargentii

sar-JEN-tee-eye

Named after Charles Sprague Sargent (1841–1927), dendrologist and director of the Arnold Arboretum, Harvard, USA, as in *Sorbus sargentiana*

sarmaticus

sar-MAT-ih-kus

sarmatica, sarmaticum

From Sarmatia, historic territory now partly in Poland, partly in Russia, as in *Campanula sarmatica*

sarmentosus

sar-men-TOH-sus

sarmentosa, sarmentosum

Producing runners, as in *Androsace sarmentosa*

Sarmienta

sar-me-EN-tuh

Named after Martín Sarmiento (1695–1772), Spanish cleric and naturalist (*Gesneriaceae*)

sarniensis [5]

sarn-ee-EN-sis

sarniensis, sarniense

From the island of Sarnia (Guernsey), as in *Nerine sarniensis*

Sarracenia [6]

sa-ruh-SEE-nee-uh

Named after Michel Sarrazin (1659–1734), French-born Canadian botanist and physician (*Sarraceniaceae*)

Saruma

suh-ROO-muh

An anagram of the related genus *Asarum* (*Aristolochiaceae*)

Sasa

SA-suh

From Japanese, the vernacular name for these bamboos (*Poaceae*)

sasanqua

suh-SAN-kwuh

From the Japanese name for *Camellia sasanqua*

4

Sapindus saponaria,
soapberry

5

Nerine sarniensis,
Guernsey lily

6

Sarracenia leucophylla,
white trumpet

1 Castanea sativa, sweet chestnut

2 Saururus cernuus, lizard's tail

Sassafras
SAS-uh-fras
From Spanish/French *sasafras*, most likely derived from a Native American name (*Lauraceae*)

sativus [1]
sa-TEE-vus
sativa, sativum
Cultivated, as in *Castanea sativa*

Satureja
sat-ew-REE-uh
The classical Latin name for this herb, possibly derived from Arabic (*Lamiaceae*)

saundersii
son-DER-see-eye
Commemorates various eminent Saunders, for example Sir Charles Saunders (1857–1935); as in *Pachypodium saundersii*

Sauromatum
saw-roo-MAY-tum
From Greek *sauros* meaning 'lizard', as the mottled spathe resembles reptile skin (*Araceae*)

Saururus [2]
saw-ROO-rus
From Greek *sauros* meaning 'lizard' and *oura* meaning 'tail', alluding to the shape of the flower spike (*Saururaceae*)

Saussurea
saw-SOO-ree-uh
Named after father and son Horace Bénédict (1740–99) and Nicolas Théodore (1767–1845) de Saussure, Swiss naturalists (*Asteraceae*)

saxatilis
saks-A-til-is
saxatilis, saxatile
Of rocky places, as in *Aurinia saxatilis*

Saxegothaea
saks-uh-GOTH-ee-uh
Named after Prince Albert of Saxe-Coburg and Gotha (1819–61), German-born husband to Queen Victoria (*Podocarpaceae*)

saxicola
saks-IH-koh-luh
Growing in rocky places, as in *Juniperus saxicola*

Saxifraga [3]
saks-i-FRAH-gah
From Latin *saxum* meaning 'stone' and *frangere* meaning 'to break', as these alpines often grow in rock crevices (*Saxifragaceae*)

saxorum
saks-OR-um
Of the rocks, as in *Streptocarpus saxorum*

saxosus
saks-OH-sus
saxosa, saxosum
Of rocky places, as in *Gentiana saxosa*

scaber
SKAB-er
scabra, scabrum
Rough, as in *Eccremocarpus scaber*

Scabiosa
ska-bee-OH-suh
From Latin *scabies* meaning 'itch', referring to the use of this plant to cure skin ailments (*Caprifoliaceae*)

scabiosifolius

skab-ee-oh-sih-FOH-lee-us

scabiosifolia, scabiosifolium

With leaves like scabious (*Scabiosa*), as in *Salvia scabiosifolia*

scabiosus

skab-ee-OH-sus

scabiosa, scabiosum

Scabrous, or relating to scabies, as in *Centaurea scabiosa*

Scadoxus

ska-DOKS-us

From Greek *skia* meaning 'shade' and *doxa* meaning 'glory', as the attractive bulbs grow in shady forests (*Amaryllidaceae*)

Scaevola

skuh-VOH-luh

From Greek *scaeva* meaning 'left-handed', as the flowers look like a hand (*Goodeniaceae*)

scalaris

skal-AH-ris

scalaris, scalare

Like a ladder, as in *Sorbus scalaris*

scandens

SKAN-denz

Climbing, as in *Cobaea scandens*

3

Saxifraga hieracifolia,
hawkweed-leaf saxifrage

HANDY HABITAT HINTS

Latin names can indicate the natural habitat that plants reside in, making it easier for gardeners to give their plants what they want. Species epithets such as *aquatica* (in water), *palustris* (marsh), *sylvatica* (woodland), *alpina* (high elevation), *rivalis* (by rivers) and *maritima* (seaside) all help to build a picture of your plant's requirements. Sometimes, however, the message may be more subtle. The buttercup genus *Ranunculus* gets its name from the Latin word for frog, as many buttercup species live in water or marsh. *Nyssa* is named for a water nymph in Greek mythology, while *Saxifraga* means 'breaking rock', alluding to the alpine habitat of many species.

scaposus

ska-POH-sus

scaposa, scaposum

With leafless flowering stems (scapes) as in *Aconitum scaposum*

scariosus

skar-ee-OH-sus

scariosa, scariosum

Shrivelled, as in *Liatris scariosa*

sceptrum

SEP-trum

Like a sceptre, as in *Isoplexis sceptrum*

schafta

SHAF-tuh

A Caspian vernacular name for *Silene schafta*

Schefflera

SHEF-lu-ruh

Named after Jacob Christoph Scheffler (1698–1742), German physician and botanist (*Araliaceae*)

schidigera

ski-DEE-ger-ruh

Bearing a spine or splinter, as in *Yucca schidigera*

schillingii

shil-LING-ee-eye

Named after Tony Schilling (b. 1935), British plantsman, as in *Euphorbia schillingii*

Schima

SHEE-muh

From Greek *skia* meaning 'shade', alluding to the dense canopy of evergreen leaves (*Theaceae*)

Schinus

SHY-nus

From Greek *schinos*, the vernacular name for mastic tree, *Pistacia lentiscus*, to which it resembles (*Anacardiaceae*)

Schisandra

sky-ZAN-druh

From Greek *schisis* meaning 'splitting' and *andros* meaning 'male'; the anthers are cleft in two (*Schisandraceae*)

Schizachyrium

sky-ZAK-ree-um

From Greek *schisis* meaning 'splitting' and *achryon* meaning 'chaff', as the lemmas (bracts in the flower spikelet) are divided (*Poaceae*)

Schizanthus

sky-ZAN-thus

From Greek *schisis* meaning 'splitting' and *anthos* meaning 'flower', as the petals are split into lobes (*Solanaceae*)

schizopetalus

ski-zo-pe-TAY-lus

schizopetala, schizopetalum

With cut petals, as in *Hibiscus schizopetalus*

Schizophragma

sky-zoh-FRAG-muh

From Greek *schisis* meaning 'splitting' and *phragma* meaning 'fence', alluding to the interior walls of the fruits, which are split into fibres (*Hydrangeaceae*)

schizophyllus

skits-oh-FIL-us

schizophylla, schizophyllum

With cut leaves, as in *Syagurus schizophylla*

Schlumbergera [1]

shloom-BERG-uh-ruh

Named after Frédéric Schlumberger (1823–93), French horticulturist (*Cactaceae*)

schmidtianus

shmit-ee-AH-nus

schmidtiana, schmidtianum

—

schmidtii

SHMIT-ee-eye

Commemorates various eminent botanists called Schmidt, as in *Artemisia schmidtiana*

schoenoprasum

skee-no-PRAY-zum

Epithet for chives (*Allium schoenoprasum*), meaning 'rush-leek' in Greek

schottii

SHOT-ee-eye

Can commemorate various naturalists called Schott, for example Arthur Carl Victor Schott (1814–75), as in *Yucca schottii*

schubertii

shoo-BER-tee-eye

Named after Gotthilf von Schubert (1780–1860), German naturalist, as in *Allium schubertii*

schumannii

shoo-MAHN-ee-eye

Named after Dr Karl Moritz Schumann (1851–1904), German botanist, as in *Abelia schumannii*

Sciadopitys

skee-ah-DO-pit-is

From Greek *skia* meaning 'shade', which can also be interpreted as 'umbrella' or 'canopy', plus *pitys* meaning 'pine' (*Sciadopityaceae*)

Scilla

SIL-uh

From Greek *skilla* meaning 'squill' or 'sea onion', possibly referring to the Mediterranean squill, *Drimia maritima* (*Asparagaceae*)

scillaris

sil-AHR-is

scillaris, scillare

Like *Scilla*, as in *Ixia scillaris*

scillifolius

sil-ih-FOH-lee-us

scillifolia, scillifolium

With leaves like *Scilla*, as in *Roscoea scillifolia*

scilloides

sil-OY-deez

Resembling *Scilla*, as in *Puschkinia scilloides*

scilloniensis

sil-oh-nee-EN-sis

scilloniensis, scilloniense

From the Isles of Scilly, England, as in *Olearia* × *scilloniensis*

Scirpus

SKIR-pus

The classical Latin name for a type of rush, possibly *Schoenoplectus lacustris* (*Juncaceae*)

sclarea

SKLAR-ee-uh

From *clarus*, 'clear', as in *Salvia sclarea*

sclerophyllus

skler-oh-FIL-us

sclerophylla, sclerophyllum

With hard leaves, as in *Castanopsis sclerophylla*

Scoliopus

skoh-lee-OH-pus

From Greek *skolios* meaning 'crooked' and *pous* meaning 'footed', as the pedicels holding each flower are twisted (*Liliaceae*)

scolopendrius

skol-oh-PEND-ree-us

scolopendria, scolopendrium

From the Greek word for *Asplenium scolopendrium*, from a supposed likeness of the underside of its fronds to a millipede or centipede (Greek *skolopendra*)

scolymus

SKOL-ih-mus

From the Greek for an edible kind of thistle or artichoke, as in *Cynara scolymus*

scoparius

sko-PAIR-ee-us

scoparia, scoparium

Like broom, as in *Cytisus scoparius*

1

Schlumbergera truncata, **Christmas cactus**

Scorzonera hispanica,
black salsify

Scrophularia vernalis,
yellow figwort

Sedum aizoon,
Aizoon stonecrop

Scopolia
skuh-POH-lee-uh
Named after Giovanni Antonio Scopoli
(1723–88), Italian physician and naturalist
(*Solanaceae*)

scopulorum
sko-puh-LOR-um
Of crags or cliffs, as in *Cirsium scopulorum*

scorodoprasum
skor-oh-doh-PRAY-zum
Greek name for a plant between leek and
garlic, as in *Allium scorodoprasum*

scorpioides
skor-pee-OY-deez
Resembling a scorpion's tail, as in *Myosotis
scorpioides*

Scorzonera [2]
skor-ZON-uh-ruh
From French *scorzonère* meaning 'viper's
grass', possibly due to the medicinal use of
the roots in treating snake bites (*Asteraceae*)

scorzonerifolius
skor-zon-er-ih-FOH-lee-us
scorzonerifolia, scorzonerifolium
With leaves like *Scorzonera*, as in *Allium
scorzonerifolium*

scoticus
SKOT-ih-kus
scotica, scoticum
Connected with Scotland, as in *Primula
scotica*

scouleri
SKOOL-er-ee
Named after Dr John Scouler (1804–71),
Scottish botanist, as in *Hypericum scouleri*

Scrophularia [3]
skrof-ew-LAIR-ee-uh
From Latin *scrofula*, or tuberculosis of the
lymph nodes, which when swollen are said
to resemble this plant's rhizomes
(*Scrophulariaceae*)

scutatus
skut-AH-tus
scutata, scutatum
—

scutellaris
skew-tel-AH-ris
scutellaris, scutellare
—

scutellatus
skew-tel-LAH-tus
scutellata, scutellatum
Shaped like a shield or platter, as in *Rumex
scutatus*

Scutellaria
skew-tuh-LAIR-ee-uh
From Latin *scutella*, a small dish; the calyx
holding the fruits resembles a dish-like
skull-cap (*Lamiaceae*)

Secale
SEK-uh-lee
From classical Latin name for rye, *S. cereale*,
or derived from Celtic *sega* meaning 'sickle'
(*Poaceae*)

secundatus
see-kun-DAH-tus
secundata, secundatum
—

secundiflorus
sek-und-ee-FLOR-us
secundiflora, secundiflorum
—

secundus
se-KUN-dus
secunda, secundum
With leaves or flowers growing on one side
of a stalk only, as in *Echeveria secunda*

Sedum [4]
SEE-dum
From Latin *sedeo* meaning 'to sit', alluding to
the compact habit of many species
(*Crassulaceae*)

seemannianus

see-mahn-ee-AH-nus

seemanniana, seemannianum

—

seemannii

see-MAN-ee-eye

Named after Berthold Carl Seemann (1825–71), German plant collector, as in *Hydrangea seemannii*

segetalis

seg-UH-ta-lis

segetalis, segetale

—

segetum

seg-EE-tum

Of cornfields, as in *Euphorbia segetalis*

Selaginella

sel-aj-uh-NEL-uh

From Latin *selago*, the savin juniper (*Juniperus sabina*), plus diminutive *ella* as the foliage bears a resemblance; *selago* also refers to the similar-looking genus *Lycopodium* (Selaginellaceae)

selaginoides

sel-aj-ee-NOY-deez

Resembling clubmoss (*Selaginella*), as in *Athrotaxis selaginoides*

Selago

suh-LAY-goh

An ancient name for *Lycopodium*, to which this plant bears a superficial resemblance; alternatively, the name may derive from Celtic *sel* meaning 'sight' and *jach* meaning 'salutary', suggesting a herb beneficial to the sight (Scrophulariaceae)

Selenicereus

suh-len-i-SER-ee-us

Named after Selene, goddess of the moon in Greek mythology, plus *Cereus*, a related genus; these cacti flower at night (Cactaceae)

Selinum

suh-LEE-num

The Greek *selinon*, the vernacular name for the related celery, *Apium graveolens* (Apiaceae)

selloanus

sel-lo-AH-nus

selloana, selloanum

Named after Friedrich Sellow (Sello), 19th-century German explorer and plant collector, as in *Cortaderia selloana*

Semele

SEM-uh-lee

Named after Semele, mother of Dionysus in Greek mythology (Asparagaceae)

Semiaquilegia

sem-ee-ak-wi-LEE-juh

From Latin *semi* meaning 'half', plus *Aquilegia*, a related genus; these plants lack the spurs typical in *Aquilegia* blooms (Ranunculaceae)

Semiarundinaria

sem-ee-ah-roon-di-NAIR-ee-uh

From Latin *semi* meaning 'half', plus *Arundinaria*, a related genus (Poaceae)

semperflorens

sem-per-FLOR-enz

Ever-blooming, as in *Grevillea × semperflorens*

sempervirens

sem-per-VY-renz

Evergreen, as in *Lonicera sempervirens*

sempervivoides

sem-per-vi-VOY-deez

Resembling houseleek (*Sempervivum*), as in *Androsace sempervivoides*

Sempervivum

Houseleeks are succulent plants with neat leaf rosettes and strange, spidery flowers. As succulents, they are adept at surviving with minimal moisture and so are popular choices for rockeries and dry-stone walls. They also grow well on tiled roofs, where legend has it they will prevent lightning strikes. With a name like 'houseleek', you might expect them to cause your roof to leak, but the 'leek' comes from Anglo-Saxon *laec* meaning 'plant'. This word was also applied to members of the onion family, such as garlic (*garlaec*) and leeks, but suggests that *Sempervivum* was a good plant to grow on your house.

Sempervivum tectorum, **houseleek**

Sempervivum

sem-per-VY-vum

From Latin *semper* meaning 'always' and *vivere* meaning 'to live', as these succulents cling to life tenaciously (*Crassulaceae*)

Senecio

suh-NEE-see-oh

From Latin *senex* meaning 'old man', as the bristles around the fruits are white (*Asteraceae*)

senegalensis

sen-eh-gal-EN-sis

senegalensis, senegalense

From Senegal, Africa, as in *Persicaria senegalensis*

senescens

sen-ESS-enz

Seeming to grow old (i.e. white or grey), as in *Allium senescens*

senilis

SEE-nil-is

senilis, senile

With white hair, as in *Rebutia senilis*

Senna

SEN-uh

From Arabic *sana*, the vernacular name (*Fabaceae*)

sensibilis

sen-si-BIL-is

sensibilis, sensibile

—

sensitivus

sen-si-TEE-vus

sensitiva, sensitivum

Sensitive to light or touch, as in *Onoclea sensibilis*

sepium

SEP-ee-um

Growing along hedgerows, as in *Calystegia sepium*

sept-

Used in compound words to denote seven

septemfidus

sep-TEM-fee-dus

septemfida, septemfidum

With seven divisions, as in *Gentiana septemfida*

Sequoiadendron giganteum, giant redwood

septemlobus

sep-tem-LOH-bus

septemloba, septemlobum

With seven lobes, as in *Primula septemloba*

septentrionalis

sep-ten-tree-oh-NAH-lis

septentrionalis, septentrionale

From the north, as in *Beschorneria septentrionalis*

Sequoia

se-KWOY-uh

Named after Sequoyah (c. 1767–1843), Native American silversmith and creator of a syllabary for the Cherokee language (*Cupressaceae*)

Sequoiadendron [1]

se-kwoy-uh-DEN-dron

From the related genus *Sequoia*, plus Greek *dendron* meaning 'tree' (*Cupressaceae*)

sericanthus

ser-ee-KAN-thus

sericantha, sericanthum

With silky flowers, as in *Philadelphus sericanthus*

sericeus

ser-IK-ee-us

sericea, sericeum

Silky, as *Rosa sericea*

Serissa

suh-RIS-uh

From an Indian language name for *S. japonica* (*Rubiaceae*)

serotinus

se-roh-TEE-nus

serotina, serotinum

With flowers or fruit late in the season, as in *Iris serotina*

serpens

SUR-penz

Creeping, as in *Agapetes serpens*

serpyllifolius

ser-pil-ly-FOH-lee-us

serpyllifolia, serpyllifolium

With leaves like wild or creeping thyme (*Thymus serpyllum*), as in *Arenaria serpyllifolia*

serpyllum

ser-PIE-lum

From the Greek word for a kind of thyme, as in *Thymus serpyllum*

serratifolius

sair-rat-ih-FOH-lee-us

serratifolia, serratifolium

With leaves that are serrated or saw-toothed, as in *Photinia serratifolia*

Serratula [1]

suh-RAT-ew-luh

From Latin *serrula* meaning 'little saw', a reference to the serrated leaves (*Asteraceae*)

serratus

sair-AH-tus

serrata, serratum

With small-toothed leaf margins, as in *Zelkova serrata*

serrulatus

ser-yoo-LAH-tus

serrulata, serrulatum,

With small serrations at the leaf margins, as in *Enkianthus serrulatus*

Seseli

SE-suh-lee

From Greek *seseli*, the name for a plant in this family, in English cicely (*Apiaceae*)

Sesleria

sez-LEER-ee-uh

Named after Leonardo Sesler (?–1785), Italian physician and botanist (*Poaceae*)

sesquipedalis

ses-kwee-ped-AH-lis

sesquipedalis, sesquipedale

Eighteen inches long, as in *Angraecum sesquipedale*

sessili-

Used in compound words to denote stalkless

sessiliflorus

sess-il-ee-FLOR-us

sessiliflora, sessililforum

With stalkless flowers, as in *Libertia sessiliflora*

sessilifolius

ses-il-ee-FOH-lee-us

sessilifolia, sessilifolium

With stalkless leaves, as in *Uvularia sessilifolia*

sessilis [2]

SES-sil-is

sessilis, sessile

Without a stalk, as in *Trillium sessile*

1

Serratula tinctoria,
saw-wort

2

Trillium sessile,
toadshade

Setaria viridis,
green bristle grass

Deutzia setchuenensis,
Sichuan deutzia

setaceus
se-TAY-see-us
setacea, setaceum
With bristles, as in *Pennisetum setaceum*

Setaria [3]
suh-TAIR-ee-uh
From Latin *seta* meaning 'bristle', as the inflorescence is bristly
(*Poaceae*)

setchuenensis [4]
sech-yoo-en-EN-sis
setchuenensis, setchuenense
From Sichuan province, China, as in *Deutzia setchuenensis*

seti-
Used in compound words to denote bristled

setiferus
set-IH-fer-us
setifera, setiferum
With bristles, as in *Polystichum setiferum*

setifolius
set-ee-FOH-lee-us
setifolia, setifolium
With bristly leaves, as in *Lathyrus setifolius*

setiger
set-EE-ger
—

setigerus
set-EE-ger-us
setigera, setigerum
Bearing bristles, as in *Gentiana setigera*

setispinus
set-i-SPIN-us
setispina, setispinum
With bristly spines, as in *Thelocactus setispinus*

setosus
set-OH-sus
setosa, setosum
With many bristles, as in *Iris setosa*

setulosus
set-yoo-LOH-sus
setulosa, setulosum
With many small bristles, as in *Salvia setulosa*

sex-
Used in compound words to denote six

sexangularis
seks-an-gew-LAH-ris
sexangularis, sexangulare
With six angles, as in *Sedum sexangulare*

1

Silene vulgaris,
bladder campion

2

Silphium terebinthinaceum,
prairie burdock

3

Silybum marianum,
milk thistle

sexstylosus
seks-sty-LOH-sus
sexstylosa, sexstylosum
With six styles, as in *Hoheria sexstylosa*

Shepherdia
shep-ERD-ee-uh
Named after John Shepherd (1764–1836),
British botanist (*Elaeagnaceae*)

sherriffii
sher-RIF-ee-eye
Named after George Sherriff (1898–1967),
Scottish plant collector, as in *Rhododendron
sherriffii*

Shibataea
shib-uh-TAY-uh
Named after Keita Shibata (1877–1949),
Japanese botanist (*Poaceae*)

shirasawanus
shir-ah-sa-WAH-nus
shirasawana, shirasawanum
Named after Homi (or Miho) Shirasawa
(1868–1947), Japanese botanist, as in *Acer
shirasawanum*

Shortia
SHOR-tee-uh
Named after Charles Wilkins Short
(1794–1863), American botanist
(*Diapensiaceae*)

Sibbaldia
si-BAL-dee-uh
Named after Robert Sibbald (1641–1722),
Scottish physician (*Rosaceae*)

Sibiraea
si-bi-REE-uh
Named after Siberia, where the first
specimens were collected (*Rosaceae*)

sibiricus
sy-BEER-ih-kus
sibirica, sibiricum
Connected with Siberia, as in *Iris sibirica*

Sibthorpia
sib-THOR-pee-uh
Named after Humphrey Waldo Sibthorp
(1713–97), British botanist
(*Plantaginaceae*)

sichuanensis
sy-CHOW-en-sis
sichuanensis, sichuanense
From Sichuan province, China, as in
Cotoneaster sichuanensis

siculus
SIK-yoo-lus
sicula, siculum
From Sicily, Italy, as in *Nectaroscordum
siculum*

Sida
SEE-duh
From Greek *side* meaning 'water lily', for
reasons unknown (*Malvaceae*)

Sidalcea
si-DAL-see-uh
A combination of two related genera, *Sida*
and *Alcea* (*Malvaceae*)

Sideritis
sid-uh-RY-tiss
From Greek *sideros* meaning 'iron', as the
plant was used to heal wounds from iron
weapons (*Lamiaceae*)

sideroxylon
sy-der-oh-ZY-lon
Wood like iron, as in *Eucalyptus sideroxylon*

sieberi
sy-BER-ee
Named after Franz Sieber (1789–1844),
Prague-born botanist and plant collector, as
in *Crocus sieberi*

sieboldianus
see-bold-ee-AH-nus
sieboldiana, sieboldianum
—

sieboldii
see-bold-ee-eye
Named after Philipp Franz von Siebold
(1796–1866), German doctor who collected
plants in Japan, as in *Magnolia sieboldii*

signatus

sig-NAH-tus

signata, signatum

Well-marked, as in *Saxifraga signata*

sikkimensis

sik-im-EN-sis

sikkimensis, sikkimense

From Sikkim, India, as in *Euphorbia sikkimensis*

Silene [1]

sy-LEE-nee

Named after Silenus, intoxicated companion of Dionysus in Greek mythology; often portrayed as being covered in foam, and some *Silene* produce a foam-like secretion (*Caryophyllaceae*)

siliceus

sil-ee-SE-us

silicea, siliceum

Growing in sand, as in *Astragalus siliceus*

siliquastrum

sil-ee-KWAS-trum

Roman name for a plant with pods, as in *Cercis siliquastrum*

Silphium [2]

SIL-fee-um

From Greek *silphion*, the name for an unknown plant (*Asteraceae*)

silvaticus

sil-VAT-ih-kus

silvatica, silvaticum

—

silvestris

sil-VES-tris

silvestris, silvestre

Growing in woodlands, as in *Polystichum silvaticum*

Silybum [3]

SIL-i-bum

From Greek *silybon*, a type of thistle (*Asteraceae*)

similis

SIM-il-is

similis, simile

Similar; like, as in *Lonicera similis*

Simmondsia

sim-ONDZ-ee-uh

Named after Thomas William Simmonds (1767–1804), British physician and botanist (*Simmondsiaceae*)

simplex

SIM-plecks

Simple; without branches, as in *Actaea simplex*

simplicifolius

sim-plik-ih-FOH-lee-us

simplicifolia, simplicifolium

With simple leaves, as in *Astilbe simplicifolia*

simulans

sim-YOO-lanz

Resembling, as in *Calochortus simulans*

sinensis [4]

sy-NEN-sis

sinensis, sinense

From China, as in *Corylopsis sinensis*

sinicus

SIN-ih-kus

sinica, sinicum

Connected with China, as in *Amelanchier sinica*

Sinningia

sin-INJ-ee-uh

Named after Wilhelm Sinning (c. 1794–1874), German horticulturist (*Gesneriaceae*)

Sinobambusa

sy-noh-bam-BOO-suh

From Greek *sino* meaning 'China', plus the related genus *Bambusa* (*Poaceae*)

Sinofranchetia

sy-noh-fran-CHET-ee-uh

Named after Adrien René Franchet (1834–1900), French botanist, plus Greek *sino* meaning 'China' (*Lardizabalaceae*)

Sinojackia

sy-noh-JAK-ee-uh

Named after John George Jack (1861–1949), American botanist, plus Greek *sino* meaning 'China' (*Styracaceae*)

Sinowilsonia

sy-noh-wil-SOH-nee-uh

Named after Ernest Henry Wilson (1876–1930), British botanist, plus Greek *sino* meaning 'China' (*Hamamelidaceae*)

sinuatus

sin-yoo-AH-tus

sinuata, sinuatum

With a wavy margin, as in *Salpiglossis sinuata*

siphiliticus

sigh-fy-LY-tih-kus

siphilitica, siphiliticum

Connected with syphilis, as in *Lobelia siphilitica*

4

Wisteria sinensis,
Chinese wisteria

Sisyrinchium
(also sysrinchium)
sis-uh-RIN-kee-um

From Greek *sisyrinchion*, the name for the related *Moraea sisyrinchium*, possibly derived from *sisyra* meaning 'goat-hair coat', alluding to the shaggy tunic surrounding the corms; alternatively, derived from *sys* meaning 'pig' and *rynkhos* meaning 'snout', referring to pigs digging for the roots (*Iridaceae*)

sitchensis
sit-KEN-sis

sitchensis, sitchense

From Sitka, Alaska, as in *Sorbus sitchensis*

Skimmia
SKIM-ee-uh

From Japanese *miyama shikimi*, the vernacular name for *S. japonica* (*Rutaceae*)

skinneri
SKIN-ner-ee

Named after George Ure Skinner (1804–67), Scottish plant collector, as in *Cattleya skinneri*

smilacinus
smil-las-SY-nus

smilacina, smilacinum

Relating to greenbriar (*Smilax*), as in *Disporum smilacinum*

Smilax
SMY-laks

From Greek *smilax*, a vernacular name for bindweed, or from the nymph Smilax in Greek mythology (*Smilacaceae*)

smithianus
SMITH-ee-ah-nus

smithiana, smithianum

—

smithii
SMITH-ee-eye

May commemorate any of several Smiths, including Sir James Edward Smith (1759–1828), as in *Senecio smithii*

Smyrnium
SMUR-nee-um

From Greek *smyrna*, 'to smell of myrrh' (*Apiaceae*)

soboliferus
soh-boh-LIH-fer-us

sobolifera, soboliferum

With creeping rooting stems, as in *Geranium soboliferum*

socialis
so-KEE-ah-lis

socialis, sociale

Forming colonies, as in *Crassula socialis*

Solandra
soh-LAN-druh

Named after Daniel Carlsson Solander (1733–82), Swedish botanist (*Solanaceae*)

Solanum
soh-LAY-num

From classical Latin name for a nightshade (*Solanaceae*)

Soldanella
sol-duh-NEL-uh

From Italian *solda* meaning 'coin', plus diminutive *ella*, as the leaves resemble small coins (*Primulaceae*)

Soleirolia
soh-lay-ROH-lee-uh

Named after Joseph-François Soleirol (1781–1863), French botanist (*Urticaceae*)

Solenostemon
soh-len-oh-STEM-on

From Greek *solen* meaning 'tube' and *stemon* meaning 'stamen', as the four stamens are partially fused into a tube (*Lamiaceae*)

Solidago
so-li-DAY-goh

From Latin *solidus* meaning 'whole' and *ago* meaning 'becoming', alluding to medicinal properties (*Asteraceae*)

solidus
SOL-id-us

solida, solidum

Solid; dense, as in *Corydalis solida*

somaliensis
soh-mal-ee-EN-sis

somaliensis, somaliense

From Somalia, Africa, as in *Cyanotis somaliensis*

somniferus
som-NIH-fer-us

somnifera, somniferum

Inducing sleep, as in *Papaver somniferum*

sonchifolius
son-chi-FOH-lee-us

sonchifolia, sonchifolium

With leaves like sowthistle (*Sonchus*), as in *Francoa sonchifolia*

Sonchus
SON-kuss

From Greek *sonkos*, the vernacular name for a thistle (*Asteraceae*)

Sophora
SOF-o-ruh

From Arabic *sophera*, the vernacular name for a leguminous tree (*Fabaceae*)

Sorbaria
sor-BAIR-ee-uh

Resembling the related genus *Sorbus* (*Rosaceae*)

sorbifolius
sor-bih-FOH-lee-us

sorbifolia, sorbifolium

With leaves like mountain ash (*Sorbus*), as in *Xanthoceras sorbifolium*

Sorbus
SOR-bus

From classical Latin vernacular name for *S. domestica* (*Rosaceae*)

sordidus
SOR-deh-dus

sordida, sordidum

Dirty-looking, as in *Salix* × *sordida*

Sorghum
SOR-goom

From Italian *sorgo*, the vernacular name for *S. bicolor* (*Poaceae*)

soulangeanus
soo-lan-jee-AH-nus

soulangeana, soulangeanum

Commemorates Étienne Soulange-Bodin (1774–1846), French diplomat and secretary to the Société Royale et Centrale d'Agriculture (now the Académie d'Agriculture de France), who raised *Magnolia* × *soulangeana*

spachianus
spak-ee-AH-nus

spachiana, spachianum

Named after Édouard Spach (1801–79), French botanist, as in *Genista* × *spachiana*

Sparaxis
spuh-RAKS-iss

From Greek *sparasso* meaning 'to tear', referring to the lacerated bracts surrounding the flowers (*Iridaceae*)

Solanum melongena,
aubergine

1

2

3

Sparganium erectum,
branched burr reed

Hylotelephium spectabile,
showy stonecrop

Blechnum spicant,
hard fern

Sparganium [1]
spar-GAY-nee-um
From Greek *sparganon* meaning 'swaddling band', for the strap-like leaves (*Typhaceae*)

Sparmannia
spar-MAN-ee-uh
Named after Anders Sparrman (1748–1820), Swedish botanist (*Malvaceae*)

sparsiflorus
spar-see-FLOR-us
sparsiflora, sparsiflorum
With sparse or scattered flowers, as in *Lupinus sparsiflorus*

Spartium
SPAR-tee-um
Both this and the grass genus *Spartina* (*Poaceae*) derive from Greek *spartion* meaning 'cord' and also 'broom'; both were weaved into cordage and the latter into brooms, though *Spartium junceum* is known as Spanish broom (*Fabaceae*)

spathaceus
spath-ay-SEE-us
spathacea, spathaceum
With a spathe, spathe-like, as in *Salvia spathacea*

Spathiphyllum
spat-i-FIL-um
From Greek *spathe*, the bract surrounding the inflorescence, plus *phyllon* meaning 'leaf', alluding to the white leaf-like spathe (*Araceae*)

spathulatus
spath-yoo-LAH-tus
spathulata, spathulatum
Spatulate, with a broader, flattened end, as in *Aeonium spathulatum*

speciosus
spee-see-OH-sus
speciosa, speciosum
Showy, as in *Ribes speciosum*

spectabilis [2]
speck-TAH-bih-lis
spectabilis, spectabile
Spectacular; showy, as in *Hylotelephium spectabile*

Speirantha
spy-RAN-thuh
From Greek *speiro* meaning 'coiled' and *anthos* meaning 'flower', alluding to a twist in the flowers (*Asparagaceae*)

Sphaeralcea
sfair-AL-see-uh
From Greek *sphaera* meaning 'sphere', plus the related genus *Alcea*; the fruits are spherical (*Malvaceae*)

sphaericus
SFAY-rih-kus
sphaerica, sphaericum
Shaped like a sphere, as in *Mammillaria sphaericus*

sphaerocarpos
sfay-ro-KAR-pus
sphaerocarpa, sphaerocarpum
With round fruits, as in *Medicago sphaerocarpos*

sphaerocephalon
sfay-ro-SEF-uh-lon
—

sphaerocephalus
sfay-ro-SEF-uh-lus
sphaerocephala, sphaerocephalum
With a round head, as in *Allium sphaerocephalon*

spicant [3]
SPIK-ant
Word of uncertain origin; possibly a German corruption of *spica*, spike, tuft, as in *Blechnum spicant*

spicatus
spi-KAH-tus
spicata, spicatum
With ears that grow in spikes, as in *Mentha spicata*

spiciformis
spik-ee-FOR-mis
spiciformis, spiciforme
In the shape of a spike, as in *Celastrus spiciformis*

spicigerus
spik-EE-ger-us
spicigera, spicigerum
Bearing spikes, as in *Justicia spicigera*

spiculifolius

spik-yoo-lih-FOH-lee-us

spiculifolia, spiculifolium

Like small spikes, as in *Erica spiculifolia*

Spigelia

spy-JEE-lee-uh

Named after Adriaan van den Spiegel (1578–1625), Flemish botanist and anatomist (*Loganiaceae*)

Spinacia

spin-AY-see-uh

From Persian *ispanakh*, the vernacular name for spinach, *S. oleracea* (*Amaranthaceae*)

spinescens

spy-NES-enz

—

spinifex

SPIN-ee-feks

—

spinosus

spy-NOH-sus

spinosa, spinosum

With spines, as in *Acanthus spinosus*

spinosissimus [4]

spin-oh-SIS-ih-mus

spinosissima, spinosissimum

Very spiny, as in *Rosa spinosissima*

spinulosus

spin-yoo-LOH-sus

spinulosa, spinulosum

With small spines, as in *Woodwardia spinulosa*

Spiraea

spy-REE-uh

From Greek *speiro* meaning 'coiled', as the flexible stems can be weaved into garlands (*Rosaceae*)

spiralis

spir-AH-lis

spiralis, spirale

Spiral, as in *Macrozamia spiralis*

splendens

SPLEN-denz

—

splendidus

splen-DEE-dus

splendida, splendidum

Splendid, as in *Fuchsia splendens*

Sprekelia

spruh-KEE-lee-uh

Named after Johann Heinrich von Spreckelsen (1691–1764), German lawyer and civil servant (*Amaryllidaceae*)

sprengeri

SPRENG-er-ee

Named after Carl Ludwig Sprenger (1846–1917), German botanist and plantsman, who bred and introduced many new plants, as in *Tulipa sprengeri*

spurius

SPEW-eee-us

spuria, spurium

False; spurious, as in *Iris spuria*

squalidus

SKWA-lee-dus

squalida, squalidum

Dirty-looking, dingy, as in *Leptinella squalida*

squamatus

SKWA-ma-tus

squamata, squamatum

With small scale-like leaves or bracts, as in *Juniperus squamata*

squamosus

skwa-MOH-sus

squamosa, squamosum

With many scales, as in *Annona squamosa*

squarrosus

skwa-ROH-sus

squarrosa, squarrosum

With spreading or curving parts at the extremities, as in *Dicksonia squarrosa*

stachyoides

stah-kee-OY-deez

Resembling betony (*Stachys*), as in *Buddleja stachyoides*

Stachys

STA-kiss

From Greek *stachys* meaning 'ear of grain', as the flowers are in wheat-like spikes (*Lamiaceae*)

Stachyurus

stak-ee-EW-rus

From Greek *stachys* meaning 'ear of grain' and *oura* meaning 'tail', a reference to the pendulous flower spikes (*Stachyuraceae*)

4

Rosa spinosissima, **burnet rose**

Staphylea pinnata,
common bladdernut

Stellaria nemorum,
wood stitchwort

Stephanotis floribunda,
Madagascar jasmine

stamineus

stam-IN-ee-us

staminea, stamineum

With pronounced stamens, as in *Vaccinium stamineum*

standishii

stan-DEE-shee-eye

Named after John Standish (1814–1875), British nurseryman, who raised plants collected by Robert Fortune, as in *Lonicera standishii*

Stangeria

stan-JEER-ee-uh

Named after William Stanger (1811–54), British surveyor, botanist and physician (*Stangeriaceae*)

stans

STANZ

Erect; upright, as in *Clematis stans*

Stapelia

stay-PEE-lee-uh

Named after Johannes Bodaeus van Stapel (1602–36), physician and botanist (*Apocynaceae*)

stapeliiformis

sta-pel-ee-ih-FOR-mis

stapeliiformis, stapeliiforme

Like *Stapelia*, as in *Ceropegia stapeliiformis*

Staphylea [1]

staf-uh-LEE-uh

From Greek *staphyle* meaning 'cluster', as the flowers are clustered (*Staphyleaceae*)

Stauntonia

stawn-TOH-nee-uh

Named after George Leonard Staunton (1737–1801), Irish physician and diplomat (*Lardizabalaceae*)

Stellaria [2]

stuh-LAIR-ee-uh

From Latin *stella* meaning 'star', as the flowers are star-shaped (*Caryophyllaceae*)

stellaris

stell-AH-ris

stellaris, stellare

—

stellatus

stell-AH-tus

stellata, stellatum

Starry, as in *Magnolia stellata*

Stenanthium

stuh-NAN-thee-um

From Greek *stenos* meaning 'narrow' and *anthos* meaning 'flower', alluding to the narrow tepals (*Melanthiaceae*)

steno-

Used in compound words to denote narrow

Stenocactus

sten-oh-KAK-tus

From Greek *stenos* meaning 'narrow' and cactus, referring to the narrow stem ribs (*Cactaceae*)

stenocarpus

sten-oh-KAR-pus

stenocarpa, stenocarpum

With narrow fruits, as in *Carex stenocarpa*

Stenocereus

sten-oh-SER-ee-us

From Greek *stenos* meaning 'narrow' and *Cereus*, a related genus (*Cactaceae*)

stenopetalus

sten-oh-PET-al-lus

stenopetala, stenopetalum

With narrow petals, as in *Genista stenopetala*

stenophyllus

sten-oh-FIL-us

stenophylla, stenophyllum

With narrow leaves, as in *Berberis* × *stenophylla*

stenostachyus

sten-oh-STAK-ee-us

stenostachya, stenostachyum

With narrow spikes, as in *Buddleja stenostachya*

Stephanandra

stef-uh-NAN-druh

From Greek *stephanos* meaning 'crown' and *andros* meaning 'male', as the stamens are persistent and form a ring around the fruit (*Rosaceae*)

Stephanotis [3]

stef-uh-NOH-tis

From Greek *stephanos* meaning 'crown' and and *otis* meaning 'ear', as the stamens are arranged in a ring and have ear-like lobes (*Apocynaceae*)

sterilis

STER-ee-lis

sterilis, sterile

Infertile; sterile, as in *Potentilla sterilis*

Sternbergia

sturn-BUR-gee-uh

Named after Kaspar Maria von Sternberg (1761–1838), Czech botanist and entomologist (*Amaryllidaceae*)

sternianus

stern-ee-AH-nus

sterniana, sternianum

—

sternii

STERN-ee-eye

Named after Sir Frederick Claude Stern (1884–1967), British horticulturist and author with a particular interest in gardening on chalk, as in *Cotoneaster sternianus*

Stevia [4]

STEE-vee-uh

Named after Pedro Jaime Esteve (1500–56), Spanish physician and botanist (*Asteraceae*)

Stewartia [5]

stew-ART-ee-uh

Named after John Stuart (1713–92), Scottish nobleman and British prime minister (*Theaceae*)

Stipa

STEE-puh

From Greek *tuppe* meaning 'tow' or 'fibre', as the grass was used to weave rope (*Poaceae*)

stipulaceus

stip-yoo-LAY-see-us

stipulacea, stipulaceum

—

stipularis

stip-yoo-LAH-ris

stipularis, stipulare

—

stipulatus

stip-yoo-LAH-tus

stipulata, stipulatum

With stipules, as in *Oxalis stipularis*

stoechas

STOW-kas

From *stoichas*, meaning in rows, the Greek name for *Lavandula stoechas*

Stokesia

STOHKS-see-uh

Named after Jonathan Stokes (1755–1831), British physician and botanist (*Asteraceae*)

stoloniferus

sto-lon-IH-fer-us

stolonifera, stoloniferum

With runners that take root, as in *Saxifraga stolonifera*

Stranvaesia

stran-VEE-zee-uh

Named after William Thomas Horner Fox-Strangways (1795–1865), British diplomat and politician (*Rosaceae*)

Stratiotes (also stratiotes)

stra-tee-OH-teez

From Greek *stratio* meaning 'soldier' alluding to the sword-shaped leaves (*Hydrocharitaceae*)

Strelitzia

stre-LIT-zee-uh

Named after Charlotte of Mecklenburg-Strelitz (1744–1818), German botanist and wife to King George III (*Strelitziaceae*)

strepto-

Used in compound words to denote twisted

Streptocarpus

strep-toh-KAR-pus

From Greek *streptos* meaning 'twisted' and *karpos* meaning 'fruit', as the seed capsules are twisted, untwisting slightly to open (*Gesneriaceae*)

streptophyllus

strep-toh-FIL-us

streptophylla, streptophyllum

With twisted leaves, as in *Ruscus streptophyllum*

Streptopus

strep-TOH-pus

From Greek *streptos* meaning 'twisted' and *pous* meaning 'foot', referring to the bent or twisted flower stalk (*Liliaceae*)

Streptosolen

strep-toh-SOH-len

From Greek *streptos* meaning 'twisted' and *solen* meaning 'tube', for the slight twist in the petal tube (*Solanaceae*)

striatus

stree-AH-tus

striata, striatum

With stripes, as in *Bletilla striata*

4

Stevia ovata,
candyleaf

5

Stewartia ovata,
mountain camellia

Streptocarpus

Commonly known as Cape primroses, *Streptocarpus* are tender plants, often grown as houseplants. Most cultivated hybrids have no stems and clusters of elongated tongue-like leaves. This habit is termed 'rosulate', but two other distinctive growth forms exist. Unifoliate plants, such as *S. wendlandii*, only produce a single, large leaf, which keeps growing from the base throughout the life of the plant. Many unifoliates die after flowering. In contrast, caulescent species such as *S. saxorum* produce distinct stems and numerous, small leaves, and can live for many years.

Streptocarpus wendlandii,
Cape primrose

strictus
STRIK-tus
stricta, strictum
Erect; upright, as in *Penstemon strictus*

strigosus
strig-OH-sus
strigosa, strigosum
With stiff bristles, as in *Rubus strigosus*

striolatus
stree-oh-LAH-tus
striolata, striolatum
With fine stripes or lines, as in *Dendrobium striolatum*

Strobilanthes
stroh-bi-LANTH-eez
From Greek *strobilus* meaning 'cone' and *anthos* meaning 'flower', as in some species, the flowers are arranged in cone-shaped inflorescences (*Acanthaceae*)

strobiliferus
stroh-bil-IH-fer-us
strobilifera, strobiliferum
Producing cones, as in *Epidendrum strobiliferum*

strobus [1]
STROH-bus
From Greek *strobos*, a whirling motion (cf. Greek *strobilos*, pine cone), or Latin *strobus*, an incense-bearing tree in Pliny, as in *Pinus strobus*

Strongylodon
strong-EYE-loh-don
From Greek *strongylus* meaning 'round' and *odontos* meaning 'tooth', as the calyx lobes are rounded (*Fabaceae*)

strumosus
stroo-MOH-sus
strumosa, strumosum
With cushion-like swellings. as in *Nemesia strumosa*

struthiopteris
struth-ee-OP-ter-is
Like an ostrich wing, as in *Matteuccia struthiopteris*

stygianus
sty-jee-AH-nuh
stygiana, stygianum
Dark, as in *Euphorbia stygiana*

Stylidium
sty-LID-ee-um
From Greek *stylos* meaning 'column' and refers to the unique mechanism at the centre of the flower. Male and female parts are fused into a column and, when insects visit the flower, they trigger this column to spring forward and dab pollen on the insect's body, or collect pollen from it (*Stylidiaceae*)

1

Pinus strobus,
Weymouth pine

Stylophorum
sty-loh-FOR-um
From Greek *stylos* meaning 'column' and *phoreus* meaning 'bearer';
these flowers have a style in the flower, unusual in poppies
(*Papaveraceae*)

stylosus
sty-LOH-sus
stylosa, stylosum
With pronounced styles, as in *Rosa stylosa*

Styphnolobium
stif-noh-LOH-bee-um
From Greek *stryphnos* meaning 'astringent' and *lobion* meaning 'pod',
referring to the sour taste of the fruits (*Fabaceae*)

styracifluus
sty-rak-IF-lu-us
styraciflua, styracifluum
Producing gum, from *styrax*, the Greek name for storax, as in
Liquidambar styraciflua

Styrax
STY-raks
From Arabic *assthirak*, the vernacular name for *S. officinalis*
(*Styracaceae*)

suaveolens
swah-vee-OH-lenz
With a sweet fragrance, as in *Brugmansia suaveolens*

suavis
SWAH-vis
suavis, suave
Sweet; with a sweet scent, as in *Asperula suavis*

sub-
Used in compound words to denote a variety of meanings such as
almost, partially, slightly, rather, under

subacaulis
sub-a-KAW-lis
subacaulis, subacaule
Without much stem, as in *Dianthus subacaulis*

subalpinus
sub-al-PY-nus
subalpina, subalpinum
Growing at the lower levels of mountain ranges, as in *Viburnum
subalpinum*

subcaulescens
sub-kawl-ESS-enz
With a small stem, as in *Geranium subcaulescens*

subcordatus
sub-kor-DAH-tus
subcordata, subcordatum
Shaped rather like a heart, as in *Alnus subcordata*

suberosus
sub-er-OH-sus
suberosa, suberosum
With cork bark, as in *Scorzonera suberosa*

subhirtellus
sub-hir-TELL-us
subhirtella, subhirtellum
Rather hairy, as in *Prunus × subhirtella*

submersus
sub-MER-sus
submersa, submersum
Submerged, as in *Ceratophyllum submersum*

subsessilis
sub-SES-sil-is
subsessilis, subsessile
Fixed, as in *Nepeta subsessilis*

subterraneus

sub-ter-RAY-nee-us

subterranea, subterraneum

Underground, as in *Parodia subterranea*

subtomentosus

sub-toh-men-TOH-sus

subtomentosa, subtomentosum

Almost hairy, as in *Rudbeckia subtomentosa*

subulatus

sub-yoo-LAH-tus

subulata, subulatum

Awl- or needle-shaped, as in *Phlox subulata*

subvillosus

sub-vil-OH-sus

subvillosa, subvillosum

With rather soft hairs, as in *Begonia subvillosa*

Succisa [1]

suk-SY-zuh

From Latin *succis* meaning 'cut off', as the short rhizomes end abruptly, as if cut off (*Caprifoliaceae*)

succulentus

suk-yoo-LEN-tus

succulenta, succulentum

Fleshy; juicy, as in *Oxalis succulenta*

suffrutescens

suf-roo-TESS-enz

—

suffruticosus

suf-roo-tee-KOH-sus

suffruticosa, suffruticosum

Rather shrubby, as in *Paeonia suffruticosa*

sulcatus

sul-KAH-tus

sulcata, sulcatum

With furrows, as in *Rubus sulcatus*

sulphureus

sul-FER-ee-us

sulphurea, sulphureum

Sulphur-yellow, as in *Lilium sulphureum*

suntensis

sun-TEN-sis

suntensis, suntense

Named after Sunte House, Sussex, England, as in *Abutilon* × *suntense*

1

Succisa pratensis,
devil's-bit scabious

superbiens

soo-PER-bee-enz

—

superbus

soo-PER-bus

superba, superbum

Superb, as in *Salvia* × *superba*

supinus

sup-EE-nus

supina, supinum

Prostrate, as in *Verbena supina*

surculosus

sur-ku-LOH-sus

surculosa, surculosum

Producing suckers, as in *Dracaena surculosa*

suspensus

sus-PEN-sus

suspensa, suspensum

Hanging, as in *Forsythia suspensa*

sutchuenensis

sech-yoo-en-EN-sis

sutchuenensis, sutchuenense

From Sichuan province, China, as in *Adonis sutchuenensis*

Sutherlandia [2]

suth-er-LAN-dee-uh

Named after James Sutherland (1639–1719), Scottish botanist (*Fabaceae*)

2

Sutherlandia frutescens,
balloon pea

sutherlandii

suth-er-LAN-dee-eye

Named after Dr Peter Sutherland (1822–1900), who discovered *Begonia sutherlandii*

Swainsona

swayn-SOH-nuh

Named after Isaac Swainson (1746–1812), British physician and horticulturist (*Fabaceae*)

Syagrus

sy-AG-rus

From classical Latin name for a palm, possibly the date, *Phoenix dactylifera* (*Arecaceae*)

Sycopsis

sy-KOP-sis

From Greek *sykon* meaning 'fig', a plant they are said to resemble (*Hamamelidaceae*)

sylvaticus

sil-VAT-ih-kus

sylvatica, sylvaticum

—

sylvester

sil-VESS-ter

—

sylvestris

sil-VESS-tris

sylvestris, sylvestre

—

sylvicola

sil-VIH-koh-luh

Growing in woodlands, as in *Pinus sylvestris*, *Nyssa sylvatica*

Symphoricarpos

sim-for-ee-KAR-pos

From Greek *symphora* meaning 'gathering' and *karpos* meaning 'fruit', as the fruits cluster closely together (*Caprifoliaceae*)

Symphyotrichum

sim-fy-oh-TREE-kum

From Greek *symphysis* meaning 'junction' and *trichos* meaning 'hair'; the botanist who established this genus noticed the hairs around each flower were fused together in a ring, but unfortunately, this is not the case in most species (*Asteraceae*)

Symphytum

sim-FY-tum

From Greek *symphyo* meaning 'grow together' and *phyton* meaning 'plant', alluding to the use of comfrey to heal broken bones (*Boraginaceae*)

Symplocos

sim-PLOK-us

From Greek *symplokos* meaning 'entwined', as the stamens are partially fused together and to the petals in some species (*Symplocaceae*)

Syneilesis

sy-nuh-LEE-sis

From Greek *syneilesis* meaning 'rolled up', referring to the unfurling leaves in spring (*Asteraceae*)

Syngonium

sin-GOH-nee-um

From Greek *syn* meaning 'together' and *gone* meaning 'gonad', as the ovaries are fused together (*Araceae*)

Synthyris

sin-THY-ris

From Greek *syn* meaning 'together' and *thyris* meaning 'little door', referring to the small valves that release the seeds (*Plantaginaceae*)

syriacus

seer-ee-AH-kus

syriaca, syriacum

Connected with Syria, as in *Asclepias syriaca*

Syringa [3]

suh-RING-uh

From Greek *syrinx* meaning 'pipe', as the stems are easily hollowed (*Oleaceae*)

Syzygium

sy-ZEE-jee-um

From Greek *syzygos* meaning 'yoked together', as the first species described had paired leaves (*Myrtaceae*)

szechuanicus

se-CHWAN-ih-kus

szechuanica, szechuanicum

Connected with Szechuan, China, as in *Populus szechuanica*

3

Syringa vulgaris, common lilac

NAMING A GIANT

The giant redwood (*Sequoiadendron giganteum*) is a marvel of the natural world. Its first Latin name, *Wellingtonia gigantea*, honoured the great British war hero and Prime Minister Arthur Wellesley, Duke of Wellington (1769–1852), who had recently died, but unfortunately, *Wellingtonia* had already been published in another plant family (*Sabiaceae*). The naming of an American giant after a British soldier did not go unnoticed. An American botanist christened the tree *Washingtonia californica*, after the first US president, but that too was thwarted as *Washingtonia* is a conserved name for a palm genus. Ultimately, the big tree became *Sequoiadendron*, recognising its similarity to the related *Sequoia*.

Tabernaemontana

tab-ur-nay-mon-TAN-uh

Named after Jakob Theodor von Bergzabern (1525–90), German physician and botanist, who Latinised his family name as Tabernaemontanus (*Apocynaceae*)

tabularis

tab-yoo-LAH-ris

tabularis, tabulare

—

tabuliformis

tab-yoo-lee-FORM-is

tabuliformis, tabuliforme

Flat, as in *Blechnum tabulare*

Tacca

TAK-uh

From Indonesian *taka*, the vernacular name (*Dioscoreaceae*)

Tagetes

TAJ-uh-teez

Etymology uncertain, though possibly named after Tages, a god in Etruscan mythology (*Asteraceae*)

tagliabuanus

tag-lee-ah-boo-AH-nus

tagliabuana, tagliabuanum

Commemorates Alberto and Carlo Tagliabue, 19th-century Italian nurserymen, as in *Campsis* × *tagliabuana*

taiwanensis

tai-wan-EN-sis

taiwanensis, taiwanense

From Taiwan, as in *Chamaecyparis taiwanensis*

takesimanus

tak-ess-ih-MAH-nus

takesimana, takesimanum

Connected with the Liancourt Rocks (Takeshima in Japanese), as in *Campanula takesimana*

taliensis

tal-ee-EN-sis

taliensis, taliense

From the Tali Range, Yunnan, China, as in *Lobelia taliensis*

Talinum

TAL-in-um

Possibly from Greek *taleia* meaning 'abundant blooms' (*Talinaceae*)

Tamarix

TAM-ur-iks

From Latin *tamariscus*, the vernacular name (*Tamaricaceae*)

tanacetifolius

tan-uh-kee-tih-FOH-lee-us

tanacetifolia, tanacetifolium

With leaves like tansy (*Tanacetum*), as in *Phacelia tanacetifolia*

Tanacetum

tan-uh-SEE-tum

From Greek *athanasia* meaning 'immortality', as the flowers are everlasting (*Asteraceae*)

Tanakaea

tuh-NAH-kee-uh

Named after Tanaka Yoshio (1838–1916), Japanese civil servant and botanist (*Saxifragaceae*)

tangelo

TAN-jel-oh

A hybrid of tangerine (*Citrus reticula*) and pomelo (*C. maxima*), as in *Citrus* × *tangelo*

tanguticus

tan-GOO-tih-kus

tangutica, tanguticum

Connected with the Tangut region of Tibet, as in *Daphne tangutica*

Taraxacum [1]

tuh-RAKS-uh-kum

From Arabic *tarakhshaqun*, a bitter herb, possibly chicory, *Cichorium intybus* (*Asteraceae*)

tardiflorus

tar-dee-FLOR-us

tardiflora, tardiflorum

Flowering late in the season, as in *Cotoneaster tardiflorus*

1

Taraxacum officinalis, dandelion

tardus

TAR-dus

tarda, tardum

Late, as in *Tulipa tarda*

tasmanicus

tas-MAN-ih-kus

tasmanica, tasmanicum

Connected with Tasmania, Australia, as in *Dianella tasmanica*

Tasmannia

tas-MAN-ee-uh

Named after Abel Janszoon Tasman (1603–59), Dutch explorer and the first European to reach Tasmania, where some species occur (*Winteraceae*)

tataricus

tat-TAR-ih-kus

tatarica, tataricum

Connected with the historical region of Tartary (now the Crimea), as in *Lonicera tatarica*

tatsienensis

tat-see-en-EN-sis

tatsienensis, tatsienense

From Tatsienlu, China, as in *Delphinium tatsienense*

tauricus

TAW-ih-kus

taurica, tauricum

Connected with Taurica (now Crimea), as in *Onosma taurica*

taxifolius

taks-ih-FOH-lee-us

taxifolia, taxifolium

With leaves like yew (*Taxus*), as in *Prumnopitys taxifolia*

Taxodium

taks-OH-dee-um

Resembling the conifer genus *Taxus*, despite being deciduous (*Cupressaceae*)

Taxus [2]

TAK-sus

The classical Latin name for yew, *T. baccata* (*Taxaceae*)

tazetta [3]

taz-ET-tuh

Little cup, as in *Narcissus tazetta*

Tecoma

te-KOH-muh

From Nahuatl (Mexico) *tecomaxochitl*, vernacular name for a flower that resembles a clay vessel (*Bignoniaceae*)

Tecophilaea

tek-oh-FIL-ee-uh

Named after Tecophila Billoti (1824–?), Italian botanical artist (*Tecophilaeaceae*)

tectorum [1]

tek-TOR-um

Of house roofs, as in *Sempervivum tectorum*

Telekia [4]

te-LEE-kee-uh

Named after Sámuel Teleki de Szék (1739–1822), Chancellor of Transylvania and book collector (*Asteraceae*)

Tellima [5]

TEL-i-muh

An anagram of the related genus *Mitella* (*Saxifragaceae*)

Telopea

tel-OH-pee-uh

From Greek *telopos* meaning 'seen from afar', alluding to the remarkable flowers (*Proteaceae*)

temulentus

tem-yoo-LEN-tus

temulenta, temulentum

Inebriated, as in *Lolium temulentum*

1

Sempervivum tectorum, **houseleek**

2

Taxus baccata, **English yew**

3

Narcissus tazetta, **paperwhite narcissus**

tenax
TEN-aks
Tough; matted, as in *Phormium tenax*

tenebrosus
teh-neh-BROH-sus
tenebrosa, tenebrosum
Connected with dark and shady places, as in *Catasetum tenebrosum*

tenellus
ten-ELL-us
tenella, tenellum
Tender; delicate, as in *Prunus tenella*

tener
TEN-er
tenera, tenerum
Slender; soft, as in *Adiantum tenerum*

tentaculatus
ten-tak-yoo-LAH-tus
tentaculata, tentaculatum
With tentacles, as in *Nepenthes tentaculata*

tenuicaulis
ten-yoo-ee-KAW-lis
tenuicaulis, tenuicaule
With slender stems, as in *Dahlia tenuicaulis*

tenuis
TEN-yoo-is
tenuis, tenue
Slender; thin, as in *Bupleurum tenue*

tenuiflorus
ten-yoo-ee-FLOR-us
tenuiflora, tenuiflorum
With slender flowers, as in *Muscari tenuiflorum*

tenuifolius
ten-yoo-ih-FOH-lee-us
tenuifolia, tenuifolium
With slender leaves, as in *Pittosporum tenuifolium*

tenuissimus
ten-yoo-ISS-ih-mus
tenuissima, tenuissimum
Very slender; thin, as in *Stipa tenuissima*

tequilana
te-kee-lee-AH-nuh
Connected with Tequila (Jalisco), Mexico, as in *Agave tequilana*

terebinthifolius
ter-ee-binth-ih-FOH-lee-us
terebinthifolia, terebinthifolium
With leaves that smell of turpentine, as in *Schinus terebinthifolius*

teres
TER-es
With a cylindrical form, as in *Vanda teres*

Terminalia
ter-min-AY-lee-uh
From Latin *terminus*, as the leaves are clustered at the tips of branches (*Combretaceae*)

terminalis
term-in-AH-lis
terminalis, terminale
Ending, as in *Erica terminalis*

ternatus
ter-NAH-tus
ternata, ternatum
With clusters of three, as in *Choisya ternata*

Ternstroemia
tern-STROH-mee-uh
Named after Christopher Tärnström (1711–46), Swedish botanist (*Pentaphylacaceae*)

terrestris
ter-RES-tris
terrestris, terrestre
From the ground; growing in the ground, as in *Lysimachia terrestris*

tessellatus
tess-ell-AH-tus
tessellata, tessellatum
Chequered, as in *Indocalamus tessellatus*

testaceus
test-AY-see-us
testacea, testaceum
Brick-coloured, as in *Lilium × testaceum*

testicularis
tes-tik-yoo-LAY-ris
testicularis, testiculare
Shaped like testicles, as in *Argyroderma testiculare*

testudinarius
tes-tuh-din-AIR-ee-us
testudinaria, testudinarium
Shaped like a tortoise shell, as in *Durio testudinarius*

tetra-
Used in compound words to denote four

4

Telekia speciosa,
heart-leaved ox-eye

5

Tellima grandiflora,
fringe cups

Tetradium ruticarpum

Teucrium botrys,
cut-leaved germander

Tetracentron
tet-ruh-SEN-tron
From Greek *tetra* meaning 'four' and *kentron* meaning 'spur', as the fruits have four prominent protrusions (*Trochodendraceae*)

Tetradium [1]
tet-RAD-ee-um
From Greek *tetra* meaning 'four', allegedly as the flower parts are in fours, but they can also be in fives (*Rutaceae*)

tetragonus
tet-ra-GON-us
tetragona, tetragonum
With four angles, as in *Nymphaea tetragona*

tetrandrus
tet-RAN-drus
tetrandra, tetrandrum
With four anthers, as in *Tamarix tetrandra*

Tetrapanax
tet-ruh-PAN-aks
From Greek *tetra* meaning 'four' and *Panax*, a related genus; flower parts in fours, unlike in *Panax*, where they are in fives (*Araliaceae*)

tetraphyllus
tet-ruh-FIL-us
tetraphylla, tetraphyllum
With four leaves, as in *Peperomia tetraphylla*

tetrapterus
tet-rap-TER-us
tetraptera, tetrapterum
With four wings, as in *Sophora tetraptera*

Tetrastigma
tet-ruh-STIG-muh
From Greek *tetra* meaning 'four', as the stigma has four lobes (*Vitaceae*)

Teucrium [2]
TEW-kree-um
From Greek *teukrion*, the vernacular name, possibly derived from Teucer, first king of Troy (*Lamiaceae*)

texanus
tek-SAH-nus
texana, texanum
—
texensis
tek-SEN-sis
texensis, texense
Of or from Texas, USA, as in *Echinocactus texensis*

textilis
teks-TIL-is
textilis, textile
Relating to weaving, as in *Bambusa textilis*

Thalia
THA-lee-uh
Named after Johann Thal (1542–83), German physician and botanist (*Marantaceae*)

thalictroides
thal-ik-TROY-deez
Resembling meadow rue (*Thalictrum*), as in *Anemonella thalictroides*

290

Theobroma cacao,
cacao

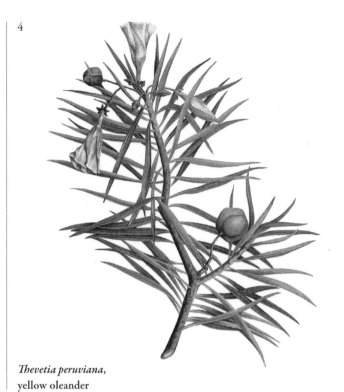

4

Thevetia peruviana,
yellow oleander

Thalictrum
tha-LIK-trum
From Greek *thaliktron,* a plant with divided leaves (*Ranunculaceae*)

Thamnocalamus
tham-noh-KAL-uh-mus
From Greek *thamnos* meaning 'shrub' and *kalamos* meaning 'reed', a compact, bushy bamboo (*Poaceae*)

Thelypteris
thel-IP-tur-iss
From Greek *thelys* meaning 'female' and *pteris* meaning 'fern', due to a supposed resemblance to lady fern, *Athyrium filix-femina* (*Thelypteridaceae*)

Theobroma [3]
thee-oh-BROH-muh
From Greeks *theos* meaning 'god' and *broma* meaning 'food', an appropriate name for chocolate, *T. cacao* (*Malvaceae*)

Thermopsis
thur-MOP-sis
From Greek *thermos* meaning 'lupine', a resemblance (*Fabaceae*)

Thevetia [4]
thu-VEE-tee-uh
Named after André Thevet (1502–92), French cleric and explorer (*Apocynaceae*)

thibetanus
ti-bet-AH-nus
thibetana, thibetanum
—
thibeticus
ti-BET-ih-kus
thibetica, thibeticum
Connected with Tibet, as in *Rubus thibetanus*

Thlaspi
THLAS-pee
From Greek *thalo* meaning 'to compress', as the fruits are flat and disc-like (*Brassicaceae*)

thomsonii
tom-SON-ee-eye
Named after Dr Thomas Thomson, 19th-century Scottish naturalist and Superintendent of the Calcutta Botanic Garden, India, as in *Clerodendrum thomsoniae*

Thrinax
THRI-naks
From Greek *thrinax* meaning 'trident', a reference to the pointed leaflets (*Arecaceae*)

Thuja
THOO-yuh
From classical Greek name for a juniper or other similar conifer (*Cupressaceae*)

Thujopsis
thoo-YOP-sis
Resembling the related genus *Thuja* (*Cupressaceae*)

A
B
C
D
E
F
G
H
I
J
K
L
M
N
O
P
Q
R
S
T
U
V
W
X
Y
Z
i

Thunbergia

thun-BER-jee-uh

Named after Carl Peter Thunberg (1743–1828), Swedish botanist and physician (*Acanthaceae*)

thunbergii

thun-BER-jee-eye

Named after Carl Peter Thunberg (1743–1828), Swedish botanist, as in *Spiraea thunbergii*

thymifolius

ty-mih-FOH-lee-us

thymifolia, thymifolium

With leaves like thyme (*Thymus*), as in *Lythrum thymifolium*

thymoides

ty-MOY-deez

Resembling thyme (*Thymus*), as in *Eriogonum thymoides*

Thymus

TY-muss

From Greek *thymos* meaning thyme, *T. vulgaris*; derived from *thyein* meaning 'to smoke/cure', as the plant has a smoky scent and may have been used as incense (*Lamiaceae*)

thyrsiflorus

thur-see-FLOR-us

thyrsiflora, thyrsiflorum

With thyrse-like flower clusters, a central spike with side branches also bearing flower clusters, as in *Ceanothus thyrsiflorus*

thyrsoideus

thurs-OY-dee-us

thyrsoidea, thyrsoideum

–

thyrsoides

thurs-OY-deez

Like a Bacchic staff, as in *Ornithogalum thyrsoides*

Tiarella

tee-uh-REL-uh

From Greek *tiara* meaning 'crown', plus diminutive *ella*, as the seed capsule resembles a small hat (*Saxifragaceae*)

tiarelloides

tee-uh-rell-OY-deez

Resembling *Tiarella*, as in × *Heucherella tiarelloides*

tibeticus

ti-BET-ih-kus

tibetica, tibeticum

Connected with Tibet, as in *Roscoea tibetica*

Tibouchina

ti-boo-CHEE-nuh

From *tibouche*, the vernacular name in a Guyanese indigeneous language (*Melastomataceae*)

Tigridia

ti-GRID-ee-uh

From Latin *tigris* meaning 'tiger', for the patterning on the petals (*Iridaceae*)

tigrinus

tig-REE-nus

tigrina, tigrinum

With stripes like the Asiatic tiger or with spots like a jaguar (known as 'tiger' in South America), as in *Faucaria tigrina*

Tilia

TIL-ee-uh

From Latin *tilia*, the vernacular name for linden, *T. cordata* or *T. platyphyllos* (*Malvaceae*)

Tillandsia [1]

ty-LAND-zee-uh

Named after Elias Erici Tillandz (1640–93), Swedish physician and botanist (*Bromeliaceae*)

tinctorius

tink-TOR-ee-us

tinctoria, tinctorium

Used as a dye, as in *Genista tinctoria*

tingitanus

ting-ee-TAH-nus

tingitana, tingitanum

Connected with Tangiers, as in *Lathyrus tingitanus*

Titanopsis

ty-tan-OP-sis

From Greek *titanos* meaning 'limestone' and *opsis* meaning 'resembling'; this succulent masquerades as rock (*Aizoaceae*)

titanus

ti-AH-nus

titana, titanum

Enormous, as in *Amorphophallus titanum*

1

Tillandsia cyanea,
pink quill

2

Trachelospermum jasminoides,
Confederate jasmine

Tithonia
ty-THOW-nee-uh
Named after Tithonus, prince of Troy in
Greek mythology; Tithonus was made
immortal by Zeus, but not granted eternal
youth and his name may have been used here
as some *Tithonia* have white hairs on the
foliage; another etymology relates to Eos,
goddess of dawn, who chose Tithonus as her
consort, the orange flowers resembling the
sun (*Asteraceae*)

tobira
TOH-bir-uh
From the Japanese name, as in *Pittosporum
tobira*

Tolmiea
TOL-mee-uh
Named after William Fraser Tolmie
(1812–86), Scottish surgeon and politician
(*Saxifragaceae*)

tomentosus
toh-men-TOH-sus
tomentosa, tomentosum
Very woolly; matted, as in *Paulownia
tomentosa*

tommasinianus
toh-mas-see-nee-AH-nus
tommasiniana, tommasinianum
Named after Muzio Giuseppe Spirito de'
Tommasini, 19th-century Italian botanist, as
in *Campanula tommasiniana*

Toona
TOO-nuh
From Sanskrit *toon* or *tunna*, the vernacular
name for *T. ciliata* (*Meliaceae*)

Torenia
to-REE-nee-uh
Named after Olof Torén (1718–53),
Swedish cleric and botanist (*Linderniaceae*)

Torreya
TOR-ay-uh
Named after John Torrey (1796–1873),
American botanist, chemist and physician
(*Taxaceae*)

torreyanus
tor-ree-AH-nus
torreyana, torreyanum
Named after Dr John Torrey (1796–1873),
American botanist, as in *Pinus torreyana*

tortifolius
tor-tih-FOH-lee-us
tortifolia, tortifolium
With twisted leaves, as in *Narcissus tortifolius*

tortilis
TOR-til-is
tortilis, tortile
Twisted, as in *Acacia tortilis*

tortuosus
tor-tew-OH-sus
tortuosa, tortuosum
Very twisted, as in *Arisaema tortuosum*

tortus
TOR-tus
torta, tortum
Twisted, as in *Masdevallia torta*

totara
toh-TAR-uh
From the Maori name for this tree, as in
Podocarpus totara

tournefortii
toor-ne-FOR-tee-eye
Named after Joseph Pitton de Tournefort
(1656–1708), French botanist, first to
define the genus, as in *Crocus tournefortii*

Townsendia
town-ZEN-dee-uh
Named after David Townsend (1787–
1858), American botanist (*Asteraceae*)

toxicarius
toks-ih-KAH-ree-us
toxicaria, toxicarium
Poisonous, as in *Antiaris toxicaria*

Toxicodendron
toks-i-koh-DEN-dron
From Greek *toxikon pharmakon* meaning
'poison' and *dendron* meaning 'tree', a fitting
name for poison ivy, *T. radicans*
(*Anacardiaceae*)

Trachelium (also trachelium)
tra-KEE-lee-um
From Greek *trachelos* meaning 'neck', as the
plant is used to treat ailments of the throat
(*Campanulaceae*)

Trachelospermum [2]
trak-uh-loh-SPER-mum
From Greek *trachelos* meaning 'neck' and
sperma meaning 'seed', referring to the shape
of the seed or perhaps the fruit
(*Apocynaceae*)

Trachycarpus
tra-kee-KAR-pus
From Greek *trachys* meaning 'rough' and
karpos meaning 'fruit', as the fruits are
irregularly shaped (*Arecaceae*)

trachyspermus
trak-ee-SPER-mus
trachysperma, trachyspermum
With rough seeds, as in *Sauropus
trachyspermus*

Trachystemon
tra-kee-STEM-on
From Greek *trachys* meaning 'rough' and
stemon meaning 'stamen'; the stamen
filaments are hairy (*Boraginaceae*)

Tradescantia
tra-duh-SKAN-tee-uh
Named after father and son John Tradescant
the Elder (c. 1570–1638) and John
Tradescant (1608–62), British botanists
(*Commelinaceae*)

tragophylla
tra-go-FIL-uh
Literally goat leaf, as in *Lonicera tragophylla*

Tragopogon

tra-goh-POH-gon

From Greek *tragos* meaning 'goat' and *pogon* meaning 'beard', alluding to the silky, parachute-like hairs attached to the fruits (*Asteraceae*)

transcaucasicus

tranz-kaw-KAS-ih-kus

transcaucasica, transcaucasicum

Connected with Caucasus, Turkey, as in *Galanthus transcaucasicus*

transitorius

tranz-ee-TAW-ree-us

transitoria, transitorum

Short-lived, as in *Malus transitoria*

transsilvanicus

tranz-il-VAN-ih-kus

transsilvanica, transsilvanicum

—

transsylvanicus

transsylvanica, transsylvanicum

Connected with Romania, as in *Hepatica transsilvanica*

trapeziformis

tra-pez-ih-FOR-mis

trapeziformis, trapeziforme

With four unequal sides, as in *Adiantum trapeziforme*

Trautvetteria

trout-vet-EER-ee-uh

Named after Ernst Rudolph von Trautvetter (1809–89), Baltic German botanist (*Ranunculaceae*)

traversii

trav-ERZ-ee-eye

Named after William Travers (1819–1903), New Zealand lawyer and plant collector, as in *Celmisia traversii*

tremulus

TREM-yoo-lus

tremula, tremulum

Quivering; trembling, as in *Populus tremula*

tri-

Used in compound words to denote three

triacanthos

try-a-KAN-thos

With three spines, as in *Gleditsia triacanthos*

triandrus

TRY-an-drus

triandra, triandrum

With three stamens, as in *Narcissus triandrus*

triangularis

try-an-gew-LAH-ris

triangularis, triangulare

—

triangulatus

try-an-gew-LAIR-tus

triangulata, triangulatum

With three angles, as in *Oxalis triangularis*

tricho-

Used in compound words to denote hairy

trichocarpus

try-ko-KAR-pus

trichocarpa, trichocarpum

With hairy fruit, as in *Rhus trichocarpa*

trichomanes

try-KOH-man-ees

Relating to a Greek name for fern, as in *Asplenium trichomanes*

trichophyllus

try-koh-FIL-us

tricophylla, tricophyllum

With hairy leaves, as in *Ranunculus trichophyllus*

trichotomus

try-KOH-toh-mus

trichotoma, trichotomum

With three branches, as in *Clerodendrum trichotomum*

tricolor [1]

TRY-kull-lur

With three colours, as in *Tropaeolum tricolor*

tricuspidatus

try-kusp-ee-DAH-tus

tricuspidata, tricuspidatum

With three points, as in *Parthenocissus tricuspidata*

Tricyrtis

try-SUR-tis

From Greek *treis* meaning 'three' and *kyrtos* meaning 'humped', referring to the swollen nectaries at the base of the flower (*Liliaceae*)

Viola tricolor, heart's ease

Trientalis

try-EN-tuh-lis

From Latin *trientalis* meaning 'third of a foot', referring to diminutive stature (*Primulaceae*)

trifasciata

try-fask-ee-AH-tuh

Three groups or bundles, as in *Sansevieria trifasciata*

trifidus

TRY-fee-dus

trifida, trifidum

Cut in three, as in *Carex trifida*

triflorus

TRY-flor-us

triflora, triflorum

With three flowers, as in *Acer triflorum*

trifoliatus

try-foh-lee-AH-tus

trifoliata, trifoliatum

—

trifolius

try-FOH-lee-us

trifolia, trifolium

With three leaves, as in *Gillenia trifoliata*

Trifolium [2]

try-FOH-lee-um
From Greek *triphyllon* meaning 'three-leaved', as clover leaves are made up of three leaflets (*Fabaceae*)

trifurcatus

try-fur-KAH-tus
trifurcata, trifurcatum
With three forks, as in *Artemisia trifurcata*

Trigonella

trig-oh-NEL-uh
From Greek *trigonella* meaning fenugreek (*T. foenum-graecum*) seeds; derived from *trigonon* meaning 'triangle', plus diminutive *ella*, referring to the shape of the leaflets (*Fabaceae*)

trigonophyllus

try-gon-oh-FIL-us
trigonophylla, trigonophyllum
With triangular leaves, as in *Acacia trigonophylla*

Trillium

TRIL-ee-um
From Latin *trilix* meaning 'triple' as the flower parts are in threes (*Melanthiaceae*)

trilobatus

try-lo-BAH-tus
trilobata, trilobatum
—

trilobus

try-LO-bus
triloba, trilobum
With three lobes, as in *Aristolochia trilobata*

trimestris

try-MES-tris
trimestris, trimestre
Of three months, as in *Lavatera trimestris*

trinervis

try-NER-vis
trinervis, trinerve
With three nerves, as in *Coelogyne trinervis*

tripartitus

try-par-TEE-tus
tripartita, tripartitum
With three parts, as in *Eryngium × tripartitum*

tripetalus

try-PET-uh-lus
tripetala, tripetalum
With three petals, as in *Moraea tripetala*

triphyllus

try-FIL-us
triphylla, triphyllum
With three leaves, as in *Penstemon triphyllus*

triplinervis

trip-lin-ner-vis
triplinervis, triplinerve
With three veins, as in *Anaphalis triplinervis*

tripteris

TRIPT-er-is
—

tripterus

TRIPT-er-us
triptera, tripterum
With three wings, as in *Coreopsis tripteris*

Tripterygium

trip-tur-IJ-ee-um
From Greek *tri* meaning 'three' and *pteryx* meaning 'wing', referring to the three-winged fruits (*Celastraceae*)

tristis

TRIS-tis
tristis, triste
Dull; sad, as in *Gladiolus tristis*

Tritelaia

try-tuh-LEE-uh
From Greek *treis* meaning 'three' and *teleios* meaning 'perfect', as the flower parts are in threes (*Asparagaceae*)

triternatus

try-tern-AH-tus
triternata, triternatum
Literally three threes, referring to leaf shape, as in *Corydalis triternata*

Tritonia

try-TOH-nee-uh
From Latin *triton* meaning 'weather vane', as the stamens can point in several directions (*Iridaceae*)

trivialis

tri-vee-AH-lis
trivialis, triviale
Common; ordinary; usual, as in *Rubus trivialis*

2

Trifolium reflexum,
buffalo clover

Tropaeolum

The nasturtium is a familiar garden annual with colourful flowers and sprawling stems. The flowers and foliage are also edible with a peppery taste. It's worth noting that the Latin name for nasturtium is *Tropaeolum majus*, because *Nasturtium* is also a genus name, but for an entirely different plant. Watercress is *Nasturtium officinale*, and is also known for its peppery taste. The shared flavour is the result of glucosinolates, a group of chemicals common to all plant families in order *Brassicales*, which includes *Brassicaceae* (*Nasturtium*) and *Tropaeolaceae* (*Tropaeolum*). Glucosinolates also provide the pungent taste of horseradish, wasabi and mustard.

Tropaeolum majus,
nasturtium

Trochodendron
trok-oh-DEN-dron
From Greek *trochos* meaning 'wheel' and *dendron* meaning 'tree', alluding to the stamens, which radiate like spokes (*Trochodendraceae*)

Trollius
TROL-ee-us
From German *troll* meaning 'round', the shape of the flowers (*Ranunculaceae*)

Tropaeolum
trop-ee-OH-lum
From Latin *tropaeum* meaning 'trophy'; the leaves of nasturtium (*T. majus*) resemble a shield and the flowers a helmet, and both were hung in a tree as a trophy by the victor after battle (*Tropaeoleaceae*)

truncatus
trunk-AH-tus
truncata, truncatum
Cut square, as in *Haworthia truncata*

tsariensis
sar-ee-EN-sis
tsariensis, tsariense
From Tsari, China, as in *Rhododendron tsariense*

tschonoskii
chon-OSK-ee-eye
Named after Sugawa Tschonoski (1841–1925), Japanese botanist and plant collector, as in *Malus tschonoskii*

Tsuga
TSOO-guh
From Japanese *tsuga*, the vernacular name for hemlock (*Pinaceae*)

tsussimensis
tsoos-sim-EN-sis
tsussimensis, tsussimense
From Tsushima Island, between Japan and Korea, as in *Polystichum tsussimense*

tuberculatus
too-ber-kew-LAH-tus
tuberculata, tuberculatum
—

tuberculosus
too-ber-kew-LOH-sus
tuberculosa, tuberculosum
Covered in lumps, as in *Anthemis tuberculata*

tuberosus
too-ber-OH-sus
tuberosa, tuberosum
Tuberous, as in *Polianthes tuberosa*

tubiferus

too-BIH-fer-us

tubifera, tubiferum

—

tubulosus

too-bul-OH-sus

tubulosa, tubulosum

Shaped like a tube or pipe, as in *Clematis tubulosa*

tubiflorus

too-bih-FLOR-us

tubiflora, tubiflorum

With trumpet-shaped flowers, as in *Salvia tubiflora*

Tulbaghia

tool-BAG-ee-uh

Named after Ryk Tulbagh (1699–1771), Dutch governor of the Cape Colony, now South Africa (*Amaryllidaceae*)

Tulipa [1]

TEW-lip-uh

From Turkish *tulbend* meaning 'turban', the shape of the flowers (*Liliaceae*)

tulipiferus

too-lip-IH-fer-us

tulipifera, tulipiferum

Producing tulips or tulip-like flowers, as in *Liriodendron tulipifera*

tuolumnensis

too-ah-lum-NEN-sis

tuolumnensis, tuolumnense

From Tuolumne County, California, USA, as in *Erythronium tuolumnense*

tupa

TOO-pa

Local name for *Lobelia tupa*

turbinatus

turb-in-AH-tus

turbinata, turbinatum

Swirling around, as in *Aesculus turbinata*

turczaninowii

tur-zan-in-NOV-ee-eye

Named after Nicholai S. Turczaninov (1796–1863), Russian botanist, as in *Carpinus turczaninowii*

turkestanicus

tur-kay-STAN-ih-kus

turkestanica, turkestanicum

Connected with Turkestan, as in *Tulipa turkestanica*

Tussilago

tew-si-LAH-goh

From Latin *tussis* meaning 'cough'; coltsfoot (*T. farfara*) was used as an expectorant (*Asteraceae*)

1

Tulipa gesneriana,
garden tulip

Tweedia

TWEE-dee-uh

Named after John (James) Tweedie (1775–1862), Scottish horticulturist (*Apocynaceae*)

tweedyi

TWEE-dee-eye

Named after Frank Tweedy, 19th-century American topographer, as in *Lewisia tweedyi*

Typha

TY-fuh

From Greek *typhe* meaning 'cat's tail', possibly derived from *typhos* meaning 'smoke', as the tiny seeds disperse in a cloud and also make excellent tinder (*Typhaceae*)

typhinus

ty-FEE-nus

typhina, typhinum

Like *Typha* (reedmace), as in *Rhus typhina*

Typhonium

ty-FOH-nee-um

From Greek *typhonion*, a type of lavender, an allusion to the shape of the spadix (*Araceae*)

Ugni

UG-nee

From Mapuche (Chile) *uñi*, the vernacular name for *U. molinae* (*Myrtaceae*)

Ulex

EW-leks

From *ulicis*, the vernacular Latin name for a shrub resembling rosemary (*Fabaceae*)

ulicinus

yoo-lih-SEE-nus

ulicina, ulicinum

Like gorse (*Ulex*), as in *Hakea ulicina*

uliginosus

yoo-li-gi-NOH-sus

uliginosa, uliginosum

From swampy and wet regions, as in *Salvia uliginosa*

ulmaria

ul-MAR-ee-uh

Like elm (*Ulmus*), as in *Filipendula ulmaria*

ulmifolius

ul-mih-FOH-lee-us

ulmifolia, ulmifolium

With leaves like elm (*Ulmus*), as in *Rubus ulmifolius*

Ulmus [1]

UL-mus

The classical Latin name for an elm tree (*Ulmaceae*)

umbellatus [2]

um-bell-AH-tus

umbellata, umbellatum

With umbels, as in *Butomus umbellatus*

Umbellularia

um-bel-ew-LAIR-ee-uh

From Latin *umbellula*, meaning 'small umbel', alluding to the flower arrangement (*Lauraceae*)

Umbilicus

um-bil-i-kus

From Latin *umbilicus* meaning 'navel', as the leaves appear to have a 'belly button' (*Crassulaceae*)

umbrosus

um-BROH-sus

umbrosa, umbrosum

Growing in shade, as in *Phlomis umbrosa*

uncinatus

un-sin-NA-tus

uncinata, uncinatum

With a hooked end, as in *Uncinia uncinata*

Uncinia

un-SIN-ee-uh

From Latin *uncinus* meaning 'hook', for the hook-like appendage on the fruits (*Cyperaceae*)

1

Ulmus minor,
field elm

2

Iberis umbellata,
common candytuft

Iris unguicularis,
Algerian iris

Urtica dioica,
stinging nettle

undatus
un-DAH-tus
undata, undatum
—

undulatus
un-dew-LAH-tus
undulata, undulatum
Wavy; undulating, as in *Hosta undulata*

unedo
YOO-nee-doe
Edible but of doubtful taste, from *unum edo*, 'I eat one', as in *Arbutus unedo*

Ungnadia
un-GNAH-dee-uh
Named after David Ungnad von Sonnegg (c. 1535–1600), Austrian diplomat (*Sapindaceae*)

unguicularis [1]
un-gwee-kew-LAH-ris
unguicularis, unguiculare
—

unguiculatus
un-gwee-kew-LAH-tus
unguiculata, unguiculatum
With claws, as in *Iris unguicularis*

uni-
Used in compound words to denote one

unicolor
YOO-nih-ko-lor
Of one colour, as in *Lachenalia unicolor*

uniflorus
yoo-nih-FLOR-us
uniflora, uniflorum
With one flower, as in *Silene uniflora*

unifolius
yoo-nih-FOH-lee-us
unifolia, unifolium
With one leaf, as in *Allium unifolium*

unilateralis
yoo-nih-LAT-uh-ra-lis
unilateralis, unilaterale
One-sided, as in *Penstemon unilateralis*

uplandicus
up-LAN-ih-kus
uplandica, uplandicum
Connected with Uppland, Sweden, as in *Symphytum × uplandicum*

urbanus
ur-BAH-nus
urbana, urbanum
—
urbicus
UR-bih-kus
urbica, urbicum
—
urbius
UR-bee-us
urbia, urbium
From towns, as in *Geum urbanum*

urceolatus
ur-kee-oh-LAH-tus
urceolata, urceolatum
Shaped like an urn, as in *Galax urceolata*

urens
UR-enz
Stinging; burning, as in *Urtica urens*

Urginea
ur-JIN-ee-uh
Named after an Algerian tribe, the Beni-Urgin (*Asparagaceae*)

urophyllus
ur-oh-FIL-us
urophylla, urophyllum
With leaves with a tip like a tail, as in *Clematis urophylla*

Ursinia
ur-SIN-ee-uh
Named after Johann Heinrich Ursinus (1608–67), German theologian (*Asteraceae*)

ursinus
ur-SEE-nus
ursina, ursinum
Like a bear, as in *Eriogonum ursinum*

Urtica [2]
UR-tik-uh
From Latin *urere* meaning 'to burn', alluding to the sting of nettles, *U. dioica* (*Urticaceae*)

urticifolius
ur-tik-ih-FOH-lee-us
urticifolia, urticifolium
With leaves like nettle (*Urtica*), as in *Agastache urticifolia*

uruguayensis
ur-uh-gway-EN-sis
uruguayensis, uruguayense
From Uruguay, South America, as in *Gymnocalycium uruguayense*

urumiensis
ur-um-ee-EN-sis
urumiensis urumiense
From Urmia, Iran, as in *Tulipa urumiensis*

urvilleanus
ur-VIL-ah-nus
urvilleana, urvilleanum
Named after J.S.C. Dumont d'Urville (1790–1842), French botanist and explorer, as in *Tibouchina urvilleana*

ussuriensis
oo-soo-ree-EN-sis
ussuriensis, ussuriense
From the River Ussuri, Asia, as in *Pyrus ussuriensis*

utahensis
yoo-tah-EN-sis
utahensis, utahense
From Utah, USA, as in *Agave utahensis*

utilis
YOO-tih-lis
utilis, utile
Useful, as in *Betula utilis*

Utricularia [3]
oo-trik-ew-LAIR-ee-uh
From Latin *utriculus* meaning 'small bag', alluding to the pouch-like traps of many bladderworts (*Lentibulariaceae*)

utriculatus
uh-trik-yoo-LAH-tus
utriculata, utriculatum
Like a bladder, as in *Alyssoides utriculata*

uva-crispa
OO-vuh-KRIS-puh
Curled grape, as in *Ribes uva-crispa*

uva-ursi
OO-va UR-see
Bear's grape, as in *Arctostaphylos uva-ursi*

uvaria
oo-VAR-ee-uh
Like a bunch of grapes, as in *Kniphofia uvaria*

Uvularia
oo-vew-LAIR-ee-uh
From Latin *uvula*, the structure hanging from the back of the human soft palate, to which the flowers are said to resemble (*Colchicaceae*)

Utricularia alpina,
alpine bladderwort

vacciniifolius

vak-sin-ee-FOH-lee-us

vacciniifolia, vacciniifolium

With leaves like blueberry (*Vaccinium*), as in
Persicaria vacciniifolia

vaccinioides

vak-sin-ee-OY-deez

Resembling blueberry (*Vaccinium*), as in
Rhododendron vaccinioides

Vaccinium

vak-SIN-ee-um

From classical Latin name for bilberry,
V. myrtillus (*Ericaceae*)

vagans

VAG-anz

Widely distributed, as in *Erica vagans*

vaginalis

vaj-in-AH-lis

vaginalis, vaginale

—

vaginatus

vaj-in-AH-tus

vaginata, vaginatum

With a sheath, as in *Primula vaginata*

valdivianus

val-div-ee-AH-nus

valdiviana, valdivianum

Connected with Valdivia, Chile, as in *Ribes
valdivianum*

valentinus

val-en-TEE-nus

valentina, valentinum

Connected with Valencia, Spain, as in
Coronilla valentina

Valeriana

val-eer-ee-AH-nuh

From classical Latin name for valerian,
V. officinalis; from *valere* meaning 'to be
healthy/strong', alluding to medicinal
properties (*Caprifoliaceae*)

Vancouveria

van-koo-VEER-ee-uh

Named after George Vancouver (1757–98),
British naval officer and explorer
(*Berberidaceae*)

Vanda

VAN-duh

From Sanskrit *vanda*, the name for an
epiphytic plant (*Orchidaceae*)

Vanilla

vuh-NIL-uh

From Spanish *vainilla* meaning 'little pod',
alluding to the fruits of *V. planifolia*
(*Orchidaceae*)

variabilis

var-ee-AH-bih-lis

variabilis, variabile

—

varians

var-ee-anz

—

variatus

var-ee-AH-tus

variata, variatum

Variable, as in *Eupatorium variabile*

varicosus

var-ee-KOH-sus

varicosa, varicosum

With dilated veins, as in *Oncidium
varicosum*

variegatus

var-ee-GAH-tus

variegata, variegatum

Variegated, as in *Pleioblastus variegatus*

GENUS SPOTLIGHT

Vaccinium

The genus *Vaccinium* comprises evergreen and
deciduous shrubs widely distributed around the northern
hemisphere, though with the odd outlier in tropical
locations such as Hawaii and Madagascar. *Vaccinium*
is the source of numerous edible berries, including
blueberries, cranberries, lingonberries and bilberries.
Blueberries and kin prefer an ericaceous soil, the name
deriving from their family *Ericaceae*. Ericaceous
composts are acidic and popular with plants that grow
in nutrient-poor or peat-rich soils, such as camellias,
magnolias, Japanese maples and, of course, most
members of family *Ericaceae* (heathers, rhododendrons
and azaleas).

Vaccinium corymbosum,
highbush blueberry

varius
VAH-ree-us
varia, varium
Diverse, as in *Calamagrostis varia*

vaseyi
VAS-ee-eye
Named after George Richard Vasey
(1822–93), American plant collector, as in
Rhododendron vaseyi

vedrariensis
ved-rar-ee-EN-sis
vedrariensis, vedrariense
From Verrières-le-Buisson, France, and the
nurseries of Vilmorin-Andrieux & Cie, as in
Clematis × vedrariensis

vegetus
veg-AH-tus
vegeta, vegetum
Vigorous, as in *Ulmus × vegeta*

veitchianus
veet-chee-AH-nus
veitchiana, veitchianum
—

veitchii
veet-chee-EYE
Named after members of the Veitch family,
nurserymen of Exeter and Chelsea, as in
Paeonia veitchii

Vellozia
vel-OH-zee-uh
Named after José Mariano da Conceição
Vellozo (1742–1811), Brazilian botanist
(*Velloziaceae*)

Veltheimia
vel-THY-me-uh
Named after August Ferdinand Graf von
Veltheim (1741–1801), German geologist
(*Asparagaceae*)

velutinus
vel-oo-TEE-nus
velutina, velutinum
Like velvet, as in *Musa velutina*

venenosus
ven-ee-NOH-sus
venenosa, venenosum
Very poisonous, as in *Caralluma venenosa*

venosus
ven-OH-sus
venosa, venosum
With many veins, as in *Vicia venosa*

1

Veratrum nigrum,
black false hellebore

ventricosus
ven-tree-KOH-sus
ventricosa, ventricosum
With a swelling on one side, belly-like, as in
Ensete ventricosum

venustus
ven-NUSS-tus
venusta, venustum
Handsome, as in *Hosta venusta*

Veratrum [1]
vuh-RAT-rum
From Latin *vere* meaning 'truth' and *ater*
meaning 'black', as some species have black
roots (*Melanthiaceae*)

verbascifolius
ver-bask-ih-FOH-lee-us
verbascifolia, verbascifolium
With leaves like mullein (*Verbascum*), as in
Celmisia verbascifolia

Verbascum
ver-BAS-kum
From Latin *barbascum* meaning 'bearded',
referring to the hairy stamen filaments
(*Scrophulariaceae*)

Verbena
ver-BEE-nuh
From Latin *verbena* meaning 'sacred bough',
fragrant stems carried in religious
processions, though probably not the plants
called *Verbena* today (*Verbenaceae*)

Verbesina
ver-bes-EE-nuh
Indicating a resemblance to *Verbena*
(*Asteraceae*)

verecundus
ver-ay-KUN-dus
verecunda, verecundum
Modest, as in *Columnea verecunda*

veris
VER-is
Relating to spring; flowering in spring, as in
Primula veris

vernalis
ver-NAH-lis
vernalis, vernale
Relating to spring; flowering in spring, as in
Pulsatilla vernalis

vernicifluus

ver-nik-IF-loo-us

verniciflua, vernicifluum

Producing varnish, as in *Rhus verniciflua*

vernicosus

vern-ih-KOH-sus

vernicosa, vernicosum

Varnished, as in *Hebe vernicosa*

Vernonia

ver-NOH-nee-uh

Named after William Vernon (c. 1666–1715), British naturalist (*Asteraceae*)

vernus

VER-nus

verna, vernum

Relating to spring, as in *Leucojum vernum*

Veronica

vuh-RON-i-kuh

Named after Saint Veronica, who gave a cloth to Jesus, so he could mop his brow on the way to Calvary; some species have flowers with markings said to resemble the imprint of Christ's face on that cloth (*Plantaginaceae*)

Veronicastrum

vuh-ron-i-KAS-trum

Somewhat resembling the related genus *Veronica* (*Plantaginaceae*)

verrucosus

ver-oo-KOH-sus

verrucosa, verrucosum

Covered with warts, as in *Brassia verrucosa*

verruculosus

ver-oo-ko-LOH-sus

verruculosa, verruculosum

With small warts, as in *Berberis verruculosa*

versicolor

VER-suh-kuh-lor

With various colours, as in *Oxalis versicolor*

verticillatus [2]

ver-ti-si-LAH-tus

verticillata, verticillatum

With a whorl or whorls, as in *Sciadopitys verticillata*

Verticordia

vur-ti-KOR-dee-uh

From Latin *vertere* meaning 'to turn' and *cordatus* meaning 'good heart', a reference to the Roman goddess Venus, who could turn hearts; her floral emblem was myrtle (*Myrtus communis*), a member of the same family, and *Verticordia* blooms are extremely attractive (*Myrtaceae*)

verus

VER-us

vera, verum

True; standard; regular, as in *Aloe vera*

vescus

VES-kus

vesca, vescum

Thin; feeble, as in *Fragaria vesca*

vesicarius

ves-ee-KAH-ree-us

vesicaria, vesicarium

—

vesiculosus

ves-ee-kew-LOH-sus

vesiculosa, vesiculosum

Like a bladder; with small bladders, as in *Eruca vesicaria*

vespertinus

ves-per-TEE-nus

vespertina, vespertinum

Relating to the evening; flowering in the evening, as in *Moraea vespertina*

Vestia

VES-tee-uh

Named after Lorenz Chrysanth von Vest (1776–1840), Austrian physician and botanist (*Solanaceae*)

vestitus

ves-TEE-tus

vestita, vestitum

Covered; clothed, as in *Sorbus vestita*

vexans

VEKS-anz

Vexatious or troublesome in some respect, as in *Sorbus vexans*

vialii

vy-AL-ee-eye

Named after Paul Vial (1855–1917), as in *Primula vialii*

2

Sciadopitys verticillata,
Japanese umbrella pine

vialis

vee-AH-lis

vialis, viale

From the wayside, as in *Calyptocarpus vialis*

viburnifolius

vy-burn-ih-FOH-lee-us

viburnifolia, viburnifolium

With leaves like *Viburnum*, as in *Ribes viburnifolium*

viburnoides

vy-burn-OY-deez

Resembling *Viburnum*, as in *Pileostegia viburnoides*

Viburnum

vy-BUR-num

From the classical Latin name for *V. lantana* (*Adoxaceae*)

Vicia

VISS-ee-uh

From Latin *vincere* meaning 'to bind', referring to the tendrils (*Fabaceae*)

Victoria

vik-TOR-ee-uh

Named after Queen Victoria (1819–1901), the genus was named in 1837, the year she ascended the throne (*Nymphaeaceae*)

victoriae

vik-TOR-ee-ay

—

victoriae-reginae

vik-TOR-ee-ay re-JEE-nay

Named after Queen Victoria (1819–1901), British monarch, as in *Agave victoriae-reginae*

vigilis

VIJ-il-is

—

vigilans

VIJ-il-anz

Vigilant, as in *Diascia vigilis*

villosus

vil-OH-sus

villosa, villosum

With soft hairs, as in *Photinia villosa*

vilmorinianus

vil-mor-in-ee-AH-nus

vilmoriniana, vilmorinianum

—

vilmorinii

vil-mor-IN-ee-eye

Named after Maurice de Vilmorin (1849–1918), French nurseryman, as in *Cotoneaster vilmorinianus*

viminalis

vim-in-AH-lis

viminalis, viminale

—

vimineus

vim-IN-ee-us

viminea, vimineum

With long, slender shoots, as in *Salix viminalis*

Vinca

VIN-kuh

From Latin *vincere* meaning 'to bind', as the stems were used for wreath-making (*Apocynaceae*)

viniferus

vih-NIH-fer-us

vinifera, viniferum

Producing wine, as in *Vitis vinifera*

Viola

vee-OH-luh

From Latin *viola*, the name for several plants with fragrant flowers (*Violaceae*)

violaceus

vy-oh-LAH-see-us

violacea, violaceum

Violet-coloured, as in *Hardenbergia violacea*

violescens

vy-oh-LESS-enz

Turning violet, as in *Phyllostachys violescens*

virens

VEER-enz

Green, as in *Penstemon virens*

virescens

veer-ES-enz

Turning green, as in *Carpobrotus virescens*

virgatus

vir-GA-tus

virgata, virgatum

Twiggy, as in *Panicum virgatum*

virginalis

vir-jin-AH-lis

virginalis, virginale

—

virgineus

vir-JIN-ee-us

virginea, virgineum

White; virginal, as in *Anguloa virginalis*

virginianus

vir-jin-ee-AH-nus

virginiana, virginianum

—

virginicus

vir-JIN-ih-kus

virginica, virginicum

—

virgineus

vir-JIN-ee-us

virginea, virgineum

Connected with Virginia, USA, as in *Hamamelis virginiana*

viridi-

Used in compound words to denote green

viridescens

vir-ih-DESS-enz

Turning green, as in *Ferocactus viridescens*

viridiflorus

vir-id-uh-FLOR-us

viridiflora, viridiflorum

With green flowers, as in *Lachenalia viridiflora*

viridis

VEER-ih-dis

viridis, viride

Green, as in *Trillium viride*

viridissimus

vir-id-ISS-ih-mus

viridissima, viridissimum

Very green, as in *Forsythia viridissima*

viridistriatus

vi-rid-ee-stry-AH-tus

viridistriata, viridistriatum

With green stripes, as in *Pleioblastus viridistriatus*

viridulus

vir-ID-yoo-lus

viridula, viridulum

Rather green, as in *Tricyrtis viridula*

Viscum

European mistletoe (*Viscum album*) is a parasitic plant that relies on its host tree for water and soil nutrients, though it can manufacture its own food via photosynthesis. As it can only survive when attached to a host, mature plants must find a way to transport their seeds to other suitable hosts, and birds are key. Mistle thrushes (*Turdus viscivorus*) feed on the white berries, providing a courier service. The berry flesh is sticky (viscous, thus *Viscum*), so once the bird eats the berry, a very sticky excrement that can adhere to tree branches transfers seed to the perfect site for germination on a new host.

Viscum album,
mistletoe

viscidus
VIS-kid-us
viscida, viscidum
Sticky; clammy, as in *Teucrium viscidum*

viscosus
vis-KOH-sus
viscosa, viscosum
Sticky; clammy, as in *Rhododendron viscosum*

Viscum
VIS-kum
The classical Latin name for mistletoe (*V. album*); also used for birdlime, a sticky substance used to catch birds and manufactured from mistletoe berries; the viscid nature of the fruits allows the seeds to stick to tree branches (*Santalaceae*)

vitaceus
vee-TAY-see-us
vitacea, vitaceum
Like vine (*Vitis*), as in *Parthenocissus vitacea*

vitellinus
vy-tel-LY-nus
vitellina, vitellinum
The colour of egg yolk, as in *Encyclia vitellina*

Vitex
VI-teks
The classical Latin name for chaste tree, *V. agnus-castus* (*Lamiaceae*)

viticella
vy-tee-CHELL-uh
Small vine, as in *Clematis viticella*

vitifolius
vy-tih-FOH-lee-us
vitifolia, vitifolium
With leaves like vine (*Vitis*), as in *Abutilon vitifolium*

Vitis
VY-tis
The classical Latin name for grapevine, *V. vinifera* (*Vitaceae*)

vitis-idaea
VY-tiss-id-uh-EE-uh
Vine of Mount Ida, as in *Vaccinium vitis-idaea*

vittatus
vy-TAH-tus
vittata, vittatum
With lengthwise stripes, as in *Billbergia vittata*

vivax
VY-vaks
Long-lived, as in *Phyllostachys vivax*

viviparus
vy-VIP-ar-us
vivipara, viviparum
Producing plantlets; self-propagating, as in *Persicaria vivipara*

volubilis
vol-OO-bil-is
volubilis, volubile
Twining, as in *Aconitum volubile*

vomitorius
vom-ih-TOR-ee-us
vomitoria, vomitorium
Emetic, as in *Ilex vomitoria*

Vriesea
vry-EEZ-ee-uh
Named after Willem Hendrik de Vriese (1806–62), Dutch botanist and physician (*Bromeliaceae*)

vulgaris
vul-GAH-ris
vulgaris, vulgare
—

vulgatus
vul-GAIT-us
vulgata, vulgatum
Common, as in *Aquilegia vulgaris*

Wachendorfia [1]
wak-un-DORF-ee-uh
Named after Evert Jacob van Wachendorff (1703–58), Dutch botanist (*Haemodoraceae*)

wagnerii
wag-ner-EE-eye
—

wagneriana
wag-ner-ee-AH-nuh
—

wagnerianus
wag-ner-ee-AH-nus
Named after Warren Wagner (1920–2000), American botanist, as in *Trachycarpus wagnerianus*

Wahlenbergia
wal-un-BERG-ee-uh
Named after Georg Göran Wahlenburg (1780–1851), Swedish botanist (*Campanulaceae*)

Waldsteinia
wald-STY-nee-uh
Named after Franz de Paula Adam von Waldstein (1759–1823), Austrian soldier and botanist (*Rosaceae*)

walkerae
WAL-ker-ah
Commemorates various Walkers, including Ernest Pillsbury Walker (1891–1969), American zoologist, as in *Chylismia walkeri*

wallerianus
wall-er-ee-AH-nus
walleriana, wallerianum
Named after Horace Waller (1833–96), British missionary, as in *Impatiens walleriana*

wallichianus [2]
wal-ik-ee-AH-nus
wallichiana, wallichianum
Named after Dr Nathaniel Wallich (1786–1854), Danish botanist and plant hunter, as in *Pinus wallichiana*

walteri
WAL-ter-ee
Named after Thomas Walter, 18th-century American botanist, as in *Cornus walteri*

wardii
WAR-dee-eye
Named after Frank Kingdon-Ward (1885–1958), British botanist and plant collector, as in *Roscoea wardii*

warscewiczii
vark-zeh-wik-ZEE-eye
Named after Joseph Warsczewicz (1812–66), Polish orchid collector, as in *Kohleria warscewiczii*

Washingtonia
wash-ing-TOH-nee-uh
Named after George Washington (1732–99), first President of the United States (*Arecaceae*)

A B C D E F G H I J K L M N O P Q R S T U V W X Y Z i

1

Wachendorfia paniculata,
marsh butterfly lily

2

Pinus wallichiana,
Bhutan pine

1

2

3

Weigela floribunda,
weigelia

Westringia eremicola,
slender western rosemary

Rhododendron wightii,
Wight's rhododendron

watereri
wat-er-EER-eye
Named after Waterers Nurseries, Knaphill,
England, as in *Laburnum* × *watereri*

Watsonia
wat-SOH-nee-uh
Named after William Watson (1715–87),
British physician and scientist (*Iridaceae*)

webbianus
web-bee-AH-nus
webbiana, webbianum
Named after Philip Barker Webb (1793–
1854), British botanist and traveller, as in
Rosa webbiana

Weigela [1]
WY-juh-luh
Named after Christian Ehrenfried Weigel
(1748–1831), German scientist
(*Caprifoliaceae*)

Weinmannia
wine-MAN-ee-uh
Named after Johann Wilhelm Weinmann
(1683–1741), German apothecary
(*Cunoniaceae*)

Westringia [2]
west-RING-ee-uh
Named after Johan Petrus Westring
(1753–1833), Swedish physician and
botanist (*Lamiaceae*)

weyerianus
wey-er-ee-AH-nus
weyeriana, weyerianum
Named after William van de Weyer, 20th-
century horticulturist, who bred *Buddleja* ×
weyeriana

Wikstroemia
wik-STROH-mee-uh
Named after Johan Emanuel Wikström
(1789–1856), Swedish botanist
(*Thymelaeaceae*)

Wisteria
wis-TEER-ee-uh
Named after Caspar Wistar (1761–1818),
American physician and anatomist; the
spelling was deliberately altered from
'*Wistaria*' to produce a better sound, but
perhaps also to honour his friend Charles
Jones Wister (1782–1865) (*Fabaceae*)

wheeleri
WHEE-ler-ee
Named after George Montague Wheeler
(1842–1905), American surveyor, as in
Dasylirion wheeleri

wherryi
WHER-ee-eye
Named after Dr Edgar Theodore Wherry
(1885–1982), American botanist and
geologist, as in *Tiarella wherryi*

whipplei
WHIP-lee-eye
Named after Lieutenant Amiel Weeks
Whipple (1818–63), American surveyor, as
in *Yucca whipplei*

wichurana
whi-choo-re-AH-nuh
Named after Max Ernst Wichura
(1817–1866), German botanist, as in *Rosa
wichurana*

wightii [3]
WIGHT-ee-eye
Named after Robert Wight (1796–1872),
botanist and Superintendent of Madras
Botanic Garden, as in *Rhododendron wightii*

wildpretii
wild-PRET-ee-eye
Named after Hermann Josef Wildpret,
19th-century Swiss botanist, as in *Echium
wildpretii*

wilkesianus
wilk-see-AH-nus
wilkesiana, wilkesianum
Named after Charles Wilkes (1798–1877),
American naval officer and explorer, as in
Acalypha wilkesiana

williamsii
wil-yams-EE-eye
Named for various eminent botanists and horticulturists called Williams, including John Charles Williams, 19th-century British plant collector, as in *Camellia × williamsii*

willmottianus
wil-mot-ee-AH-nus
willmottiana, willmottianum
—

willmottiae
wil-MOT-ee-eye
Named after Ellen Willmott (1858–1934), British horticulturist, of Warley Place, Essex, as in *Rosa willmottiae*

wilsoniae
wil-SON-ee-ay
—

wilsonii
wil-SON-ee-eye
Named after Dr Ernest Henry Wilson (1876–1930), British plant hunter, as in *Spiraea wilsonii*. The epithet *wilsoniae* commemorates his wife Helen

wintonensis
win-ton-EN-sis
wintonensis, wintonense
From Winchester; used especially of Hillier Nurseries, Hampshire, England, as in *Halimiocistus × wintonensis*

wisleyensis
wis-lee-EN-sis
wisleyensis, wisleyense
Named after RHS Garden Wisley, Surrey, England, as in *Gaultheria × wisleyensis*

wittrockianus
wit-rok-ee-AH-nus
wittrockiana, wittrockianum
Named after Professor Veit Brecher Wittrock (1839–1914), Swedish botanist, as in *Viola × wittrockiana*

Wollemia
wo-LEM-ee-uh
Named after Wollemi National Park in New South Wales, Australia, where *W. nobilis* was discovered in 1994 (*Araucariaceae*)

Woodsia
WOOD-zee-uh
Named after Joseph Woods (1776–1864), British botanist and geologist (*Woodsiaceae*)

Woodwardia
wood-WARD-ee-uh
Named after Thomas Jenkinson Woodward (1745–1820), British botanist (*Blechnaceae*)

woronowii
wor-on-OV-ee-eye
Named after Georg Woronow (1874–1931), Russian botanist and plant collector, as in *Galanthus woronowii*

Worsleya
WORS-lay-uh
Named after Arthington Worsley (1861–1944), British horticulturist and engineer (*Amaryllidaceae*)

wrightii
RITE-ee-eye
Named after Charles Wright, 19th-century American botanist and plant collector, as in *Viburnum wrightii*

Wulfenia
wul-FEE-nee-uh
Named after Franz Xaver von Wulfen (1728–1805), Serbian-born Austrian cleric and scientist (*Plantaginaceae*)

GENUS SPOTLIGHT

Wollemia

Wollemia nobilis, a conifer in the monkey-puzzle family (*Araucariaceae*), is native to New South Wales, Australia. Only described in 1995, its discovery the year before created a sensation in the botanical world. It was found in Wollemi National Park, less than 100 miles from Sydney, but how could a whole new conifer genus be discovered so close to a major city? It seems the reason is the park is pretty large, and the wollemia pines were in quite a remote location. There were only a few of them, among thousands of other trees, and it took an alert, and intrepid, botanist to discover these trees for what they were. The plants are rare in the wild too with fewer than 100 adult trees, and they're threatened by an introduced fungal pathogen. In order to ensure their survival, plants were propagated, and the offspring sold with profits being used to support *Wollemia* conservation.

Reconstruction of fossil
***Wollemia nobilis*,**
Wollemi pine

Xanthoceras sorbifolium,
yellow horn

Xerophyllum asphodeloides,
turkey beard

xanth-
Used in compound words to denote yellow

xanthinus
zan-TEE-nus
xanthina, xanthinum
Yellow, as in *Rosa xanthina*

xanthocarpus
zan-tho-KAR-pus
xanthocarpa, xanthocarpum
With yellow fruits, as in *Rubus xanthocarpus*

Xanthoceras [1]
zan-tho-SEER-as
From Greek *xanthos* meaning 'yellow' and *keras* meaning 'horn',
referring to the horn-like glands between the petals (*Sapindaceae*)

Xanthocyparis
zan-tho-SIP-uh-ris
From Greek *xanthos* meaning 'yellow' and *cyparissos* meaning
'cypress', alluding to the colour of the wood (*Cupressaceae*)

xantholeucus
zan-THO-luh-cus
xantholeuca, xantholeucum
Yellow-white, as in *Sobralia xantholeuca*

Xanthorhiza
zan-tho-RY-zuh
From Greek *xanthos* meaning 'yellow' and *rhiza* meaning 'root', as the
rhizomes are yellow (*Ranunculaceae*)

Xanthosoma
zan-tho-SOH-muh
From Greek *xanthos* meaning 'yellow' and *soma* meaning 'body',
referring either to the stigma, or inner tissues (*Araceae*)

Xeranthemum
zeer-ANTH-uh-mum
From Greek *xeros* meaning 'dry' and *anthemon* meaning 'flower', as
the flower heads are everlasting when dry (*Asteraceae*)

Xerochrysum
zeer-oh-KRY-zum
From Greek *xeros* meaning 'dry' and *chrysos* meaning 'gold', alluding
to the papery yellow bracts (*Asteraceae*)

Xerophyllum [2]
zeer-oh-FIL-um
From Greek *xeros* meaning 'dry' and *phyllon* meaning 'leaf'; the dried
leaves are used for weaving (*Melanthiaceae*)

yakushimanus

ya-koo-shim-MAH-nus

yakushimana, yakushimanum

Connected with Yakushima Island, Japan, as in *Rhododendron yakushimanum*

yedoensis

YED-oh-en-sis

yedoensis, yedoense

—

yesoensis

yesoensis, yesoense

—

yezoensis

yezoensis, yezoense

From Tokyo, Japan, as in *Prunus × yedoensis*

Ypsilandra

ip-si-LAN-druh

From Greek *ypsilon* meaning the letter 'Y' and *andros* meaning 'male', as the stamens are supposedly Y-shaped (*Melanthiaceae*)

Yucca [1]

YUK-uh

From Caribbean *yuca*, the name for cassava (*Manihot esculenta*) roots, wrongly applied to this genus (*Asparagaceae*)

yuccifolius

yuk-kih-FOH-lee-us

yuccifolia, yuccifolium

With leaves like *Yucca*, as in *Eryngium yuccifolium*

yuccoides

yuk-KOY-deez

Resembling *Yucca*, as in *Beschorneria yuccoides*

yunnanensis

yoo-nan-EN-sis

yunnanensis, yunnanense

From Yunnan, China, as in *Magnolia yunnanensis*

Yushania

yew-SHAN-ee-uh

Named after Yushan, the highest mountain in Taiwan, where the first species was collected (*Poaceae*)

1

Yucca gloriosa,
Spanish dagger

KEEPING IT IN THE FAMILY

The Latin names given to plant families are constructed by choosing one genus from the family, such as *Erica*, then adding the suffix *-aceae*, so *Ericaceae* are plants that resemble *Erica* (heather). Typically, the genus chosen is typical of the family, but not always. *Acanthaceae* are mainly tropical shrubs, but *Acanthus* is a hardy herbaceous perennial. In a few families, the representative genus is no longer recognised, as in *Caprifoliaceae*, *Aquifoliaceae* or *Cactaceae*, but the family name remains unchanged. *Caprifolium* is a synonym of *Lonicera*, *Aquifolium* is now *Ilex*, while *Cactus* species now belong to several other genera.

zabelianus
zah-bel-ee-AH-nus
zabeliana, zabelianum
Named after Hermann Zabel, 19th-century German dendrologist, as in *Berberis zabeliana*

Zaluzianskya
zah-loo-zee-AN-ski-uh
Named after Adam Zaluziansky von Zaluzian (1558–1613), Czech physician (*Scrophulariaceae*)

zambesiacus
zam-bes-ee-AH-kus
zambesiaca, zambesiacum
Connected with the Zambezi River, Africa, as in *Eucomis zambesiaca*

Zamia
ZAY-mee-uh
From Greek *azaniae* meaning 'pine cone', as *Zamia* is a cone-producing cycad (*Zamiaceae*)

Zamioculcas
zay-mee-oh-KUL-kas
From *Zamia*, an unrelated plant of similar appearance, plus Arabic *culcas*, the vernacular name for the related *Colocasia* (*Araceae*)

Zantedeschia
zan-tuh-DESH-ee-uh
Named after Giovanni Zantedeschi (1773–1846), Italian botanist and physician (*Araceae*)

Zanthoxylum
zan-THOKS-uh-lum
From Greek *xanthos* meaning 'yellow' and *xylon* meaning 'wood'; some species have yellow heartwood (*Rutaceae*)

Zea
ZEE-uh
From Greek *zeia*, a type of cereal (*Poaceae*)

zebrinus
zeb-REE-nus
zebrina, zebrinum
With stripes like a zebra, as in *Tradescantia zebrina*

Zelkova
zel-KOH-vuh
From Georgian *dzelkva* meaning 'stone pillar', as the wood is hard and popular for construction (*Ulmaceae*)

Zenobia
zuh-NOH-bee-uh
Named after Septimia Zenobia (c. AD 240–274), Queen of Palmyra, in present-day Syria (*Ericaceae*)

Zephyranthes
zef-ur-ANTH-eez
From Greek Zephyros, god of the west wind, plus *anthos* meaning 'flower'; presumably alluding to their distribution in the western hemisphere (*Amaryllidaceae*)

GENUS SPOTLIGHT

Zamioculcas

This popular houseplant is often known as the ZZ plant, due to the initials of its Latin name *Zamioculcas zamiifolia*. Both the genus and species names recognise the similarity of this plant to the genus *Zamia*. However, the two plants are not closely related. *Zamioculcas* is an aroid, a member of the *Araceae* family, most notable for their unusual flower structure where tiny flowers cluster around a central rod (spadix), which is then enclosed within a bract (spathe). Other popular family members include peace lily (*Spathiphyllum*) and flamingo flower (*Anthurium*). *Zamia* meanwhile is a cycad, a non-flowering plant most closely related to conifers.

Zamioculcas zamiifolia,
fern arum

zeyheri
ZAY-AIR-eye
Named after Karl Ludwig Philipp Zeyher (1799–1859), German botanist and plant collector, as in *Philadelphus zeyheri*

zeylanicus
zey-LAN-ih-kus
zeylanica, zeylanicum
From Ceylon (Sri Lanka), as in *Pancratium zeylanicum*

zibethinus
zy-beth-EE-nus
zibethina, zibethinum
Smelling foul, like a civet cat, as in *Durio zibethinus*

Zigadenus
zig-uh-DEE-nus
From Greek *zygos* meaning 'pair' or 'yoke' and *aden* meaning 'gland', referring to the pair of glands on each petal of some species (*Melanthiaceae*)

Zingiber
ZIN-jib-ur
From Greek *ziggiberis*, the vernacular name for ginger, *Z. officinale* (*Zingiberaceae*)

Zinnia [1]
ZIN-ee-uh
Named after Johann Gottfried Zinn (1727–59), German botanist and ophthalmologist (*Asteraceae*)

Zizania
zy-ZAY-nee-uh
From Greek *zizanion*, a weedy grass growing amongst wheat crops (*Poaceae*)

Ziziphus [2]
ZIZ-i-fus
From Persian *zizafun*, the vernacular name for *Z. lotus* (*Rhamnaceae*)

zonalis
zo-NAH-lis
zonalis, zonale
—

zonatus
zo-NAH-tus
zonata, zonatum
With bands, often coloured, as in *Cryptanthus zonatus*

Zygopetalum
zy-goh-PET-ah-lum
From Greek *zygos* meaning 'yoke' and *petalon* meaning 'petal', as the flower lip is swollen at the base, appearing to yoke together the other petals (*Orchidaceae*)

1

Zinnia elegans,
youth on age

2

Ziziphus spina-christi,
Christ's thorn plant

The Gardener's Botanical Picture Credits

3	© RHS, Lindley Library	54	© RHS, Lindley Library	139	© RHS, Lindley Library
4	© RHS, Lindley Library	65	© RHS, Lindley Library	140	© RHS, Lindley Library
5T	© RHS, Lindley Library	68	© RHS, Lindley Library	148	© RHS, Lindley Library
6	© RHS, Lindley Library	76L	© RHS, Lindley Library	152L	© RHS, Lindley Library
12	© RHS, Lindley Library	92L	© RHS, Lindley Library	154	© RHS, Lindley Library
13	© RHS, Lindley Library	101	© RHS, Lindley Library	168	© RHS, Lindley Library
15	© RHS, Lindley Library	104	© RHS, Lindley Library	169R	© RHS, Lindley Library
16	© RHS, Lindley Library	109	© RHS, Lindley Library	179	© RHS, Lindley Library
18	© RHS, Lindley Library	118	© RHS, Lindley Library	186L	© RHS, Lindley Library
20L	© RHS, Lindley Library	120L	© RHS, Lindley Library	186R	© RHS, Lindley Library
21	© RHS, Lindley Library	122R	© RHS, Lindley Library	193R	© RHS, Lindley Library
24	© RHS, Lindley Library	123	© RHS, Lindley Library	199	© RHS, Lindley Library
34C	© RHS, Lindley Library	131R	© RHS, Lindley Library	201L	© RHS, Lindley Library
34R	© RHS, Lindley Library	134	© Emma Shepherd	205	© RHS, Lindley Library
35C	© RHS, Lindley Library	136C	© RHS, Lindley Library	214M	© RHS, Lindley Library
52R	© RHS, Lindley Library	138	© RHS, Lindley Library		

Chrysanthemum indicum,
Indian chrysanthemum

Index of common names

This index can be used to find the botanical names of some plants in the book. It is not a definitive index, but if you know the common name, it cross-references to listings for each part of the botanical name.

For example: 'Adam's needle' is a common name for *Yucca filamentosa*. The cross references for that listing direct you to entries in the main part of the book for both *Yucca* (315) and *filamentosa* (132), allowing you to understand the origins and meanings of each part of the binomial name. Some common names lead to more than one botanical name (where the same common name is applied to different species). Common names for a genus will have only one botanical term beneath them, for example: Amaryllis, *Hippeastrum* (155).

Index tabs A–Z and i along right margin

A
B
C
D
E
F
G
H
I
J
K
L
M
N
O
P
Q
R
S
T
U
V
W
X
Y
Z

i

A
B
C
D
E
F
G
H
I
J
K
L
M
N
O
P
Q
R
S
T
U
V
W
X
Y
Z

i

A
B
C
D
E
F
G
H
I
J
K
L
M
N
O
P
Q
R
S
T
U
V
W
X
Y
Z

i

A
B
C
D
E
F
G
H
I
J
K
L
M
N
O
P
Q
R
S
T
U
V
W
X
Y
Z

i

A
B
C
D
E
F
G
H
I
J
K
L
M
N
O
P
Q
R
S
T
U
V
W
X
Y
Z

i

A
B
C
D
E
F
G
H
I
J
K
L
M
N
O
P
Q
R
S
T
U
V
W
X
Y
Z

i

A
B
C
D
E
F
G
H
I
J
K
L
M
N
O
P
Q
R
S
T
U
V
W
X
Y
Z

i

A
B
C
D
E
F
G
H
I
J
K
L
M
N
O
P
Q
R
S
T
U
V
W
X
Y
Z

i

A
B
C
D
E
F
G
H
I
J
K
L
M
N
O
P
Q
R
S
T
U
V
W
X
Y
Z

i

A
B
C
D
E
F
G
H
I
J
K
L
M
N
O
P
Q
R
S
T
U
V
W
X
Y
Z

i

Please note that some Latin names are used as the common names so are also listed in the main section. These include:

Alyssum	Daphne	Iris
Aster	Forsythia	Lobelia
Aubrieta	Freesia	Magnolia
Begonia	Geranium	Petunia
Chrysanthemum	Hebe	Phlox
Clematis	Heuchera	Rhododendron
Cosmos	Hosta	
Dahlia	Hydrangea	

Dahlia,
dahlia